# LINEAR ALGEBRA AND GEOMETRY

Translated from the Dutch edition
by A. VAN DER SLUIS

# LINEAR ALGEBRA AND GEOMETRY

*by*

NICOLAAS H. KUIPER

*Professor of Mathematics*
*University of Amsterdam*

SECOND REVISED EDITION

1965

NORTH-HOLLAND PUBLISHING COMPANY – AMSTERDAM

*1st edition 1962*
*2nd printing 1963*
*2nd revised edition 1965*

PUBLISHERS:
NORTH-HOLLAND PUBLISHING CO., AMSTERDAM
SOLE DISTRIBUTORS FOR U.S.A.:
INTERSCIENCE PUBLISHERS INC., NEW YORK



PRINTED IN THE NETHERLANDS

# PREFACE

The subject which was usually designated by the names analytic geometry, affine geometry and projective geometry, has gradually grown into a new subject under the great unifying and stimulating influence of algebra. Here linear algebra plays a dominant role due to its use as a technique and also because many of the essential ideas of the subject belong to linear algebra.

In this book we follow this trend. We try to penetrate our subject-matter with the modern algebraic tools that are useful in all mathematics. However it has been our aim at the same time to preserve the aesthetically satisfying geometrical flavour of the subject. We have included many geometrical theorems, some elementary, some important in a field-free axiomatic approach (like the theorem of Desargues).

Another special feature in our treatment is that we have emphasized the idea of functions on spaces, in all those cases where it is customary to deal with the equations, curves and surfaces, which represent the level-sets of these functions. Our method is very fertile, as can be seen from the treatment of quadratic surfaces and the invariance of cross-ratio under projection.

In general we have tried to keep our treatment coordinate-free. In particular we have not followed the custom of replacing any space by a set of coordinates, and then forgetting about the space as soon as possible. In this spirit we handle homomorphisms (linear mappings) before considering matrices. While using coordinates we have been conscious of the fact that coordinates also are functions.

As far as linear algebra is concerned the main result to which this book leads is the classification of the endomorphisms of complex (**C**) and real (**R**) finite dimensional vector spaces, (Jordan normal form). We also give the classification of quadratic and hermitian functions (or forms) on euclidean and unitary vector spaces.

As far as geometry is concerned we deal with euclidean and affine spaces, particulary those of dimension two and three, with their motions and affinities, and linear and quadratic functions.

A long chapter (Ch. 20) is devoted to projective geometry, while some attention is paid to finite planes (Ch. 8), non-euclidean geometry (Ch. 21) and the topology of some very elementary varieties (Ch. 22). In Ch. 16 the theory of least squares and correlation coefficients is mentioned as the approach from our point of view and in our formulation seems clarifying and is not generally known.

While preparing the Dutch edition of this book and also during the preparation of this translation we have had the benefits of critical remarks, suggestions and help from Professor F. van der Blij, Mr. M. Keuls, Professor T. A. Springer, Mr. L. R. Verdooren, and others. We are very grateful for this help.

The translator Dr. A. van der Sluis has not restricted his work to a faithful translation, but, in cooperation with the author, he has improved on the Dutch edition in view of his own criticism and those of others. The author expresses his extreme gratitude to Dr. A. van der Sluis. The translator, in his turn, wishes to express his warm appreciation to the author for the open-mindedness and cooperation with which he welcomed any suggestion.

Dr. T. J. Willmore from Liverpool University read the text and made several improvements, particularly those of a linguistic nature. We thank him warmly for this work and his interest.

Finally we like to thank the publisher for his contribution to the book and for the pleasant cooperation.

Wageningen, September 1961.

N. H. Kuiper
A. van der Sluis

## CONTENTS


| CHAPTER | | page |
|---|---|---|
| 1. | VECTORS IN THE PLANE AND IN SPACE | 1 |
| 2. | SUBSET, PRODUCT SET, RELATION AND MAPPING | 4 |
| 3. | THE n-DIMENSIONAL VECTOR SPACE $V^n$ | 8 |
| 4. | THE PARAMETRIC REPRESENTATION OF A LINE | 13 |
| 5. | SOME FUNDAMENTAL THEOREMS | 20 |
| | The dual vector space V* | 26 |
| 6. | FIRST DEGREE FUNCTIONS ON, AND LINEAR VARIETIES IN $A^n$ | 31 |
| 7. | LINEAR FUNCTIONS AND LINES IN $A^2$ AND $A^n$. APPLICATIONS | 39 |
| | Cross-ratio | 44 |
| | Harmonic separation | 48 |
| 8. | A FINITE AFFINE PLANE | 53 |
| 9. | HOMOMORPHISMS OF VECTOR SPACES | 58 |
| | The vector space Hom (A, B) | 63 |
| | Composition (multiplication) of homomorphisms | 65 |
| | The dual homomorphism of the dual vector spaces | 68 |
| 10. | MATRICES | 71 |
| 11. | SETS OF LINEAR EQUATIONS | 81 |
| 12. | FUNCTIONS OF SEVERAL VARIABLES. DETERMINANT | 85 |
| 13. | APPLICATIONS OF DETERMINANTS. VOLUME | 98 |
| 14. | QUADRATIC AND SYMMETRIC BILINEAR FUNCTIONS | 106 |
| | A. Functions on a vector space | 106 |
| | $A_H$. Hermitian functions | 119 |
| | B. Functions on a real affine space | 121 |
| 15. | EUCLIDEAN SPACE | 128 |
| | Unitary vector space | 142 |
| 16. | SOME APPLICATIONS IN STATISTICS | 143 |
| | I. Method of least squares, linear adjustment, regression | 143 |
| | II. The correlation coefficient | 149 |
| 17. | CLASSIFICATION OF ENDOMORPHISMS | 156 |
| | Classification of endomorphisms (complex numbers) | 160 |
| | Endomorphisms of real vector spaces | 166 |
| | Symmetric endomorphisms and quadratic functions on a euclidean vector space | 170 |

Orthogonal endomorphisms . . . . . . . . . . . . . . . 173
Hermitian endomorphisms and hermitian functions on a unitary space . . . . . . . . . . . . . . . . . . . . . 176
18. QUADRATIC FUNCTIONS ON AND QUADRATIC VARIETIES IN EUCLIDEAN SPACES . . . . . . . . . . . . . . . . . . . . 179
Investigation of a given quadratic variety . . . . . . . . . . 183
19. MOTIONS AND AFFINITIES . . . . . . . . . . . . . . . . . 190
Motions . . . . . . . . . . . . . . . . . . . . . . 190
Classification of motions. . . . . . . . . . . . . . . . 195
Motion in the euclidean plane as basic notion . . . . . . . 199
Affinities in real spaces . . . . . . . . . . . . . . . . 201
Some constructions with plane affinities . . . . . . . . . . 204
20. PROJECTIVE GEOMETRY . . . . . . . . . . . . . . . . . 209
Points at infinity of an affine plane $A^2$ . . . . . . . . . 209
Projective classification of quadrics (over **C** and **R**) . . . . . 221
Classification of collineations (over **C** and **R**) . . . . . . . . 224
21. NON-EUCLIDEAN PLANES. . . . . . . . . . . . . . . . . 237
The hyperbolic plane . . . . . . . . . . . . . . . . . 237
The elliptic plane. . . . . . . . . . . . . . . . . . 244
22. SOME TOPOLOGICAL REMARKS . . . . . . . . . . . . . . 248

HINTS AND ANSWERS TO THE PROBLEMS IN CHAPTER 3–21 . . . . . 255
INDEX. . . . . . . . . . . . . . . . . . . . . . . . . 279
LIST OF SYMBOLS . . . . . . . . . . . . . . . . . . . . 285

# 1. VECTORS IN THE PLANE AND IN SPACE

In the ordinary plane (or in ordinary space) we take a fixed point $O$, that we call the *origin*. We consider arrows in the plane. An arrow can be characterized by its initial point and its endpoint. The word arrow is therefore used as synonym for "ordered pair of points", the first point of a pair being the initial point, the second the endpoint of the arrow. An arrow with $O$ as initial point will be called a *vector* [1]).

A special vector is that with $O$ as initial as well as endpoint; it is special since it cannot be drawn as an ordinary arrow. It is called the zero vector and designated by O.

There is a one-to-one relationship between points of the plane and vectors; indeed, to each point there corresponds one vector with that point as endpoint, and conversely, to any vector there belongs an endpoint.

To any arrow $BC$ (cf. fig. 1.1) there corresponds exactly one vector (the arrow with $O$ as initial point) which can be obtained from $BC$ by displacing it parallel to itself so that $O$ becomes the initial point. The vector $OA$ so obtained may thus be represented by the arrow $BC$. The vector $OA$ has many such representatives, of course. Sometimes we shall say "the vector $BC$" and mean "the vector *represented* by $BC$".

The set of all arrows in the plane (in space) with initial point $O$ is called a 2-*dimensional vector space* (a 3-dimensional vector space). Furthermore the following algebraic conventions will be observed:

---

[1]) Another (equivalent) definition which, however, is slightly less realistic to the beginner, is: a vector is a complete set (i.e. a set that cannot be extended) of arrows, each of which can be obtained from any other one by translation (a parallel displacement).

$A_1$. *Addition.* To any pair of vectors a $=OA$, b $=OB$ there corresponds a vector c $=OC$ in the following way: the arrow $BC$ must be a representative of a, or equivalently, the arrow $AC$ must

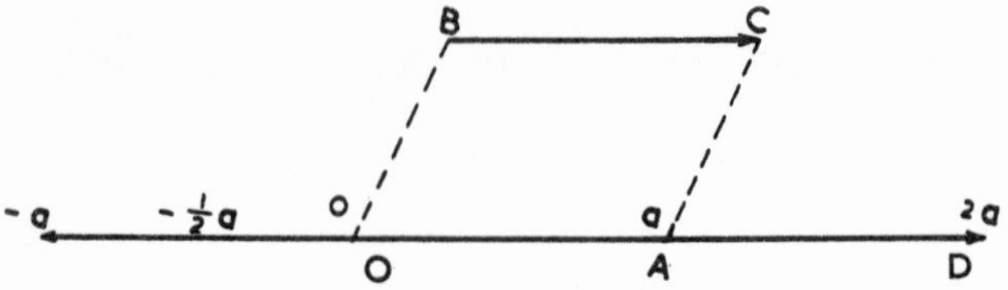


Fig. 1.1

be a representative of b, or: $C$ is the fourth vertex of a parallelogram with sides $OA$ and $OB$ (cf. fig. 1.2. The last formulation, known as the parallelogram-construction, is not unambiguous if $O$, $A$ and $B$ are collinear). This vector c is called the *sum* of a and b, and is denoted by a + b.

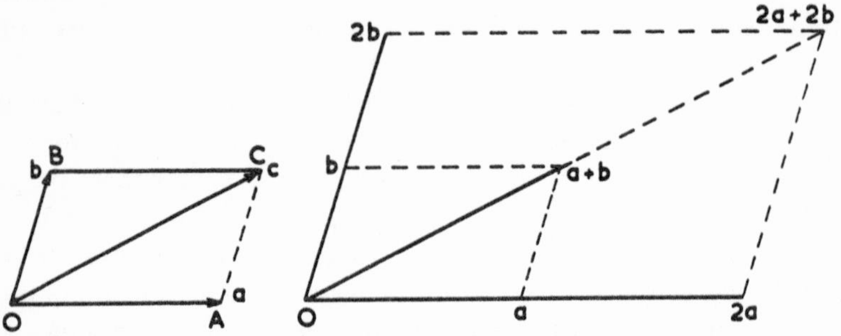


Fig. 1.2

$A_2$. *Multiplication by a real number $\lambda$.* To any pair consisting of a vector a $=OA$ and a real number $\lambda$ there corresponds a vector d $=OD$, called the *product* of $\lambda$ and a, denoted by $\lambda$a, in the following way: $O$, $A$ and $D$ lie on a line and

$$\text{length of } OD = |\lambda| \cdot \text{length of } OA,$$

whilst $A$ and $D$ will be on the same or on opposite sides of $O$ depending on whether $\lambda$ is positive or negative. $|\lambda|$ means the absolute value of $\lambda$, i.e. the non-negative one of the numbers $\lambda$ and $-\lambda$; for example $|5| = 5$, $|-7| = 7$, $|0| = 0$ (cf. fig. 1.1 with $\lambda = 2$). The concept of multiplication considered here is the *geometrical multiplication* known from plane geometry.

Combining addition and multiplication we obtain expressions in vectors and numbers like in ordinary algebra.

*These expressions satisfy a number of identities known from ordinary algebra.* E.g. whatever the vectors a and b and the number $\lambda$ may be, the vector $\lambda(\mathrm{a} + \mathrm{b})$ will always be equal to the vector $\lambda\mathrm{a} + \lambda\mathrm{b}$. This will be clear from the geometrical multiplication of the parallelogram on a and b by the factor $\lambda$.

We mention some identities which are not so very important when considered as theorems (they are almost trivial), but which will be chosen as starting point (axioms) in the following chapters. From that moment on theorems will no longer be deduced from any knowledge of plane or solid geometry, but from the axioms only. Nevertheless ordinary geometry will play an important part, simply since many theorems originate in it. Also many theorems and their proofs will be much better understood and memorized if interpreted in terms of ordinary geometry.

Important rules, true for arbitrary choice of vectors a, b, c and numbers $\lambda$, $\mu$, are the following:

| | | |
|---|---|---|
| $A_3$ | $(\mathrm{a} + \mathrm{b}) + \mathrm{c} = \mathrm{a} + (\mathrm{b} + \mathrm{c})$ | associative law |
| $A_6$ | $\mathrm{a} + \mathrm{b} = \mathrm{b} + \mathrm{a}$ | commutative law |
| $A_7$ | $1\mathrm{a} = \mathrm{a}$ | |
| $A_8$ | $\lambda(\mu\mathrm{a}) = (\lambda\mu)\mathrm{a}$ | |
| $A_9$ | $(\lambda + \mu)\mathrm{a} = \lambda\mathrm{a} + \mu\mathrm{a}$ | distributive law |
| $A_{10}$ | $\lambda(\mathrm{a} + \mathrm{b}) = \lambda\mathrm{a} + \lambda\mathrm{b}$ | |

PROBLEM (1.1). Take vectors a, b, c in space, and numbers $\lambda$, $\mu$. Construct geometrically the above expressions, and check that the relations hold.

## 2. SUBSET, PRODUCT SET, RELATION AND MAPPING

In this chapter we introduce some general notions and symbols that will be used later on.

If $A$ is a set of elements, and $a$ is one of them, we shall write $a \in A$. If any element of $A$ is also an element of the set $B$, then $A$ will be called a *subset* of $B$, denoted by $A \subset B$, or, which means the same, $B \supset A$. If moreover $A$ is different from $B$, then $A$ is called a *proper* subset of $B$. The set of all elements belonging to the set $A$ as well as to $B$, is called the *intersection* of $A$ and $B$, denoted by $A \cap B$. Fig. 2.1 shows point sets $A$ and $B$ and their intersection. Note, that $A \cap B$ is a subset of $A$: $(A \cap B) \subset A$, and of $B$.

The set of all elements belonging to $A$ or to $B$ or to both is called the *union* of $A$ and $B$, denoted by $A \cup B$.

The set of all pairs $(a, b)$ with $a \in A$ and $b \in B$, is called the *product set* of $A$ and $B$, denoted by $A \times B$. Hence $A \times A$ is the set of all ordered pairs of elements of $A$. Also any pair of the form $(a, a)$ belongs to it; but if $a \neq a'$ the pair $(a, a')$ is to be distinguished from $(a', a)$. $A \times A \times A$ is the set of all triples of elements of $A$.

A subset $R$ of $A \times B$ is called a *relation* between the elements of $A$ and those of $B$. If both $A$ and $B$ are the sets of real numbers, then the set of pairs $(a, b)$ with $a \in A$, $b \in B$ such that $a < b$, is a relation, viz. the relation "less than". In fig. 2.2 the relation $a < b$ has been shaded. Similarly we have the relations $a = 2b$ and $a^2 + b^2 = 1$ and $b \leqslant \sin a$. We will say that the relation $R$ between $a$ and $b$ holds if $(a, b) \in R$.

The relation consisting of the set of all pairs $(a, a)$ in $A \times A$ is called the *identity*. A relation $R \subset A \times A$ is called *symmetric* if $(a, b) \in R$ implies that $(b, a) \in R$, for every $a, b \in A$. The relation is called *transitive* if from $(a, b) \in R$ *and* $(b, c) \in R$ it follows that

$(a, c) \in R$, for every $a, b, c \in A$. A relation containing the identity is called *reflexive*.

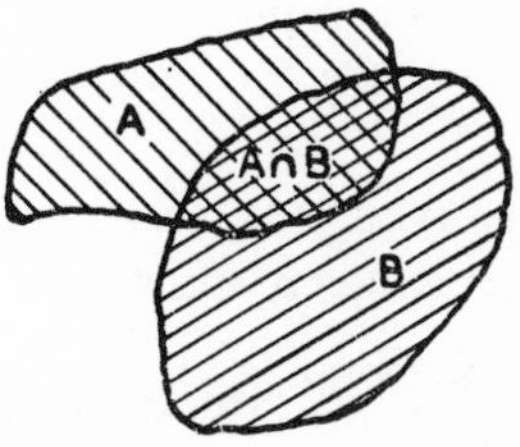


Fig. 2.1

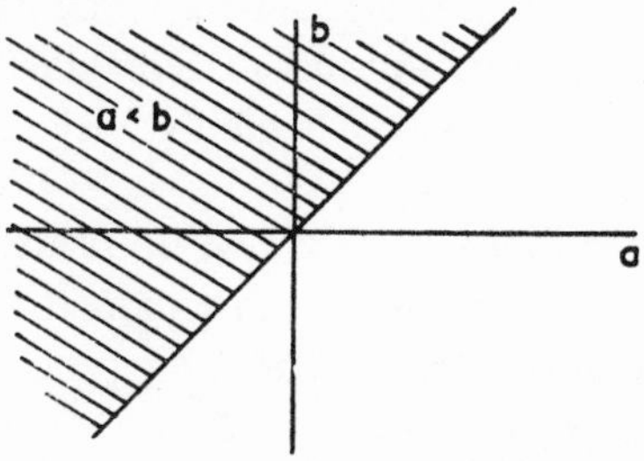


Fig. 2.2

A reflexive, symmetric, transitive relation is called an *equivalence*. We will usually denote equivalence between $a$ and $b$ by $a \sim b$, and we say: "$a$ is equivalent to $b$". From the definition it follows that for an equivalence we have:

$a \sim a$ (reflexive);
if $a \sim b$, then $b \sim a$ (symmetric);
if $a \sim b$ and $b \sim c$ then $a \sim c$ (transitive).

The relation "similarity" between plane figures is an instance of an equivalence. The identity is also an equivalence. The relation "less than" for real numbers is transitive, but it is not an equivalence.

If an equivalence $R$ in $A \times A$ is given, the elements of $A$ can be divided into classes, such that two elements belong to the same class if and only if they are equivalent. These equivalence classes can be considered as elements of a new set, denoted by $A/R$, which is called the *quotient* of $A$ by the equivalence $R$. An element of a class will sometimes be called a *representative* of that class.

For a geometrical example, consider the set $A$ of all points in a vertical plane. Two points $a$ and $b$ will be called equivalent, $a \sim b$ or $(a, b) \in R$, if they are at the same height. It can easily be seen that this relation is an equivalence. The equivalence classes are the horizontal lines.

As another application of the notion of equivalence we mention the construction of the rational numbers from the integers. Let $A$

be the set of pairs of integers $(p, q)$ with $q \neq 0$. Two elements $(p, q)$ and $(r, s)$ will be equivalent if $ps - qr = 0$. Again it is easy to see that this relation also is an equivalence. The equivalence classes are the rational numbers. The class of which $(p, q)$ is a representative, i.e. the class to which it belongs, is denoted by $p/q$, and also by $r/s$ if $ps - rq = 0$.

If in a subset $R \subset A \times B$ any element $a \in A$ occurs exactly once as leading element in a pair, then the relation is called a *mapping of A into B*. The element $b \in B$ occurring with $a \in A$ in a pair, is called the *image* of $a$ and may be denoted by $b = f(a)$, or, still shorter, by $fa$. The mapping is then denoted by $f: A \to B$. We shall also write $f: a \to b$ when $b = f(a)$.

The mapping $f$ will be called a *function* if $B$ is a set of numbers, or more generally a set of elements of a field $\mathbf{F}$ (for definition of a field cf. p. 68).

Fig. 2.3

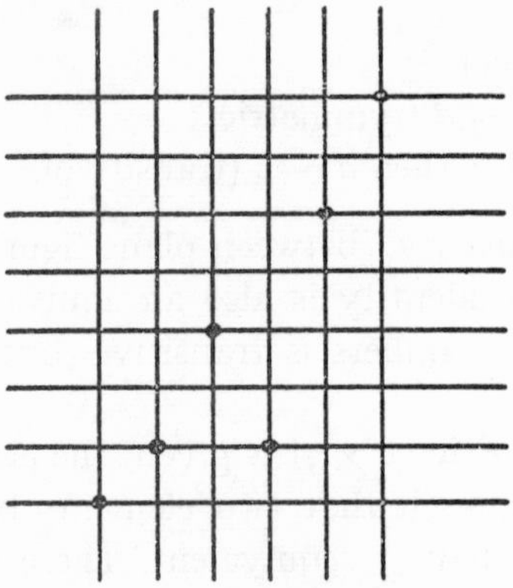

By the *image of a subset V of A under f* is meant the set of all images $fa$ of elements $a \in V$. It is denoted by $fV$. Briefly, $fA$ is called the image of the mapping $f$.

In fig. 2.3, $A$ is a set of 6 vertical lines, $B$ a set of 8 horizontal lines. Any element of the product space $A \times B$ will be a pair consisting of a vertical and a horizontal line, and can be represented by the point of intersection. A relation is given by marking a number of such points. The relation given in the figure is a mapping of $A$ into $B$. This is similar to the ordinary graph of a function.

The relation is called a *mapping of $A$ onto $B$* if the image coincides with $B$. The set of all $a \in A$ having $b$ as image is designated by $f^{-1}(b)$ and is called a *level set* of the mapping $f$. The level set of the mapping which associates to points on the earth the temperature, the atmospherical pressure or the altitude at those points, are called isotherms, isobars and isohypses respectively. Sometimes one of the points of the image space plays a special part, and is denoted by 0 (zero). In that case the level set $f^{-1}(0)$ is called the *kernel* of the mapping.

If $c \in B$ and $f(a) = c$ for all $a \in A$ then $f$ is called *the constant function $c$*. For example, *the function zero.*

If in the relation $R \subset A \times B$ any element $a \in A$ occurs exactly once as leading element in a pair, and any element $b \in B$ at most (exactly) once as second element, then the relation is called a *one-to-one mapping* into (onto).

The relations $R \subset A \times B$ and $S \subset B \times C$ determine a relation $SR \subset A \times C$ called the *composite relation,* consisting of all pairs $(a, c) \in A \times C$ for which there exists a $b \in B$ such that $(a, b) \in R$ and $(b, c) \in S$. We shall use this only in the case that the relations are mappings, say $f: A \rightarrow B$ and $g: B \rightarrow C$. The composite relation is then called the *product mapping*. The product mapping associates to any element $a \in A$ the element $gfa = g(f(a)) \in C$. It is denoted by $gf: A \rightarrow C$.

If the one-to-one mappings $f: A \rightarrow B$ and $g: B \rightarrow A$ are such that the product mapping $gf: A \rightarrow A$ is the identity, then $g$ is called the *inverse* of $f$. In that case $fg: B \rightarrow B$ is the identity in $B$, and consequently $f$ is also the inverse of $g$. The inverse of $f$ is denoted by $f^{-1}: B \rightarrow A$.

As an example we mention: the product of the mappings (in this case functions of real variables) $x \rightarrow x + 3$, $x \rightarrow x^2$, $x \rightarrow \sin x$ is the composite function $x \rightarrow \sin(x + 3)^2$.

# 3. THE $n$-DIMENSIONAL VECTOR SPACE $V^n$

We shall now present a precise formulation of our starting point by giving a definition of vector space. This definition will be such that the geometrical vector spaces of chapter 1 can be considered as (important) instances. The definition will not, however, be based on any geometrical experience of the reader. Also, in proving theorems we shall only use the definition and properties already established. Hence, all properties that the vector space will eventually have, it will have by virtue of our definitions only.

In the definition we shall make use of *scalars*. The reader may think of these as real numbers, or also as complex numbers; more generally, scalars will be elements of an arbitrary field **F** of characteristic $\neq 2$, unless in particular cases we explicitly state the contrary [1]. (A field is said to have characteristic $\neq 2$ if any non-zero element differs from its opposite). The field of real numbers will be denoted by (**F** =)**R**, the complex number field by (**F** =) **C**. We first define a linear space.

Definition: A *linear space* over the field **F** is a set V of elements a, b, $\cdots$, called *vectors*, having the following properties $A_1, \cdots, A_{10}$.

$A_1$. There is a mapping of V $\times$ V into V which is called *addition* of vectors. The image of the pair (a, b) $\in$ V $\times$ V is called the *sum* of a and b, and it is denoted by a + b.

$A_2$. There is a mapping of **F** $\times$ V into V which is called *multiplication* of vectors by scalars. The image of the pair ($\lambda$, a) $\in$ **F** $\times$ V is called the *product*, and is denoted by $\lambda$a.

---

[1]) A further generalization to arbitrary characteristic and non-commutative fields is possible, but requires too many precautions for our purposes.

For arbitrary a, b, c $\in$ V and $\lambda$, $\mu$, $\in$ **F**:

$A_3$ (a + b) + c = a + (b + c) associative law

$A_4$ There exists in V an element, denoted by O, called the *zero vector*, such that for any a $\in$ V:

$$a + O = O + a = a$$

$A_5$ For any a $\in$ V there exists an element in V, denoted by − a, such that

$$a + (-a) = (-a) + a = O$$

$A_6$ a + b = b + a commutative law

$A_7$ 1a = a

$A_8$ $\lambda(\mu a) = (\lambda\mu)a$

$A_9$ $(\lambda + \mu)a = \lambda a + \mu a$ } distributive law

$A_{10}$ $\lambda(a + b) = \lambda a + \lambda b$ } distributive law

From properties $A_3$, $\cdots A_8$ it follows that to a certain extent the manipulations with scalars and vectors are the same as in ordinary algebra. For example, $A_3$ says that no ambiguity will arise if in a sum of three or more vectors the parentheses are omitted. $A_6$ implies that altering the order in a sum of vectors has no influence on the result. For example a + (b + c) = a + (c + b) = (a + c)+ b = (c + a) + b = c + (a + b), which without any harm may be written as a + b + c or c + a + b.

PROBLEM (3.1). Using $A_3$, $\cdots A_8$ only, prove:

$$\lambda\{(\mu + \nu)(c + b)\} + (\lambda\mu)a + \nu(\lambda a) = \lambda(\mu + \nu)(a + b + c)$$

$\lambda, \mu, \nu \in$ **F**; a, b, c $\in$ V.

A *set of generators* of V will be any set of vectors $a_1, \cdots a_m$ in V such that for any vector a $\in$ V there exist scalars $\lambda_1, \cdots \lambda_m \in$ **F** satisfying

$$a = \lambda_1 a_1 + \cdots + \lambda_m a_m.$$

In this case we shall say that the vectors $a_1, \cdots a_m$ *generate* or *span* the space V.

If none of the proper subsets of the set $a_1, \cdots a_m$ is also a set of generators of V, then the set $a_1, \cdots a_m$ is called a *basis* of V.

If a finite set of generators which is not a basis, is given, then by the definition it should be possible to omit at least one of the vectors of the set and still have a set of generators. Repeating this, one finds a basis after a finite number of steps.

The properties $A_1, \cdots A_{10}$ do not imply that there exists a finite set of generators. Consider e.g. the set of all polynomials in one variable with real coefficients, or the set of all continuous functions on an interval. In this book we restrict to the case where a finite set of generators exists. We give therefore the

$A_{11}$. Definition. A *vector space* is a linear space which has a finite basis.

Since we wish to restrict ourselves in this book to a *finite set of* generators, we add:

$A_{12}$. V has a finite basis.

The smallest number occurring as the number of elements in a basis is called the *dimension* of V. If, however, V consists of exactly one vector, we shall say that the dimension is zero. A vector space of dimension n will be denoted by $V^n$.

The vectors in the ordinary plane with a fixed point $O$, as introduced in chapter 1, form a vector space over the real numbers. Since these vectors are not all multiples of one of them, the dimension is at least two. In fig. 3.1 we see that the dimension is exactly two: $a_1$ and $a_2$ are vectors different from zero and situated on two intersecting lines through $O$. It is easy to find for any vector b a parallelogram having b as diagonal and two sides along the given lines. Then there are real numbers $\lambda_1$ and $\lambda_2$ such that

$$b = \lambda_1 a_1 + \lambda_2 a_2.$$

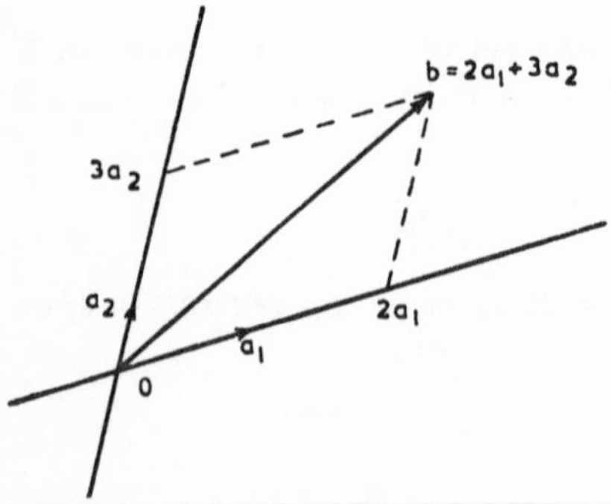


Fig. 3.1

PROBLEMS. (3.2). The vectors in ordinary space with fixed point *O* form a vector space of dimension *three*. Prove this by means of solid geometry.

(3.3). In fig. 3.1 the vectors on the line on which $a_1$ lies form a vector space of dimension *one*.

*Remark*: *If in a problem like* (3.3) *just an assertion is given, then this assertion is to be proved.*

Some corollaries of the axioms

If a and x are vectors such that $a + x = a$, then

$$(-a) + (a + x) = ((-a) + a) + x = O + x = x$$

equals

$$(-a) + a = O.$$

Hence for any vector a there is *exactly one* element $x = O$ such that $a + x = a$.

If $a + x = O$, then

$$(-a) + a + x = O + x = x$$

equals

$$(-a) + O = -a.$$

Consequently for any a there is *exactly one* element $x = -a$ such that $a + x = O$.

We observe further that for any a: $0 \cdot a + 1 \cdot a = (0 + 1)a = 1a$, hence

$$0 \cdot a + a = a \text{ and } 0 \cdot a = O.$$

Also $(-1)a + a = (-1)a + 1 \cdot a = (-1 + 1)a = 0 \cdot a = O$, hence

$$(-1)a = -a.$$

The vector x satisfying $a + x = c$ for given $a, c \in V$, is called the *difference* of c and a, and is denoted by $c - a$. From $a + x = c$ follows:

$$(-a) + a + x = O + x = x \text{ equals } (-a) + c.$$

Hence $c - a = c + (-a)$.

In fig. 1.2 $c - a$ is the vector b.

PROBLEMS. Using the definitions of vector space, subspace, basis, etc., prove the following assertions, and draw figures illustrating the low-dimensional cases. V will always be a vector space.

(3.4). If the pair $a, b \in V$ forms a basis of V, then so does the following pair of vectors ($\lambda \neq 0$):

$$a, -b; \ \lambda a, b; \ a + b, b.$$

(3.5). If $a_1, \cdots a_m$ form a basis of V, then so do

$$a_1, a_1 + a_2, a_3, a_4, \cdots a_m.$$

(3.6). If $a_1, \cdots a_k$ are vectors in V then the set B of all vectors $\lambda_1 a_1 + \cdots + \lambda_k a_k$ with arbitrary $\lambda_1, \cdots \lambda_k \in \mathbf{F}$ is also a vector space. It is called the *(sub)space generated by* $a_1, \cdots a_k$. The set of all vectors $\lambda a$ with fixed $a \in V$ and variable $\lambda \in \mathbf{F}$ is a one-dimensional space and is denoted by $\mathbf{F}a$. If $U$ and $W$ are subsets of V, then the set of all $b + c$ with $b \in U$ and $c \in W$ is denoted by $U + W$ (cf. fig. 3.2). Hence the subspace generated by $a_1, \cdots a_k$ can be represented by $\mathbf{F}a_1 + \mathbf{F}a_2 + \cdots + \mathbf{F}a_k$. Similarly $\lambda U$ may be defined.

Fig. 3.2

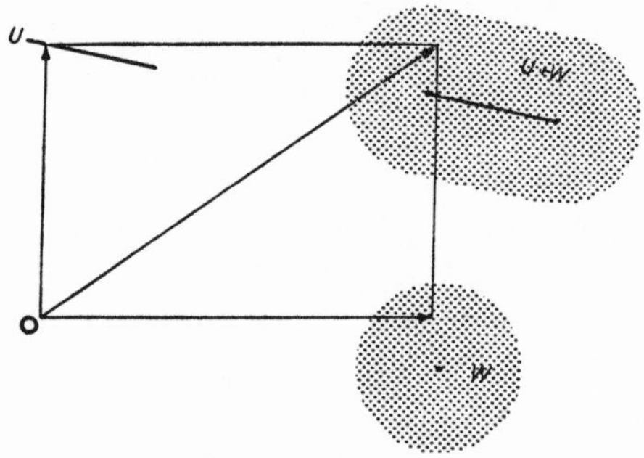


(3.7). If $W$ is a set in the two-dimensional geometrical vector space of chapter 1 and a is a point (vector), prove that $a + W$ is congruent to $W$.

(3.8). If $U$ and $W$ are non-parallel line segments in a plane, prove that $U + W$ is a parallelogram together with its interior.

(3.9). If $U$ is the interior of a triangle prove that $\frac{1}{2}(U + U) = U$.

(3.10). Let V be the set of all polynomials in x of degree $< n$ with coefficients in $\mathbf{R}$

$$\alpha_0 + \alpha_1 x + \cdots + \alpha_{n-1} x^{n-1}, \qquad \alpha_i \in \mathbf{R}.$$

Addition and multiplication with $\lambda \in \mathbf{R}$ are defined by

$$(\alpha_0 + \alpha_1 x + \cdots) + (\beta_0 + \beta_1 x + \cdots) = (\alpha_0 + \beta_0) + (\alpha_1 + \beta_1) x + \cdots,$$

$$\gamma(\alpha_0 + \alpha_1 x + \cdots) = (\gamma\alpha_0) + (\gamma\alpha_1) x + \cdots.$$

Then V is a vectorspace of dimension $n$. Which polynomial plays the role of O?

# 4. THE PARAMETRIC REPRESENTATION OF A LINE

Fig. 4.1 shows a so-called number axis. In connection with it we consider two sets:

a. the set of points on the line,
b. the set of real numbers.

The figure suggests a one-to-one mapping between the two sets, making possible the designation of points by numbers.

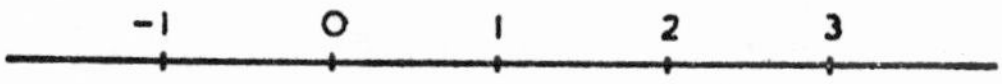


Fig. 4.1

Similarly in the geometrical plane with fixed point $O$ of chapter 1 we may consider two sets:

a. the set $A$ of points in the plane,
b. the set V of vectors.

There is again a one-to-one mapping of either of them onto the other set. Fig. 4.2 shows the two sets *apart*, and the mapping $\kappa$ is indicated by the arrow $\kappa$.

In $A$ our interest will concentrate on points, lines and other configurations, and later on motions. In V our attention will be directed to the vector algebra.

We may speak of $A$ in terms of V. For example $B$ is the point represented by vector b under the mapping $\kappa$. It will simply be called "*the point* b". For the time being we shall work with a single fixed mapping $A \rightarrow$ V; later on we shall consider various mappings $A \rightarrow$ V and we shall make a clearer distinction between $A$ and V.

After this introduction we give the following *preliminary definition* of the $n$-dimensional *affine space* $A^n$: It is a set whose elements are called points, having a one-to-one mapping

$$\kappa: A^n \to \mathrm{V}^n$$

onto the $n$-dimensional vector space $\mathrm{V}^n$.

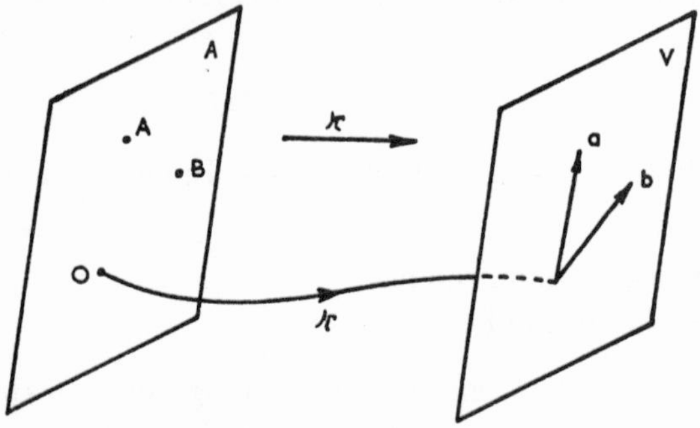


Fig. 4.2

In the following we shall alternately consider $A^n$ and $\mathrm{V}^n$; which of the two is under consideration can be seen from the terminology: points and lines belong to $A^n$, vectors and vector subspaces belong to $\mathrm{V}^n$. Moreover, vector spaces and vectors will be distinguished by roman type.

Definition: The *line* through the points (represented by the vectors) a and b is the point set (cf. fig. 4.3)

$$\mathrm{a} + \mu(\mathrm{b} - \mathrm{a}) \qquad \mu \in \mathbf{F} \tag{4.1}$$

or $$\lambda\mathrm{a} + \mu\mathrm{b} \qquad \lambda + \mu = 1;\ \lambda, \mu \in \mathbf{F}.$$

This definition of course refers to the affine space $A$; (4.1) is called the *parametric representation* of the line. b — a is called *the vector from point* a *to point* b. For $\mu = 0$ or 1 respectively we obtain the points a and b again. For $\mu = \frac{1}{2}$ we obtain the point $\mathrm{z} = \frac{1}{2}(\mathrm{a} + \mathrm{b})$, the *middle* or *centroid* of a and b.

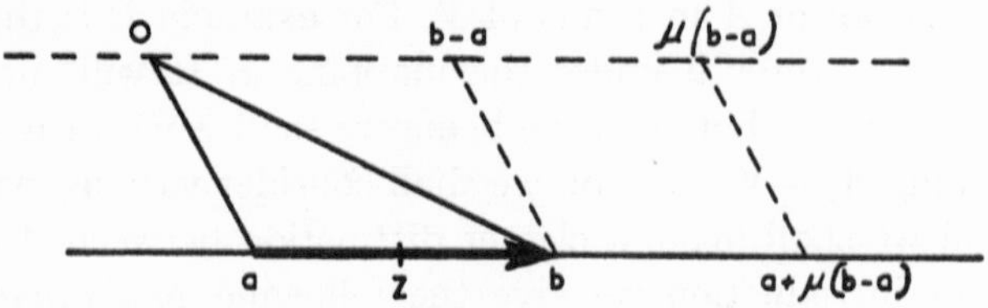


Fig. 4.3

If real numbers are being used ($\mathbf{F} = \mathbf{R}$) then the definition just gives the ordinary line through a and b. The points with $0 < \mu < 1$ lie between a and b on the line through a and b. This can be seen from the figure, but it cannot be seen independently of that, since "between" is a yet undefined term. A suitable definition is therefore: A point (4.1) on the line through a and b will be said to lie *between* a and b if $0 < \mu < 1$.

Suppose for general $\mathbf{F}$ that "the line through the different points a′ and b′" contains the points a and b($\neq$ a). We shall now prove that the line coincides with "the line through a and b".

This is expressed by

Theorem [4.1]: *There is exactly one line containing two given different points.*

Proof: Since a and b are on the line through a′ and b′ there exist scalars $\nu'$ and $\eta' \neq \nu' \in \mathbf{F}$ such that

$$a = a' + \nu'(b' - a'), \quad b = a' + \eta'(b' - a').$$

The line through a′ and b′ consists of the points

$$a' + \mu'(b' - a') \qquad \mu' \text{ variable in } \mathbf{F}.$$

The line through a and b consists of the points

$$a + \mu(b - a) = a' + \{\nu' + \mu(\eta' - \nu')\}(b' - a') \qquad \mu \in \mathbf{F}.$$

These two sets are identical: Take

$$\mu' = \nu' + \mu(\eta' - \nu'), \ \mu = (\mu' - \nu')(\eta' - \nu')^{-1}.$$

If $a \neq O$ and b are vectors such that $b = \lambda a$, then the scalar $\lambda$ is called *the ratio of* b *and* a. If also $b = \mu a$, then $\lambda a - \mu a = (\lambda - \mu)a = O$. If $\lambda - \mu \neq 0$ then $(\lambda - \mu)^{-1}(\lambda - \mu)a = a = O$, contrary to the assumption. Hence $\lambda = \mu$ and the ratio

$$\frac{b}{a} = \lambda \tag{4.2}$$

is uniquely determined.

*N.B.* For *arbitrary* vectors a and b, the left-hand side of (4.2) usually has no meaning.

Two lines are said to be *parallel* if there exist points a and b($\neq$ a) on one of them, points c and d($\neq$ c) on the other, and a scalar $\lambda$ such that

$$d - c = \lambda(b - a), \quad \lambda = \frac{d - c}{b - a}. \tag{4.3}$$

$\lambda$ is called the *ratio of the line segments* "cd" and "ab".

PROBLEMS. (4.1). If arbitrary points a′ and b′ $\neq$ a′ are chosen on one of two parallel lines and points c′ and d′($\neq$ c′) on the other one, then there exists a scalar $\lambda'$ such that $(d' - c') = \lambda'(b' - a')$.

(4.2). Given points a and b in the ordinary plane, determine a point c on ab such that the ratio of the line segments ab and ac equals (i) $-1$; (ii) $+4$; (iii) $+1$.

(4.3). If two lines are parallel to a third line then they are parallel themselves.

Three points a, b, c are said to be *collinear* if they are on one line. Three lines are said to be *concurrent* if they either pass through one point or are mutually parallel. (Fig. 4.4).

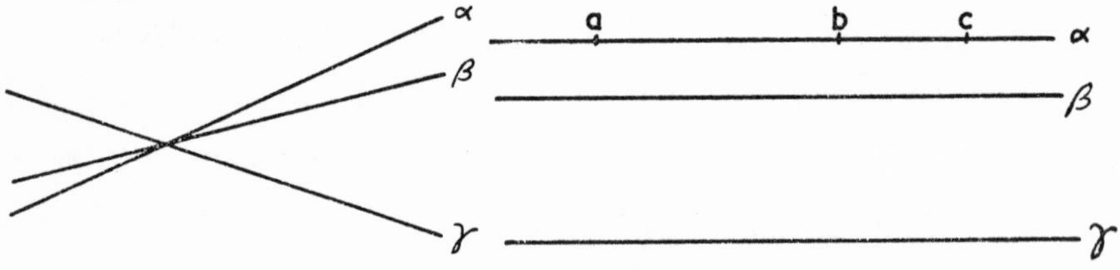


Fig. 4.4 Three concurrent lines.

As an application of what precedes we shall prove the

Theorem: *The medians of a triangle pass through one point* [1]).

Proof: Let a, b, c($\in$ V) be the vertices of an arbitrarily given triangle. We first determine an expression for the median from a to the middle of b and c: $\frac{1}{2}(b + c)$. It is: $a + \lambda\{\frac{1}{2}(b + c) - a\}$, $\lambda \in \mathbf{F}$. The choice $\lambda = 2/3$ yields the point

$$\tfrac{1}{3}(a + b + c). \tag{4.3}$$

[1]) In this theorem and the following problems we assume that the scalars are taken from a *field with characteristic* 0 such as the real or complex number fields.

On the medians from b and c we find in a similar way a point that can be obtained from (4.3) by interchanging the letters. However, (4.3) is invariant under interchange of letters; hence the point given by (4.3) lies on all medians and is then the centroid of the triangle.

(4.4). The points (represented by vectors) a, b, c lie on a line if and only if there are $\alpha, \beta, \gamma \in \mathbf{F}$ $((\alpha, \beta, \gamma) \neq (0, 0, 0))$ such that

$$\alpha \mathrm{a} + \beta \mathrm{b} + \gamma \mathrm{c} = \mathrm{O} \text{ and } \alpha + \beta + \gamma = 0.$$

(4.5). Give a definition of a parallelogram that can also be applied to a "quadrangle" having four collinear vertices. Let a, b, c, d be the consecutive vertices of a parallelogram in space. Express vector d in terms of a, b, c.

(4.6). The diagonals in a parallelogram bisect each other.

(4.7). The midpoints of the sides of an arbitrary plane or non-plane quadrangle form a parallelogram.

(4.8). Each of the sides ab and bc of a triangle is extended by itself to yield the points p and q resp. such that b is between a and p, c between b and q. Line pq intersects ac in r. Prove that c divides the segment ar into pieces with ratio 3 : 1.

(4.9). The four lines through one of the points a, b, c, d and the centroid of the other three pass through one point, the centroid of a, b, c, d.

(4.10). In a space of arbitrary dimension the *centroid of k points* $\mathrm{a}_1, \cdots \mathrm{a}_k$ is by definition the point

$$\mathrm{z} = \frac{1}{k} (\mathrm{a}_1 + \mathrm{a}_2 + \cdots + \mathrm{a}_k).$$

Prove that the line through the centroid of $\mathrm{a}_1, \cdots \mathrm{a}_p$ and the centroid of $\mathrm{a}_{p+1}, \cdots \mathrm{a}_{p+q}$ $(p + q = m)$, passes through the centroid of $\mathrm{a}_1, \cdots \mathrm{a}_m$.

What consequences does this have for a plane quadrangle and for a tetrahedron? (Take $(p, q) = (1, 3)$ and $(p, q) = (2, 2)$).

(4.11). The midpoints of the consecutive sides of the hexagon $\mathrm{a}_1\mathrm{a}_2 \cdots \mathrm{a}_6$ are $\mathrm{b}_1, \mathrm{b}_2, \cdots \mathrm{b}_6$ respectively. Prove that the triangles $\mathrm{b}_1\mathrm{b}_3\mathrm{b}_5$ and $\mathrm{b}_2\mathrm{b}_4\mathrm{b}_6$ have the same centroid.

(4.12). Give a definition of a parallelopiped. Let $\begin{matrix} e\,f\,g\,h \\ a\,b\,c\,d \end{matrix}$ be a parallelopiped; let u be the centroid of deb, v that of cfh, w′ that of bdeg, w″ that of acfh, w that of abcdefgh. Prove that w = w′ = w″ and that a, u, v, w and g are collinear. Calculate the ratio of the line segments thus formed on ag. Hint: take b = a + p, d = a + q, e = a + r and express the vertices in terms of a, p, q and r.

(4.13). A set $G$ of points of a real affine space is called *convex* if it contains together with any two points a, b also the points on ab between a and b. The intersection of two convex sets is itself convex.

(4.14). If $a_1, \cdots a_m$ are arbitrary points in a real affine space then the set $G$ of the points

$$x = \frac{\gamma_1 a_1 + \cdots + \gamma_m a_m}{\gamma_1 + \cdots + \gamma_m} \qquad \gamma_1, \cdots \gamma_m \text{ real numbers}$$

is convex.

The same is true if $\gamma_1, \cdots \gamma_m$ are required to be non-negative.

Fig. 4.5

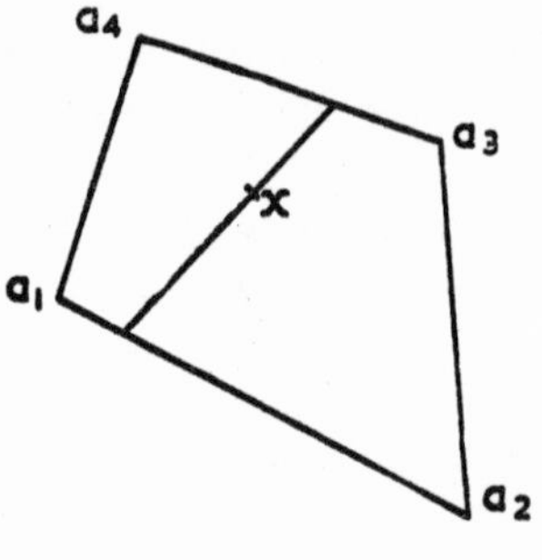


In this last case prove that we obtain the smallest convex set containing $a_1, \cdots a_m$ (cf. fig. 4.5). x is called a *weighted mean* of the vectors $a_1, \cdots a_m$ with "weights" $\gamma_1 \geqslant 0, \cdots \gamma_m \geqslant 0$.

If $m = 3$ and $a_1, a_2, a_3$ are not collinear, then this convex set is a triangle which, in this connection, is also called a *two-simplex.*

(4.15). If $x = \dfrac{\lambda a + \mu b}{\lambda + \mu}$ then a, b and x are collinear, and for $\mu \neq 0$:

$$\frac{x - b}{a - x} = \frac{\lambda}{\mu} \text{ and } \frac{x - b}{x - a} = -\frac{\lambda}{\mu}.$$

(4.16). In a triangle abc whose vertices are not collinear, the lines connecting a, b, c with points a′, b′, c′ on the opposite sides are concurrent if and only if the following ratio of line segments equals $-1$:

$$\frac{c - a'}{b - a'} \cdot \frac{a - b'}{c - b'} \cdot \frac{b - c'}{a - c'}.$$

This is Ceva's theorem, which will be proved in chapter 7.

Hint: If aa′ and bb′ intersect in a point $P$, write

$$P = \frac{\alpha a + \beta b + \gamma c}{\alpha + \beta + \gamma}.$$

(4.17). Let the non-collinear points a, b, c, d form a parallelogram in a plane not containing O. Prove that the points $\lambda$a, $\mu$b, $\nu$c and $\omega$d ($\lambda, \mu, \nu, \omega \neq 0$) are in a plane if and only if

$$\frac{1}{\lambda} + \frac{1}{\nu} = \frac{1}{\mu} + \frac{1}{\omega}.$$

(4.18*). Let $G$ be a convex set in the real plane with boundary $\partial G$, not a single point of which belongs to $G$. It may be assumed that $\partial G$ divides lines through a point $P$ of $G$ into pieces the ratio of which depends continuously on the direction. Prove that any point of $G$ bisects at least one chord of $\partial G$.

Prove also that (cf. problem 3.6)

$$\tfrac{1}{2}(\partial G + \partial G) = G \cup \partial G.$$

Hint: prove that any point belonging to the left-hand side also belongs to the right-hand side of the equation and conversely.

(4.19*). A point a in a real vector plane is called the *centre* of a point set $G$ if $a - x \in G$ whenever $a + x \in G$. Now let $G$ be a convex set with centre $a = O$ and boundary $\partial G$ which has no point in common with $G$. Also, if $\omega > 0$ let $\omega G$ and $\omega \cdot \partial G$ be the sets obtained from $G$ and $\partial G$ by geometrical multiplication from O with factor $\omega$.

Now assume that $0 < \omega < \frac{1}{2}$ and prove that $(1 - 2\omega)G$ is the set of all points in $G$ through which there exists no chord which is divided in ratio $\omega : (1 - \omega)$.

(4.20). If $U$ and $W$ are convex subsets of a real vector space then $U + W$ is also convex.

## 5. SOME FUNDAMENTAL THEOREMS

The following theorems are trivial in ordinary plane and solid geometry. Therefore figures are of no use in proving them. These theorems are needed in order to give sufficient generality to our theory.

A vector a will be called a *linear combination* of the vectors $a_1$, $a_2$, $\cdots a_m$ if it belongs to the space generated by $a_1$, $\cdots a_m$, i.e. if there are scalars $\lambda_1$, $\cdots \lambda_m$ such that

$$a = \lambda_1 a_1 + \cdots + \lambda_m a_m. \quad (5.1)$$

Then a is said to be *linearly dependent* on $a_1$, $\cdots a_m$. The vectors $a_1$, $\cdots a_m$ are said to be *linearly dependent* or short *dependent*, if at least one of them is linearly dependent on the others. This is the case if and only if there are scalars $\lambda_1$, $\cdots \lambda_m$, not all zero, such that

$$\lambda_1 a_1 + \cdots + \lambda_m a_m = O. \quad (5.2)$$

PROBLEMS. (5.1). Prove our last assertion.

(5.2). Vector a is linearly dependent on 2a + b and b. The vectors 2a and − a are linearly dependent. Also O, a and b; 2a, b and a + b.

If some vectors are not linearly dependent, then they are called *linearly independent*, or short *independent*.

Theorem [5.1]: *A basis* $a_1$, $\cdots a_m$ *of a vectorspace* V *consists of independent vectors, and conversely any independent set of generators of* V *is a basis.*

Proof: Suppose that one of the vectors $a_1$, $\cdots a_m$ of a basis is dependent on the other ones. After possible rearrangement we may assume that $a_m$ is this vector. Any vector of V may be written as a linear combination of $a_1$, $\cdots a_m$, and subsequently, by substituting the expression for $a_m$, as a linear combination of $a_1, \cdots a_{m-1}$. It follows that $a_1, \cdots a_{m-1}$ already form a set of generators of V, and $a_m$ can be omitted, contrary to the assumption that $a_1, \cdots a_m$ form a basis.

If, conversely, an independent set of generators $a_1, \cdots a_m$ of V were not a basis, then one of them, for example $a_m$ could be omitted. But in that case $a_m$ could be written as linear combination of $a_1, \cdots a_{m-1}$.

Theorem [5.2]: *Let* $a_1, \cdots a_m$ *be a basis of* V, *then for any vector* $a \in V$ *there exists exactly one set of scalars* $\lambda_1, \cdots \lambda_m$ *such that* (5.1) *holds* (*uniqueness of the representation* (5.1)).

Proof: If

$$\mu_1 a_1 + \cdots + \mu_m a_m = \nu_1 a_1 + \cdots + \nu_m a_m$$

then

$$(\mu_1 - \nu_1)a_1 + \cdots + (\mu_m - \nu_m)a_m = O$$

and, since $a_1, \cdots a_m$ are independent,

$$\mu_1 - \nu_1 = \cdots = \mu_m - \nu_m = 0.$$

A mapping (cf. chapter 2) of V into the field **F** is called a *function on* V *with values in* **F**. The function

$$\varphi: V \to \mathbf{F}$$

is called *homogeneous and linear*, or shorter: *linear*, if for every $a, b \in V$ and $\lambda, \mu \in \mathbf{F}$:

$$\varphi(\lambda a) = \lambda\varphi(a) \qquad (5.3)$$

and

$$\varphi(a + b) = \varphi(a) + \varphi(b). \qquad (5.4)$$

Consequently

$$\varphi(\lambda a + \mu b) = \varphi(\lambda a) + \varphi(\mu b) = \lambda\varphi(a) + \mu\varphi(b)$$

and for $a_1, \cdots a_m \in V$, $\lambda_1, \cdots \lambda_m \in \mathbf{F}$,

$$\varphi(\lambda_1 a_1 + \cdots + \lambda_m a_m) = \lambda_1\varphi(a_1) + \cdots + \lambda_m\varphi(a_m), \qquad (5.5)$$

hence a linear function is determined as soon as its values on $a_1, \cdots a_m$ are known.

Figure 5.1 shows two linear functions $\varphi_1$ and $\varphi_2$ in the two-dimensional vector space of chapter 1. The functions are such that $\varphi_1(a_1) = \varphi_2(a_2) = 1$, $\varphi_1(a_2) = \varphi_2(a_1) = 0$.

Theorem [5.3]: *Let* $a_1, \cdots a_m$ *be a basis of* V, *and* $\alpha_1, \cdots \alpha_m \in \mathbf{F}$, *then there exists exactly one homogeneous linear function* $\varphi$ *such that* $\varphi(a_i) = \alpha_i$, $i = 1, \cdots m$. *Any linear function on* V *can be so obtained.*

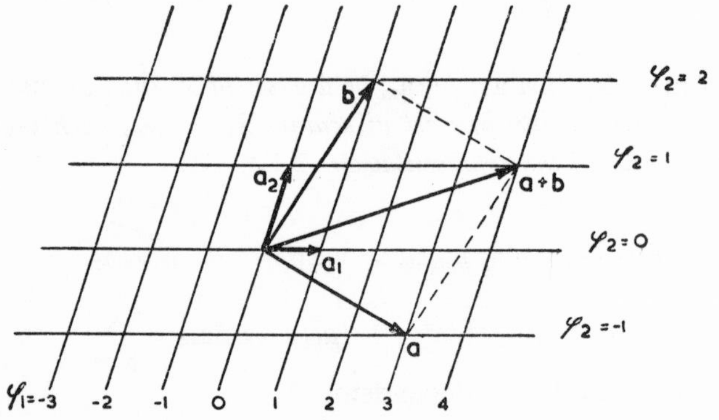


Fig. 5.1

Proof: Since by the last theorem any vector $a \in V$ can unambiguously be written in the form (5.1), we may define the following function $\varphi$ on V:

$$\varphi(a) = \varphi(\lambda_1 a_1 + \cdots + \lambda_m a_m) = \lambda_1 \alpha_1 + \cdots + \lambda_m \alpha_m \quad \lambda_i \in \mathbf{F}.$$

This function has the property that $\varphi(a_i) = \alpha_i$ and in addition it satisfies (5.3) and (5.4); hence it is the desired linear function. The last assertion in the theorem follows from (5.5).

First Dimension Theorem [5.4]: *Any basis of an n-dimensional space* $V^n$ *consists of n vectors. Any set of independent vectors in* $V^n$ *can be extended to a basis.*

*Therefore we may define the dimension of a vector space as the number of vectors of an arbitrary basis.*

Proof: The theorem holds for $n = 1$, since in a one-dimensional space with basis-vector a any vector $\lambda a \neq O$ is a generator.

We next prove, that if the theorem holds for every natural number $n < k$, it also holds for $n = k$. From the principle of *mathematical induction* it then follows that the theorem holds for every natural number $n$.

Assume now that the theorem holds for $n < k$. We consider a $k$-dimensional vector space $V^k$ with basis $b_1, \cdots b_k$. Let B be the space generated by $b_1, \cdots b_{k-1}$. These vectors are independent. They form a basis of B, which, by the induction hypothesis, has dimension $k - 1$. Let $\varphi$ be the linear function for which

$$\varphi(b_i) = \begin{Bmatrix} 0 \text{ for } i \neq k \\ 1 \text{ for } i = k \end{Bmatrix}.$$

For an arbitrary vector b we have

$$\varphi(b) = \varphi(\lambda_1 b_1 + \cdots + \lambda_k b_k) = \lambda_k$$

and this expression is zero if and only if $b \in B$. Hence $B = \text{Kernel } \varphi$.

Now let $a_1, \cdots a_r$ be another basis of $V^k$. If $\varphi(a_i) = 0$ for $i = 1, \cdots r$, then the linear function $\varphi$ is identically zero on V, contrary to the assumption. Hence, after possible rearrangement we may assume $\varphi(a_r) \neq 0$.

Next consider the $r - 1$ vectors

$$c_i = a_i - \frac{\varphi(a_i)}{\varphi(a_r)} a_r \qquad i = 1, \cdots r-1.$$

These vectors are contained in B since $\varphi(c_i) = 0$ for $i = 1, \cdots, r - 1$. They are projections in the direction of $a_r$.

They are independent, for, since $a_1, \cdots a_r$ are independent,

$$\textstyle\sum_{i=1}^{r-1} \lambda_i c_i = \sum_{i=1}^{r-1} \lambda_i a_i + [\cdots]\, a_r$$

cannot be zero, unless $\lambda_1 = \cdots = \lambda_{r-1} = 0$.

Moreover the $c_1, \cdots c_{r-1}$ are a basis of B, because for any vector $a \in B$,

$$a = \lambda_1 a_1 + \cdots + \lambda_r a_r \quad \text{with} \quad \varphi(a) = \lambda_1 \varphi(a_1) + \cdots + \lambda_r \varphi(a_r) = 0$$

we have

$$a = \lambda_1 c_1 + \cdots + \lambda_{r-1} c_{r-1} + \frac{\lambda_1 \varphi(a_1) + \cdots + \lambda_r \varphi(a_r)}{\varphi(a_r)} a_r =$$
$$= \lambda_1 c_1 + \cdots + \lambda_{r-1} c_{r-1}.$$

Hence $r - 1 = k - 1$ and $r = k$, which proves the first part of our theorem.

Now let $b_1, \cdots b_j$ be independent vectors in the $n$-dimensional space $V^n$ with basis $a_1, \cdots a_n$. Then there exists a number $k$ such that $b_1, \cdots b_j$ together with $k$ of the vectors $a_1, \cdots a_n$ form a set of generators, but such that no $k - 1$ of the $a_1, \cdots a_n$ together with the $b_1, \cdots b_j$ do so. Hence $k + j \geqslant n$. Let, after possible rearrangement, $a_1, \cdots a_k$ be such a set. If $k + j > n$ then $a_1, \cdots a_k$, $b_1, \cdots b_j$ are dependent. Then there are scalars $\alpha_1, \cdots \alpha_k$, $\beta_1, \cdots \beta_j$, not all zero, such that

$$\alpha_1 a_1 + \cdots + \alpha_k a_k + \beta_1 b_1 + \cdots + \beta_j b_j = O. \qquad (5.6)$$

If all of $\alpha_1, \cdots \alpha_k$ are zero, the dependence of $b_1, \cdots b_j$ follows, contradicting our assumption. If, however, $\alpha_i \neq 0$, then $a_i$ could be omitted, contrary to the definition of $k$. Hence $k + j = n$, which proves the final part of our theorem: the set of independent vectors $b_1, \cdots b_j$ can be extended with $k = n - j$ of the vectors $a_1, \cdots a_n$ to form a basis of $V^n$. Observe that this implies $j \leqslant n$.

Theorem [5.5]: *Let B be a subset of the vector space* $V = V^n$ *and suppose that for every* $a, b \in B$ *and* $\lambda \in \mathbf{F}$, *also* $\lambda a \in B$ *and* $a + b \in B$. *Then B together with addition and multiplication properties* $A_1$ *and* $A_2$ *of* V, *is again a vector space. The dimension of* $B =$ B *is less then or equal to* $n$.

B is called a *subspace* of V.

Proof: The reader will verify without difficulty that properties $A_3, \cdots A_8$ (cf. chapter 3) hold. To prove $A_9$, choose in B a set of independent vectors, which cannot be extended. This set, which of course consists of at most $n$ vectors, then constitutes a finite basis of B.

Problems. (5.3). If B and C are subspaces of V, then $B \cap C$ is also a subspace of V, and so is the space $B + C$ generated by B and C (cf. problem 3.6).

To prove the last assertion, let $b_1 + c_1$ and $b_2 + c_2$ ($b_1, b_2 \in B$; $c_1, c_2 \in C$) be two arbitrary vectors of $B + C$. If $\lambda \in \mathbf{F}$, then $\lambda(b_1 + c_1)$ and $(b_1 + c_1) + (b_2 + c_2)$ are also in $B + C$, since these vectors are equal to

$$\lambda b_1 + \lambda c_1 \text{ and } (b_1 + b_2) + (c_1 + c_2),$$

respectively, whereas

$$\lambda b_1, b_1 + b_2 \in B, \lambda c_1, c_1 + c_2 \in C.$$

Then B + C is a subspace, since axioms $A_3, \cdots A_8$ hold automatically, whilst a finite number of generators of B + C is obtained from a basis of B and one of C.

In fig. 5.2 the 2-dimensional vectorspaces B and C intersect in the one-dimensional space $B \cap C$; together they generate the 3-dimensional space B + C.

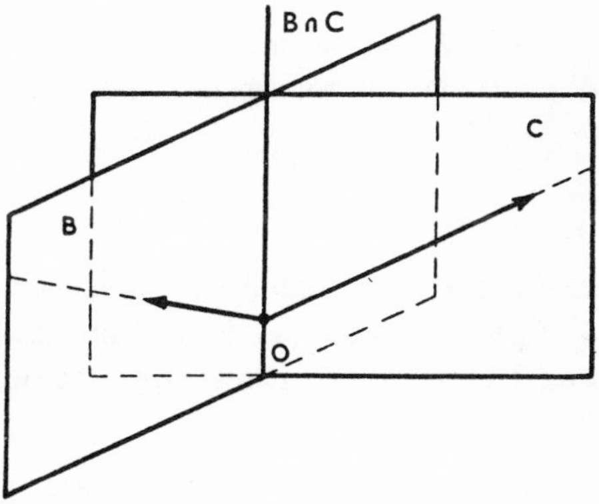


Fig. 5.2

(5.4). a and b are vectors in a real vector space. A linear function $\eta$ is known to satisfy $\eta(a + 2b) = -4$ and $\eta(2a - b) = 7$.
Calculate $\eta(3a + b)$, $\eta(2a + 4b)$, $\eta(3b)$, $\eta(a)$, $\eta(b)$.

Second Dimension Theorem [5.6]: *Let* B *and* C *be two subspaces of* V, *with intersection* $B \cap C$, *and let* B + C *be the space generated by* B *and* C. *Then the dimensions satisfy*

$$\dim (B + C) = \dim B + \dim C - \dim (B \cap C).$$

Proof: Put $\dim(B \cap C) = r$, $\dim B = r + s$, $\dim C = r + t$. Choose a basis $a_1, \cdots a_r$ in $B \cap C$, and complete this to a basis $a_1, \cdots a_r, b_1, \cdots b_s$ of B and to a basis $a_1, \cdots a_r, c_1, \cdots c_t$ of C.

Now $a_1, \cdots a_r, b_1, \cdots b_s, c_1, \cdots c_t$ form a set of generators of

$B + C$. It actually is a basis, for, if

$$\Sigma_1^r \alpha_i a_i + \Sigma_1^s \beta_j b_j + \Sigma_1^t \gamma_k c_k = 0 \tag{5.7}$$

then $- \Sigma_1^s \beta_j b_j$ is not only in B, but also in C, hence in $B \cap C$.

But then this vector is zero, since otherwise $b_1, \cdots b_s$ and $a_1, \cdots a_r$ would be dependent. Hence $\beta_1 = \cdots = \beta_s = 0$, and

$$\Sigma_1^r \alpha_i a_i + \Sigma_1^t \gamma_k c_k = 0. \tag{5.7'}$$

Since $a_1, \cdots a_r, c_1, \cdots c_t$ are independent, all coefficients in (5.7′) and (5.7) have to be zero.

Hence the dimension of $B + C$ is $r + s + t$, which proves the theorem.

PROBLEM (5.5). Apply the second dimension theorem to subspaces of a 3-dimensional vector space, and illustrate this with figures.

*The dual vector space* V*

If $\varphi$ is a linear function on V and $\lambda \in \mathbf{F}$, then $\lambda\varphi$, i.e. the function associating to $a \in V$ the value $\lambda\varphi(a)$, is also linear. If $\varphi$ and $\psi$ are linear functions on V, then $\varphi + \psi$ is also a function, in fact a linear function on V, for

$$\varphi(\mu a) + \psi(\mu a) = \mu[\varphi(a) + \psi(a)]$$

$$\varphi(a + b) + \psi(a + b) = [\varphi(a) + \psi(a)] + [\varphi(b) + \psi(b)].$$

Hence in the set of linear functions there exist addition $A_1$ and multiplication by scalars $A_2$, and it is easily verified that the relations $A_3, \cdots A_8$ are satisfied.

Theorem [5.7]. *The linear functions on an n-dimensional vector space* V *themselves form an n-dimensional vector space* V*.

Proof: If $a_1, \cdots a_n$ is a basis of V, then some examples of linear functions are

$$\varphi_i \text{ with } \varphi_i(a_j) = \delta_{ij} \quad i = 1, \cdots n; j = 1, \cdots n.$$

$\delta_{ij}$ *will always be the function with value* 1 *for* $j = i$ *and* 0 *for* $j \neq i$.

Now let $\varphi$ be an arbitrary linear function and $a = \lambda_1 a_1 + \cdots + \lambda_n a_n$.

If we put $\varphi(a_i) = \alpha_i$, then

$$\varphi(a) = \varphi(\lambda_1 a_1 + \cdots + \lambda_n a_n) = \lambda_1\varphi(a_1) + \cdots + \lambda_n\varphi(a_n) =$$
$$= \lambda_1\alpha_1 + \cdots + \lambda_n\alpha_n = \alpha_1\lambda_1 + \cdots + \alpha_n\lambda_n.$$

But $\varphi_i(a) = \lambda_i$, hence

$$\varphi(a) = \alpha_1\varphi_1(a) + \cdots + \alpha_n\varphi_n(a)$$

i.e. any linear function is linearly dependent on the functions $\varphi_1, \cdots \varphi_n$.

The functions $\varphi_1, \cdots \varphi_n$ are linearly independent, for, if $\nu_1, \cdots \nu_n$ are scalars such that $\nu_1\varphi_1 + \cdots + \nu_n\varphi_n$ is the zero function, then its value is in particular zero on $a_i$, and hence $\nu_i = 0$ for $i = 1, \cdots n$. Consequently these functions form a basis of the vectorspace V* of linear functions on V. V* is called the *dual vector space* of V. It has the same dimension as V. The basis $\varphi_1, \cdots \varphi_n$ is called the *cobasis* in V* of $a_1, \cdots a_n$ in V.

We can also consider the dual space V** of V*(!) consisting of linear functions on V*. If $a \in V$ then the mapping associating $\varphi(a)$ to $\varphi \in V^*$ is a function, which turns out to be linear on V*: If $\lambda \in \mathbf{F}$, then $\lambda\varphi \to \lambda\varphi(a)$, $\varphi + \psi \to \varphi(a) + \psi(a)$, that is, the sum of the values attached to $\varphi$ and $\psi$. In particular for $a = a_i$ we get the mapping

$$\varphi \to \varphi(a_i) \qquad \varphi \in V^*$$

with

$$\varphi_j \to \varphi_j(a_i) = \delta_{ij} \qquad \text{for } j = 1, \cdots n.$$

It follows that the linear functions $\varphi \to \varphi(a_i)$, $i = 1, \cdots n$, form a basis of V**, viz. the cobasis of the basis $\varphi_1, \cdots \varphi_n$ of V*. An arbitrary element of V** is then a mapping, which can be written as

$$\varphi \to \lambda_1\varphi(a_1) + \cdots + \lambda_n\varphi(a_n) = \varphi(\lambda_1 a_1 + \cdots + \lambda_n a_n) = \varphi(a).$$

By this mapping the elements of V** are put into one-to-one correspondence with the elements of V. The $\lambda$-product of an element of V** corresponds to the $\lambda$-product of its image in V. Moreover the sum of two elements of V** is mapped into the sum of the images in V. The reader is recommended to verify this. We can therefore denote the linear function on V*: $\varphi \to \varphi(a)$ by $a \in V$, and consider V as V**. We shall also say that V** and V *may be identified.*

If $a_1, \cdots a_n$ is a basis of $V^n$, if $\varphi_1, \cdots \varphi_n$ is the cobasis and

$$a = \lambda_1 a_1 + \cdots + \lambda_n a_n,$$

then $$\lambda_1 = \varphi_1(a), \cdots, \lambda_n = \varphi_n(a),$$

and $$a = \varphi_1(a) \cdot a_1 + \cdots + \varphi_n(a) \cdot a_n. \tag{5.8}$$

It follows that the vector $a \in V^n$ can be represented uniquely by the values $\lambda_1, \cdots \lambda_n$ of the set of functions $\varphi_1, \cdots \varphi_n$ on a. These values $\lambda_1, \cdots \lambda_n$ are also called the coordinate values or *coordinates* of the vector a with respect to the basis $a_1, \cdots a_n$. The functions $\varphi_1, \cdots \varphi_n$ are also called *coordinates.*

If a and b are characterized by the coordinates $\lambda_1, \cdots \lambda_n$ and $\mu_1, \cdots \mu_n$ respectively, then

$$\boxed{\begin{array}{c} \lambda a \text{ is characterized by } \lambda\lambda_1, \lambda\lambda_2, \cdots \lambda\lambda_n \\ \text{and } a+b \text{ is characterized by } \lambda_1+\mu_1, \lambda_2+\mu_2, \cdots \lambda_n+\mu_n. \end{array}} \tag{5.9}$$

*The vector space* $\mathbf{F}^n$. Consider the sequences of $n$ scalars $(\lambda_1, \cdots \lambda_n)$ and *define multiplication* of a sequence by a factor $\lambda$ and *addition* of sequences by (5.9). These conventions may be used as axioms $A_1$ and $A_2$ of a vector space for which, by what precedes, the other axioms are also satisfied. These axioms are also easily verified directly. The vector space so defined is called the $n$-dimensional space $\mathbf{F}^n$.

Two vector spaces are called *isomorphic* if there exists a one-to-one mapping of the first onto the second space such that the $\lambda$-product of a vector is mapped into the $\lambda$-product of the image, and the sum of two vectors is mapped into the sum of the images. We observed already that V and V** are isomorphic. By interpretation with coordinates (5.9) we obtain

Theorem [5.8]: *Any n-dimensional vector space over* **F** *is isomorphic to the n-dimensional space* $\mathbf{F}^n$.

Fig. 5.1 shows a basis and a cobasis of two linear functions on the 2-dimensional vector space of chapter 1. Moreover a is the vector with coordinates $\varphi_1(\mathrm{a}) = 3$, $\varphi_2(\mathrm{a}) = -1$; it may be denoted by $\mathrm{a} = (3, -1)$.

Problem (5.6). Prove axioms $A_3, \cdots A_8$ for $\mathbf{F}^n$.

Theorem [5.9]: *Let $\varphi$ be a proper linear function on $\mathrm{V}^n$, i.e. not the function 0. Then the kernel $\varphi^{-1}(0)$ is an $(n-1)$-dimensional subspace of* V.

Proof: If $\mathrm{a}_1, \cdots \mathrm{a}_n$ is a basis of V, then $\varphi(\mathrm{a}_j) \neq 0$ for at least one $j$, say for $j = n$; thus $\varphi(\mathrm{a}_n) \neq 0$. Then the vectors

$$\mathrm{c}_i = \mathrm{a}_i - \frac{\varphi(\mathrm{a}_i)}{\varphi(\mathrm{a}_n)} \mathrm{a}_n \qquad i = 1, \cdots n-1$$

are in the kernel and form, together with $\mathrm{a}_n$, another basis of V; moreover

$$\varphi(\mathrm{a}) = \varphi(\lambda_1\mathrm{c}_1 + \cdots + \lambda_{n-1}\mathrm{c}_{n-1} + \lambda_n\mathrm{a}_n) =$$

$$= \lambda_1\varphi(\mathrm{c}_1) + \cdots + \lambda_{n-1}\varphi(\mathrm{c}_{n-1}) + \lambda_n\varphi(\mathrm{a}_n) = \lambda_n\varphi(\mathrm{a}_n).$$

This expression is zero if and only if $\lambda_n = 0$, i.e. if a belongs to the space generated by the $n-1$ independent vectors $\mathrm{c}_1, \cdots \mathrm{c}_{n-1}$.

Theorem [5.10]: *If $\xi$ and $\eta$ are two proper linear functions on $\mathrm{V}^n$ with common kernel, then there exists a scalar $\lambda$ such that*

$$\xi = \lambda\eta.$$

Proof: For any value of $\lambda$ the function $\xi - \lambda\eta$ is also a linear function. Let the kernel of $\xi$ and $\eta$ be generated by $\mathrm{c}_1, \cdots \mathrm{c}_{n-1}$, which together with, say, $\mathrm{a}_n$ form a basis of $\mathrm{V}^n$. Choose $\lambda$ such that

$$\xi(\mathrm{a}_n) - \lambda\eta(\mathrm{a}_n) = 0.$$

Then $\xi - \lambda\eta$ is a linear function which assumes the value zero on the vectors of the basis of V, and which is, therefore, identically zero: $\xi = \lambda\eta$.

We conclude this chapter by giving the definition of functions of degree $r$. A mapping of V onto one single scalar $\lambda \in \mathbf{F}$ will be called a *constant function*, or *function of degree zero*. The sum of a proper linear function $\varphi$ (i.e. not the function 0) and a constant $\lambda$, $\varphi + \lambda$ is called a *proper first-degree function*. A function $\chi$: V $\rightarrow$ **F** will be called a *function of degree r* on V if it is equal to a sum of terms each of which is the product of at most $r$ functions of degree one. If $\chi$ is not also of degree $r - 1$, then it is said to be of *proper degree r*. If $\chi$ is equal to a sum of terms each of which is the product of $r$ (homogeneous) linear functions, then $\chi$ is called a *homogeneous* function of degree $r$.

By this definition linear functions are homogeneous functions of degree one. Likewise the term *quadratic function on a vector space* will be reserved for homogeneous second-degree functions.

If $\xi$, $\eta$ are given functions on V then by $\xi\eta$ and $\eta^2$ we mean the functions that map a $\epsilon$ V into $\xi(a)\cdot\eta(a)$ and $\{\eta(a)\}^2$ respectively. It $\xi$, $\eta$, $\zeta$ are some (proper) linear functions on V, and $\lambda$ and $\mu$ are scalars distinct from zero, then

| | |
|---|---|
| $\lambda\xi\eta + \eta^2 + \mu + \lambda\zeta$ | is a second-degree function |
| $\xi^2 + \lambda\xi\eta + \zeta^2$ | is a homogeneous second-degree function |
| $\xi + \eta + \lambda\zeta + \mu$ | is a first-degree function |
| $\xi^3 + \eta^3$ | is a homogeneous third-degree function. |

The first- and second-degree functions on vector spaces play an important part in all branches of mathematics. In the following chapters we shall discuss them at length.

PROBLEMS. (5.7). The space of homogeneous $r$-th degree functions on an $n$-dimensional vector space is of dimension

$$\binom{n + r - 1}{r} \quad (r \geqslant 0).$$

The functions of degree $r$ form a vector space of dimension $\sum_{s=0}^{r} \binom{n + s - 1}{s}$. By definition $\binom{n}{k} = \dfrac{n!}{k!\,(n - k)!}$.

(5.8). The vectors (1, 0, 0, 0), (1, 1, 0, 0), (1, 1, 1, 0) and (1, 1, 1, 1) form a basis of $\mathbf{R}^4$. Determine the values of the vectors of the cobasis on the vector (0, 0, 0, 1) and also on the vector (1, — 1, 1, — 1).

# 6. FIRST DEGREE FUNCTIONS ON, AND LINEAR VARIETIES IN $A^n$

Vectors were introduced in the ordinary plane in order to enable us to apply algebraic tools to geometry. Now it is well-known from elementary geometry that there is sometimes an advantage in choosing the origin of this vector plane in a particular point with respect to a given problem. In our example of the number axis in fig. 4.1 this amounts to considering different scales along the line, each of which provides a mapping of the line onto the real number system. Fig. 6.1 and 6.2 show two different scales along the line, and we notice that if the upper scale $\kappa$ associates the number $a$ to a given point $P$, then the lower scale $\kappa'$ associates the number $a' = a + d$ to $P$.

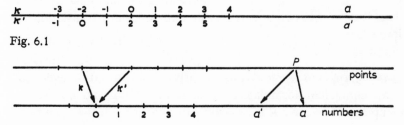

Fig. 6.1

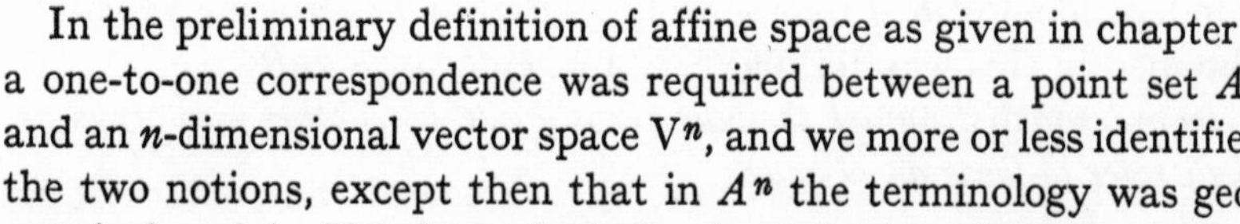

Fig. 6.2

In the preliminary definition of affine space as given in chapter 4 a one-to-one correspondence was required between a point set $A^n$ and an $n$-dimensional vector space $V^n$, and we more or less identified the two notions, except then that in $A^n$ the terminology was geometrical and in $V^n$ algebraical. In the following definition of an affine space $A^n$ we require the existence of a whole range of mappings of $A^n$ onto $V^n$, where any two mappings are interrelated in a way similar to the relation between the two scales of fig. 6.1.

In connection with the following definition it is convenient to introduce the notion of a *translation over* d in $V^n$: it is a mapping of the vector space $V^n$ onto itself which for fixed $d \in V^n$ associates to any vector $x \in V^n$ the vector $x + d$. If we are not particularly interested in the vector d, we shall just call this mapping a *translation*.

Definition: The $n$-dimensional *affine space* $A^n$ is a set of elements called points, with an atlas $\mathscr{A}$ of one-to-one mappings $\kappa, \kappa', \cdots$ of $A^n$ onto the $n$-dimensional vector space $V^n$ such that the following two properties hold (cf. fig. 6.3):

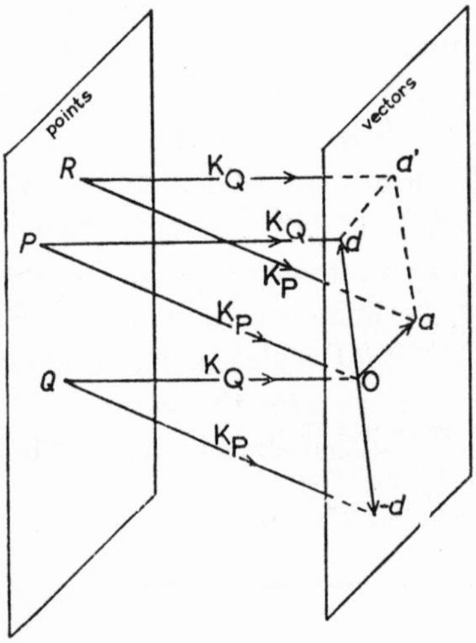


Fig. 6.3

I. To any point $P \in A^n$ there corresponds a mapping $\kappa_P \in \mathscr{A}$ which maps $P$ to the vector O of $V^n$, i.e. $\kappa_P P = O$.

II. If $\kappa_P$ and $\kappa_Q$ are two mappings in $\mathscr{A}$ then the mapping $\kappa_Q \kappa_P^{-1}$ of $V^n$ onto itself is a translation.

Note that in II the mapping $\kappa_P^{-1}$ sends O to $P$, hence the translation $\kappa_Q \kappa_P^{-1}$ maps O to $\kappa_Q P$ and consequently it is a translation over $\kappa_Q P$.

An equivalent formulation of II is that if $\kappa_P$ and $\kappa_Q$ are two mappings in $\mathscr{A}$, and $R$ is an arbitrary point of $A^n$, the vector

$$d = \kappa_Q R - \kappa_P R \tag{6.1}$$

is independent of $R$. From I it follows that any vector $d \in V^n$ can be obtained in this way (cf. fig. 6.3: $a = \kappa_P R$, $a' = \kappa_Q R$).

*In order to distinguish the mappings $\kappa \in \mathscr{A}$ from other mappings, we shall refer to these as $\mathscr{A}$-maps.*

The vector space V can also be described in terms of $A$ in another way. Consider the set of pairs of points of $A$, that is $A \times A$. Two pairs $(P, Q)$ and $(R, S)$ will be said to be equivalent if for some $\mathscr{A}$-map $\kappa$

$$\kappa(Q) - \kappa(P) = \kappa(S) - \kappa(R) \quad [\in V^n].$$

This is indeed an equivalence relation $\Omega$ and it is independent of the choice of $\kappa \in \mathscr{A}$. Any equivalence class determines a unique vector and vice versa. Hence the vectors can be considered as particular equivalence classes of pairs of points. Addition is defined by the rule that the sum of the class of $(P, Q)$ and the class of $(Q, R)$ is the class of $(P, R)$. With a similar rule for multiplication with a scalar, $(A \times A)/\Omega$ acquires a structure isomorphic to V.

In chapter 4 we introduced a few geometrical notions, such as line and ratio of parallel line segments. Since at that time we used only one single $\mathscr{A}$-map $\kappa$, these notions could be defined in terms of vectors without risk of ambiguity. But we now have to check that, for example, a set of points in $A$ that would be called a line under a particular $\mathscr{A}$-map $\kappa$, will also be a line under any other $\mathscr{A}$-map. If this were not the case, the notion of line would not be a proper notion for points in an affine space $A$. Fortunately the notions mentioned above are indeed independent of the choice of a particular map, as we shall now prove.

Let $\kappa = \kappa_P$ and $\kappa' = \kappa_Q$ be two $\mathscr{A}$-maps. If the points of a set in $A$ correspond under $\kappa$ to the vectors $\mathrm{c} = \mathrm{a} + \mu(\mathrm{b} - \mathrm{a})$ with variable $\mu \in \mathbf{F}$, then under $\kappa'$ they correspond to

$$\mathrm{c}'=\mathrm{a}+\mu(\mathrm{b}-\mathrm{a})+\mathrm{d}=\mathrm{a}+\mathrm{d}+\mu\{(\mathrm{b}+\mathrm{d})-(\mathrm{a}+\mathrm{d})\}=\mathrm{a}'+\mu(\mathrm{b}'-\mathrm{a}').$$

It follows that if the set of points is a line under $\kappa$ then it is so under $\kappa'$ and conversely.

The ratio $\mu = \dfrac{\mathrm{c} - \mathrm{a}}{\mathrm{b} - \mathrm{a}} = \dfrac{\mathrm{c}' - \mathrm{a}'}{\mathrm{b}' - \mathrm{a}'}$ too, is independent of the mapping and therefore is a property of the three collinear points represented under $\kappa$ by a, b, c.

PROBLEM (6.1). Prove that the notions of parallelism and ratio of parallel line segments as related to points of $A$, are independent of the choice of a particular $\mathscr{A}$-map. Prove also that the notions "between" and "convex", defined in a real affine space $A$ under some $\mathscr{A}$-map are independent of the choice of that $\mathscr{A}$-map.

Let $\kappa$ be an $\mathscr{A}$-map $\kappa\colon A \to \mathrm{V}$. Any function $\chi\colon \mathrm{V} \to \mathbf{F}$ represents a unique function $\chi\kappa\colon A \to \mathbf{F}$, sending the point $T \in A$ to a scalar (cf. fig. 6.4) $(\chi\kappa)(T) = \chi(\kappa(T)) = \chi(\mathrm{a})$. As long as $\kappa$ is kept fixed we can and often shall omit $\kappa$ from the notation and write $\chi$ instead of $\chi\kappa$.

We now consider some function on $A$. Let this function be $\chi\kappa$, hence represented by $\chi$ under $\kappa = \kappa_P$. The given function will not in general be expressed by $\chi$ when we use a different $\mathscr{A}$-map

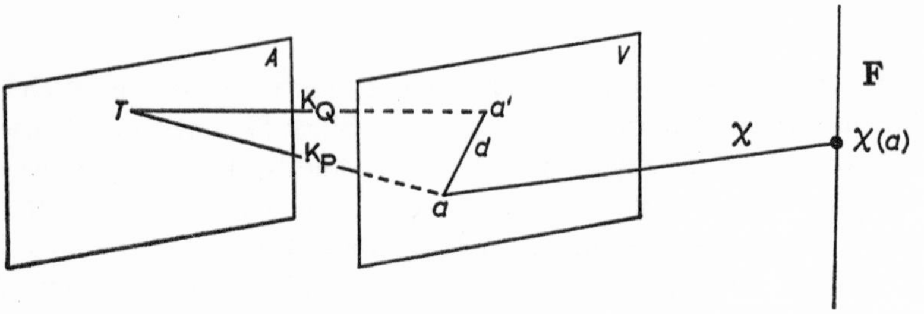


Fig. 6.4

$\kappa' = \kappa_Q$, related to $\kappa$ by (6.1). Let us consider the function value for some point $T \in A$. This value is

$$\chi\kappa_P T = \chi(\kappa_Q T - \mathrm{d}) = \chi(\mathrm{a}' - \mathrm{d}).$$

Hence the expression for the function under $\kappa'$ will now be

$$\mathrm{a}' \to \chi(\mathrm{a}' - \mathrm{d}) \overset{\mathrm{def}}{=} \chi'(\mathrm{a}') \tag{6.3}$$

($\overset{\mathrm{def}}{=}$ means: by definition).

Theorem [6.1]: *If a function on A, under a particular $\mathscr{A}$-map $A \to \mathrm{V}$ is expressed by a (proper) r-th degree function, then the same is true using any other mapping of the atlas. The function is then called a (proper) r-th degree function on A. A level set (cf. chapter 2) is called a (proper) r-th degree variety in A.*

Proof: The theorem is trivial for functions of degree zero. Since functions of degree $r$ have been defined by means of first-degree functions it will be sufficient to prove the theorem for these functions.

Let $\chi$: $\mathrm{a} \to \lambda + \xi(\mathrm{a})$, $\xi$ linear on V, be an arbitrary proper first-degree function on V, corresponding to a function $\chi\kappa$: $A \to \mathbf{F}$ by the $\mathscr{A}$-map $\kappa$. Under the $\mathscr{A}$-map $\kappa'$ the expression of this function becomes, in view of (6.3)

$$a' \to \chi(a' - d) = \lambda + \xi(a' - d) = \lambda + \xi(a') - \xi(d);$$

hence

$$a' \to \{\lambda - \xi(d)\} + \xi(a') \qquad a' \in V$$

and this, too, is a proper first-degree function on the vector space V.

If the constant part $\lambda$ of the function $\chi$ on V equals 0, then this is not usually the case for the constant part $\lambda - \xi(d) = -\xi(d)$ of the second function on V. Consequently, though it is sensible to speak of homogeneous functions on V, it makes no sense to speak of homogeneous functions on $A$.

*N.B.* A first-degree function on $A$ is also called a *linear function* on $A$. A *homogeneous* first-degree function on V is a *linear function* on V. If there might be any risk of ambiguity, we shall call the latter a homogeneous linear function on V.

A second-degree function on $A$ is also called a *quadratic function* on $A$. A homogeneous second-degree function on V is called a *quadratic function* on V. Again in danger of ambiguity we shall call the latter a homogeneous quadratic function.

Definition: A subset $A^m \subset A^n$ is called a *linear m-variety* if there exists an $\mathcal{A}$-map $\kappa$ in the atlas mapping $A^m$ onto an $m$-dimensional subspace of V.

Theorem [6.2]: *Linear* 1*-varieties are lines in A.*

Proof: Under a suitable $\mathcal{A}$-map the linear 1-variety consists of the set of points $\mu a = O + \mu(a - O)$, $a \neq O$, $\mu \in \mathbf{F}$, which is a line.

Conversely, let a line consist of the points $b + \mu(c - b)$. If we change to an other map by (6.1) with $d = -b$, we get a representation of the line by the 1-dimensional subspace

$$(b - b) + \mu(c - b) = \mu(c - b) \qquad \mu \in \mathbf{F}.$$

Theorem [6.3]: *If a line has two points in common with a linear r-variety, then it lies entirely in it.*

Proof: Choose an $\mathcal{A}$-map such that the given $r$-variety is represented by a subspace $B \subset V$. The proof then follows from the fact that $a, b \in B$ implies $a + \mu(b - a) \in B$.

Theorem [6.4]: *The linear $(n-1)$-varieties in $A^n$ are the level sets of the proper linear functions on $A^n$.*

Proof: Choose an $\mathscr{A}$-map such that the given $(n-1)$-variety is represented by a subspace $B \subset V$. Let $a_1, \cdots a_{n-1}$ be a basis of B, and $a_1, \cdots a_n$ a basis of V. The linear function $\xi$ for which $\xi(a_i) = 0$ for $i < n$, $\xi(a_n) = 1$, represents a first-degree function on $A$ whose kernel $\xi^{-1}(0)$ is the given linear variety.

Now let $\lambda + \xi$, $\lambda \in \mathbf{F}$, $\xi$ a homogeneous linear function, be a first-degree function on $A$. We consider the level set consisting of the points (represented by vectors under the given $\mathscr{A}$-map) a for which

$$\lambda + \xi(a) = \mu, \quad a \in V. \tag{6.4}$$

If $\mu - \lambda = 0$, then the assertion follows from theorem [5.9]. If not, then choose a vector b for which $\xi(b) \neq 0$, and change to another $\mathscr{A}$-map by (6.1) with $d = \alpha b$, $\alpha \in \mathbf{F}$. Then equation (6.4) of the level set changes to

$$\lambda + \xi(a' - d) = \lambda + \xi(a') - \xi(d) = \lambda + \xi(a') - \alpha\xi(b) = \mu.$$

Taking $\alpha = (\lambda - \mu)(\xi(b))^{-1}$, it becomes the equation of a linear $(n-1)$-variety:

$$\xi(a') = 0. \tag{6.5}$$

In particular it follows that in $A^2$ the level sets of linear functions are lines. Linear 2-varieties are also called *planes*. The linear $(n-1)$-varieties in $A^n$ are called *hyperplanes*.

PROBLEMS. (6.2). If the $\mathscr{A}$-map $\kappa'$: $A \to V$ is such that some point of a certain linear variety is mapped into the vector O, then $\kappa'$ maps the linear variety onto a subspace of V.

(6.3). If a given linear $r$-variety has $r + 1$ points, which are not contained in any $(r-1)$-variety, in common with an $s$-variety, then the $r$-variety lies entirely in the $s$-variety.

(6.4). If $\xi$ and $\eta$ are proper linear functions on $A^n$ that have identical kernels $\xi^{-1}(0)$ and $\eta^{-1}(0)$, then there exists a scalar $\lambda \in \mathbf{F}$ such that $\eta = \lambda\xi$. Give interpretations of this problem in plane and solid geometry.

Theorem [6.5]: *Let $\xi$ be a linear function on $A$, let the lines* (ab) *and* (cd) *be parallel, and let* $\xi(b) \neq \xi(a)$. *Then the ratio of "directed" line segments* (*cf. chapter* 4) *satisfies*

$$\frac{d - c}{b - a} = \frac{\xi(d) - \xi(c)}{\xi(b) - \xi(a)}. \tag{6.6}$$

Proof: The zero level of $\xi$ is a linear $(n - 1)$-variety. Choose an $\mathscr{A}$-map which associates a subspace of V to it. Then the first-degree function on V representing $\xi$ is homogeneous. We use the symbol $\xi$ for this function on V.

Put

$$\frac{d - c}{b - a} = \lambda \text{ so that } d - c = \lambda(b - a)$$

$$\xi(d - c) = \xi\{\lambda(b - a)\}$$

$$\xi(d) - \xi(c) = \lambda\{\xi(b) - \xi(a)\}.$$

Since $\xi(b) \neq \xi(a)$, the assertion follows (cf. problem (6.1)).

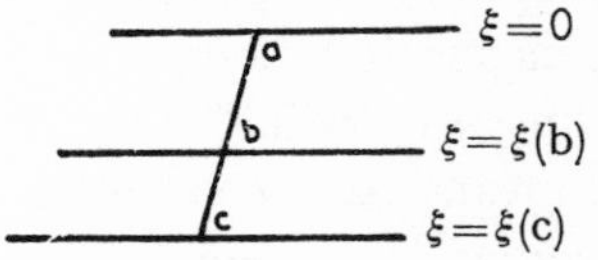


Fig. 6.5

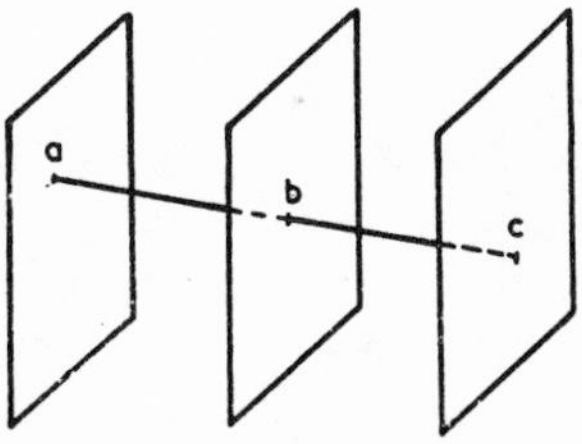


Substitution of a, b, a, c for a, b, c, d in (6.6) yields: If $\xi$ is a linear function on $A$, $\xi(a) = 0$, $\xi(b) \neq 0$, a, b and c collinear, then

$$\frac{c - a}{b - a} = \frac{\xi(c)}{\xi(b)}. \tag{6.7}$$

Fig. 6.5 illustrates this for $A^2$ and $A^3$.

PROBLEMS. (6.5). If $\xi$ and $\eta$ are linear functions on $A$ having non-identical zero-level sets, and if a is a point not on these sets, then

$$x \to \zeta(x) = \xi(a)\eta(x) - \eta(a)\xi(x) \tag{6.8}$$

is a linear function on $A$ whose zero-level passes through a, contains the entire intersection $\xi^{-1}(0) \cap \eta^{-1}(0)$ and contains not a single further point of $\xi^{-1}(0)$ nor $\eta^{-1}(0)$. Prove this, and give lower-dimensional interpretations.

(6.6). If the kernels of the linear functions $\xi$ and $\eta$ on $A$ have no point in common (parallel), then there are scalars $\alpha$ and $\beta$ such that

$$1 = \alpha\xi + \beta\eta \text{ (identically).}$$

(6.7). Three lines $\xi^{-1}(0)$, $\eta^{-1}(0)$, $\zeta^{-1}(0)$ in $A^2$ determined by the linear functions $\xi$, $\eta$ and $\zeta$, are *concurrent* if and only if $\xi$, $\eta$ and $\zeta$ are linearly dependent, i.e. if there exist scalars $\alpha, \beta, \gamma \in \mathbf{F}$, not all zero, such that $\alpha\xi + \beta\eta + \gamma\zeta$ is the zero-function.

(6.8). Let $\varphi$ and $\psi$ be two linear functions on an affine space $A^n$ over the real numbers, for which the systems of level sets are different. Prove that the following point sets are convex (cf. problem (4.13)): The points satisfying *a)* $\varphi = 0$; *b)* $\varphi = \psi = 0$; *c)* $\alpha < \varphi < \beta$; *d)* $\alpha \leqslant \varphi \leqslant \beta$; *e)* $\alpha \leqslant \varphi \leqslant \beta$ as well as $\gamma \leqslant \psi \leqslant \delta$; *f)* $\varphi^2 + \psi^2 \leqslant 1$; *g)* $\varphi^2 + \psi^2 < 1$. *h)* Prove also that any linear variety is convex. Illustrate this problem by a figure in the cases $n \leqslant 3$.

Remark: A non-constant linear function on $A$ is called a *coordinate*. $n$ linearly independent homogeneous functions on $V^n$ together with the $\mathscr{A}$-map $\kappa: A \to V^n$, define $n$ coordinates on $A$, together forming a *coordinate-system*. By means of a coordinate-system the points of $A$ are mapped one-to-one to sequences of $n$ function values, i.e. sequences of scalars.

## 7. LINEAR FUNCTIONS AND LINES IN $A^2$ AND $A^n$. APPLICATIONS

Menelaus's theorem [7.1]: *Let the points* a, b, c *be non-collinear, and let the points* $a^+$, $b^+$ *and* $c^+$ *be on the lines* bc, ca, ab *respectively, but not at the vertices of triangle* abc. *Then* $a^+$, $b^+$, $c^+$ *are collinear if and only if the following relation holds:*

$$\frac{b - a^+}{c - a^+} \frac{c - b^+}{a - b^+} \frac{a - c^+}{b - c^+} = 1. \tag{7.1}$$

Proof: (cf. fig. 7.1) If $a^+$, $b^+$, $c^+$ are collinear and lie on the line $\xi^{-1}(0)$ where $\xi$ is a (not necessarily homogeneous) linear function, then by theorem [6.5] the left-hand side of (7.1) is equal to

$$\frac{\xi(b)}{\xi(c)} \frac{\xi(c)}{\xi(a)} \frac{\xi(a)}{\xi(b)} = 1.$$

If, conversely, (7.1) holds, then take a linear function $\xi$ such that $\xi(a^+) = \xi(b^+) = 0$. Then by (7.1)

$$\frac{\xi(b)}{\xi(c)} \frac{\xi(c)}{\xi(a)} \frac{a - c^+}{b - c^+} = 1 \tag{7.2}$$

$$\xi(b) \cdot (a - c^+) = \xi(a) \cdot (b - c^+)$$

$$\xi(b)[\xi(a) - \xi(c^+)] = \xi(a)[\xi(b) - \xi(c^+)]$$

$$[\xi(a) - \xi(b)]\xi(c^+) = 0.$$

Since $\xi(c^+) \neq 0$ would imply $\xi(a) = \xi(b)$ and then by (7.2)

$$a - c^+ = b - c^+, \ a = b$$

which is a contradiction, $\xi(c^+)$ has to be zero, and the assertion follows.

Ceva's theorem [7.2]: *Let the points* a, b, c *be non-collinear, and let the points* $a^0$, $b^0$, $c^0$ *be on the lines* bc, ca, ab *respectively but not at the vertices of triangle* abc. *Then the lines* $aa^0$, $bb^0$ *and* $cc^0$ *are concurrent if and only if the following relation holds*: (cf. fig. 7.1)

$$\frac{b - a^0}{c - a^0}\,\frac{c - b^0}{a - b^0}\,\frac{a - c^0}{b - c^0} = -1. \tag{7.3}$$

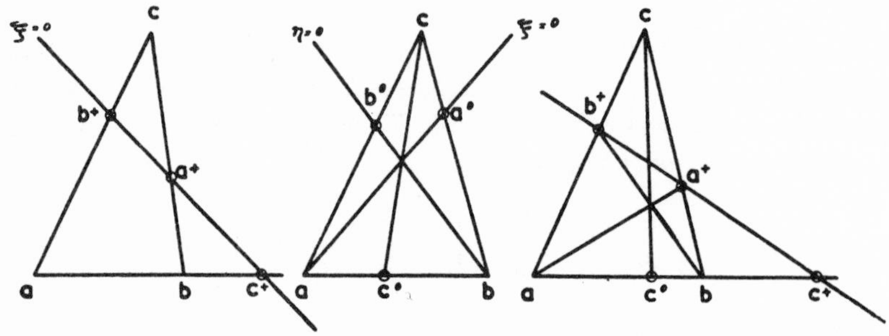


Fig. 7.1

Proof: Let $\xi$ and $\eta$ be linear functions such that

$$a,\ a^0 \in \xi^{-1}(0)\,;\ \ b,\ b^0 \in \eta^{-1}(0),\ \text{and define}$$

$$\zeta(x) = \xi(c)\eta(x) - \xi(x)\eta(c).$$

$\zeta^{-1}(0)$ is the line through c which is concurrent with $\xi^{-1}(0)$ and $\eta^{-1}(0)$ (cf. problem (6.5)). If the lines $aa^0$, $bb^0$ and $cc^0$ are concurrent, then $c^0 \in \zeta^{-1}(0)$, and the left-hand side of (7.3) equals

$$\frac{\xi(b)}{\xi(c)}\,\frac{\eta(c)}{\eta(a)}\,\frac{\zeta(a)}{\zeta(b)} = \frac{\xi(b)}{\xi(c)}\,\frac{\eta(c)}{\eta(a)}\,\frac{\xi(c)\eta(a) - \xi(a)\eta(c)}{\xi(c)\eta(b) - \xi(b)\eta(c)} = -1$$

since $\xi(a) = \eta(b) = 0$. Note that the denominators are not zero.

If, conversely, (7.3) holds, then the same definitions of $\xi$, $\eta$, $\zeta$ yield

$$\frac{\xi(b)}{\xi(c)}\,\frac{\eta(c)}{\eta(a)}\,\frac{a - c^0}{b - c^0} = -1$$

and then, since $\xi(a) = \eta(b) = 0$:

$$\frac{a - c^0}{b - c^0} = \frac{\xi(c)\eta(a) - 0}{0 - \xi(b)\eta(c)} = \frac{\xi(c)\eta(a) - \xi(a)\eta(c)}{\xi(c)\eta(b) - \xi(b)\eta(c)} = \frac{\zeta(a)}{\zeta(b)}. \tag{7.4}$$

It follows that

$$\zeta(b)\{\zeta(a) - \zeta(c^0)\} = \zeta(a)\{\zeta(b) - \zeta(c^0)\}$$
$$[\zeta(b) - \zeta(a)]\zeta(c^0) = 0.$$

If $\zeta(b) - \zeta(a) = 0$ then by (7.4) $a - c^0 = b - c^0$; hence $a = b$, which is a contradiction. Consequently $\zeta(c^0) = 0$, which proves the assertion.

*N.B.* In the third part of fig. 7.1 the points $a^+$ and $a^0$ of Menelaus's and Ceva's theorems coincide, and the same holds for the points $b^+$ and $b^0$. Under these conditions another property follows:

$$\frac{a - c^+}{b - c^+} : \frac{a - c^0}{b - c^0} = -1$$

i.e. the ratio of ratios, also called the cross-ratio, equals $-1$ (cf. page 44).

Desargues's theorem [7.3]: *If the non-degenerate triangles* abc *and* a'b'c' *are such that there exists a line m which is concurrent with the lines* bc *and* b'c', *with the lines* ca *and* c'a' *and with the lines* ab *and* a'b' *or if* bc//b'c' (// = *parallel*), ca//c'a' *and* ab//a'b' *then the lines* aa', bb' *and* cc' *are concurrent.*

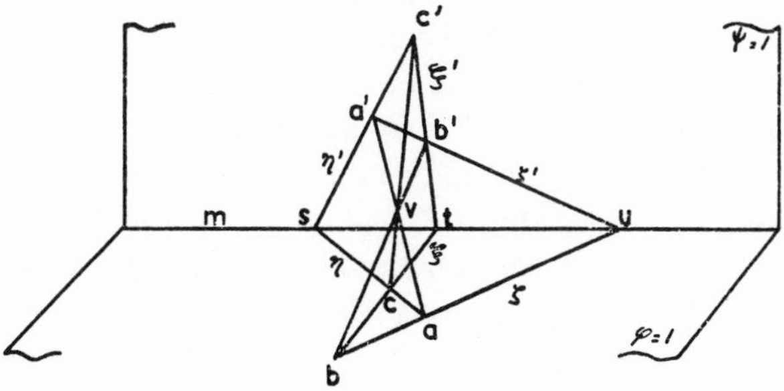


Fig. 7.2

Proof: Let $\xi, \eta, \zeta, \xi', \eta', \zeta'$, be linear functions on $A^2$ having the lines bc, ca, ab, b'c', c'a', a'b' respectively as kernel. In the first case let $\chi = 0$ be the equation of the line $m$, in the second case let $\chi$ be identically 1. In either case there exist scalars $\alpha, \alpha', \beta, \beta', \gamma, \gamma'$, such that (cf. problems 6.4; 6.5; 6.6)

$$\chi = \alpha\xi + \alpha'\xi' = \beta\eta + \beta'\eta' = \gamma\zeta + \gamma'\zeta' \text{ (equality of functions!).}$$

Then $\alpha\xi - \beta\eta = -\alpha'\xi' + \beta'\eta'$, and the kernel of this proper linear function is a line which contains c (cf. the left-hand side) and c′ (the right-hand side).

Similarly $\alpha\xi - \gamma\zeta = -\alpha'\xi' + \gamma'\zeta'$ is the linear function having the line bb′ as its kernel.

The difference of these two functions is the following function whose kernel is a line which is concurrent with cc′ and bb′:

$$-\beta\eta + \gamma\zeta = \beta'\eta' - \gamma'\zeta'$$

but this kernel is just the line aa′, which proves the theorem.

*N.B.* In chapter 20 we will also consider the converse of this theorem.

*Second proof for the case that the line m exists. Geometrical introduction*: Fig. 7.2 can also be considered as the projection of a 3-dimensional figure where a′, b′, c′ are in a vertical plane and a, b, c in a horizontal plane. The planes bcb′c′, cac′a′ and aba′b′ either intersect in a point, or their lines of intersection are parallel. In either case the lines aa′, bb′ and cc′ are concurrent in three-space, and then the same is true for their projections.

A proof along these lines, valid for an arbitrary field **F**, for example for the complex numbers, is as follows. Suppose that the given plane configuration lies in a 3-dimensional space $A^3$ which is mapped onto a vector space $V^3$ by an $\mathscr{A}$-map $\kappa$ in such a way that the image of the plane does not contain the vector O. Let the plane of the configuration (cf. fig. 7.2) have the "equation" $\psi = 1$, where $\psi$ is a homogeneous linear function. Let $\varphi = 1$ be another plane (the "horizontal plane") passing through s, t and u. $\varphi$ is homogeneous and linear, whereas $\varphi = 0$ does not contain any of the points a, b, c.

The vectors a, b and u are linearly dependent, and therefore so are

$$a^+ = \frac{a}{\varphi(a)}, \quad b^+ = \frac{b}{\varphi(b)} \quad \text{and u.}$$

These vectors represent points which are also in the plane $\varphi = 1$, as may be verified by substitution. This implies that they are collinear (cf. problem (4.4)). For, $\alpha a^+ + \beta b^+ + \gamma u = O$ implies

$$\varphi(\alpha a^+ + \beta b^+ + \gamma u) = \alpha\varphi(a^+) + \beta\varphi(b^+) + \gamma\varphi(u) = \alpha + \beta + \gamma = 0$$

and the points $a^+$, $b^+$, u, a′, b′ lie in a plane. Then the lines $a^+a'$ and $b^+b'$ are concurrent, i.e. they intersect in a point $v^+$ or are parallel.

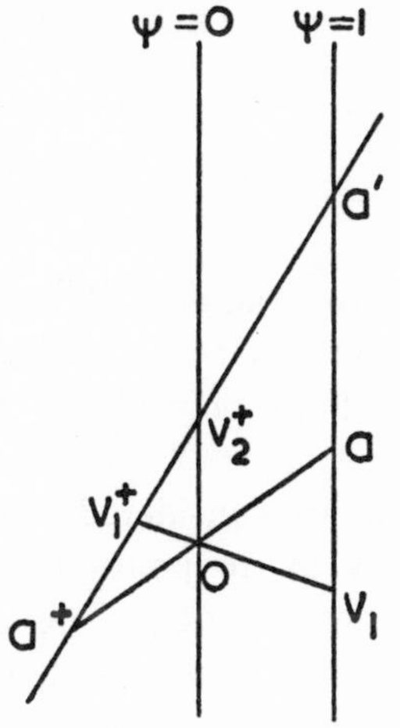


Fig. 7.3

Similar results are obtained for $a^+a'$ and $c^+c'$, and for $b^+b'$ and $c^+c'$. Since $c^+c'$ does not lie in the plane through $a^+a'$ and $b^+b'$, it intersects this plane in $v^+$ if $v^+$ exists, and the three lines intersect in $v^+$. If $v^+$ does not exist then neither do $a^+a' \cap c^+c'$ and $b^+b' \cap c^+c'$. In this case the three lines are parallel.

We now restrict ourselves to the case when $v^+$ exists, and leave the other case to the reader. The vectors a,$a^+$, a′ and $v^+$ are in a 2-dimensional vector space.

If $\psi(v^+) \neq 0$ then $v = v^+/\psi(v^+)$ is both in this space and in the plane $\psi = 1$ which contains a and a′ (cf. fig. 7.3 $v^+ = v_1^+$). Then v lies on the line aa′, and for similar reasons also on the lines bb′ and cc′.

If $\psi(v^+) = 0$ then the vector $v^+$ lies in $\psi = 0$ and is therefore parallel to the line aa′ in the plane $\psi = 1$ (cf. fig. 7.3 $v^+ = v_2^+$). Similarly the vector $v^+$ is parallel to the lines bb′ and cc′, which therefore have to be parallel to aa′.

In both cases the lines aa′, bb′ and cc′ are concurrent.

(Outline of a) *Third proof*: Again we start from the plane figure 7.2 which is represented in the plane $\psi = 1$ of a 3-dimensional vector space. Then take a homogeneous linear function $\omega$ satisfying $\omega(s) = \omega(t) = 0$, hence $\omega(u) = 0$. Now project the figure from O into the plane $\omega = 1$. Then we find the points

$\bar{a} = \dfrac{a}{\omega(a)}$, $\bar{b} = \dfrac{b}{\omega(b)}$, $\bar{c} = \dfrac{c}{\omega(c)}$, $\bar{a}' = \dfrac{a'}{\omega(a')}$, $\bar{b}' = \dfrac{b'}{\omega(b')}$ and $\bar{c}' = \dfrac{c}{\omega(c')}$.

These points form two triangles $\bar{a}\bar{b}\bar{c}$ and $\bar{a}'\bar{b}'\bar{c}'$ with parallel sides, and it is easily verified that the lines $\bar{a}\bar{a}'$, $\bar{b}\bar{b}'$ and $\bar{c}\bar{c}'$ are concurrent. Projection of the points then proves the theorem.

The configuration that we considered consists of 10 lines and 10 points, and through any of the points (on any of the lines) there pass three lines (lie three points). The configuration is called *Desargues's configuration*, and is usually denoted by Cf $(10_3, 10_3)$. It plays an important part in the synthetic axiomatic foundation of projective geometry.

*Cross-ratio*

The next part of the theory holds for all values of $n > 1$. For better understanding the reader is, however, recommended to read this part first taking $n = 2$ or 3, and to consider general $n$ at second reading.

Let a, b, c, d be four collinear points (cf. fig. 7.4). Then the expression

$$(abcd) = \frac{a - c}{b - c} : \frac{a - d}{b - d} \tag{7.5}$$

is called the *cross-ratio of these points*.

If the linear function $\zeta$ has different values on a, b, c, d, then theorem [6.5] implies

$$(abcd) = \frac{\zeta(a) - \zeta(c)}{\zeta(b) - \zeta(c)} : \frac{\zeta(a) - \zeta(d)}{\zeta(b) - \zeta(d)}. \tag{7.5'}$$

Next consider two $(n-1)$-varieties (lines in $A^2$, planes in $A^3$) with equations $\xi(\mathrm{x}) = 0$, $\eta(\mathrm{x}) = 0$, which do not contain a or b, but do contain c and d. Then by theorem [6.5] with $\xi(\mathrm{c}) = \eta(\mathrm{d}) = 0$,

$$\lambda = (\mathrm{abcd}) = \frac{\xi(\mathrm{a})}{\xi(\mathrm{b})} : \frac{\eta(\mathrm{a})}{\eta(\mathrm{b})}. \tag{7.6}$$

This is also called the *cross-ratio of the points* a *and* b *with respect to the* $(n-1)$*-varieties* $\xi^{-1}(0)$ *and* $\eta^{-1}(0)$.

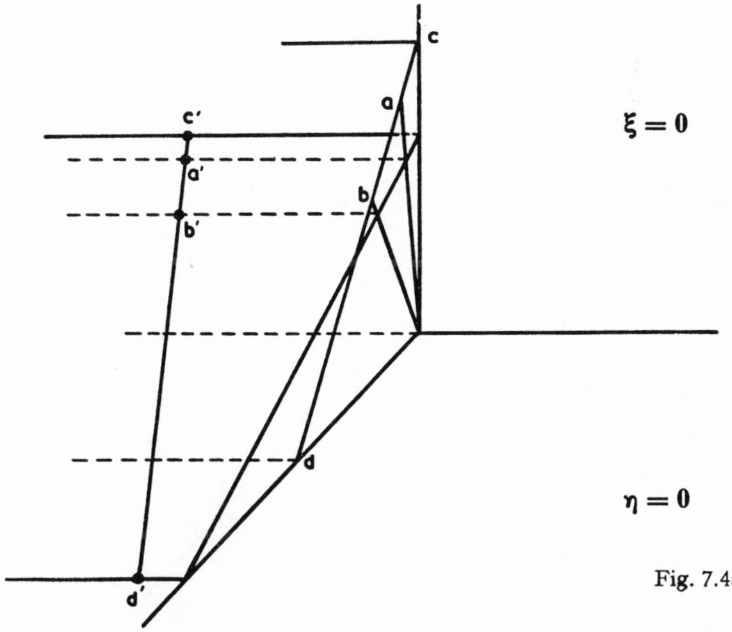


Fig. 7.4a

The unique $(n-1)$-variety which contains the intersection $\xi^{-1}(0) \cap \eta^{-1}(0)$ and the point a is

$$\xi(\mathrm{x})\eta(\mathrm{a}) - \xi(\mathrm{a})\eta(\mathrm{x}) = 0.$$

Similarly with b and a interchanged, we have

$$\xi(\mathrm{x})\eta(\mathrm{b}) - \xi(\mathrm{b})\eta(\mathrm{x}) = 0.$$

Hence for points a′ and b′ lying on the first and second variety respectively, but not on $\eta(x) = 0$, we have

$$\frac{\xi(a')}{\eta(a')} = \frac{\xi(a)}{\eta(a)} \qquad \frac{\xi(b')}{\eta(b')} = \frac{\xi(b)}{\eta(b)}.$$

Substitution in (7.6) then shows that the points a′ and b′ have the same cross-ratio with respect to $\xi^{-1}(0)$ and $\eta^{-1}(0)$ as a and b, and therefore (cf. fig. 7.4a and b)

$$(a'b'c'd') = (abcd). \tag{7.7}$$

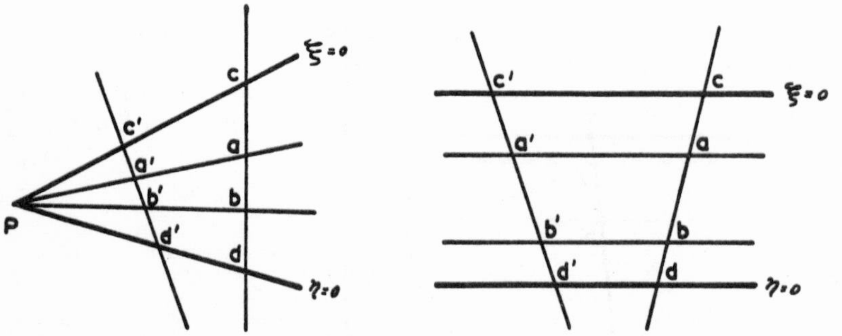


Fi.g 7.4b

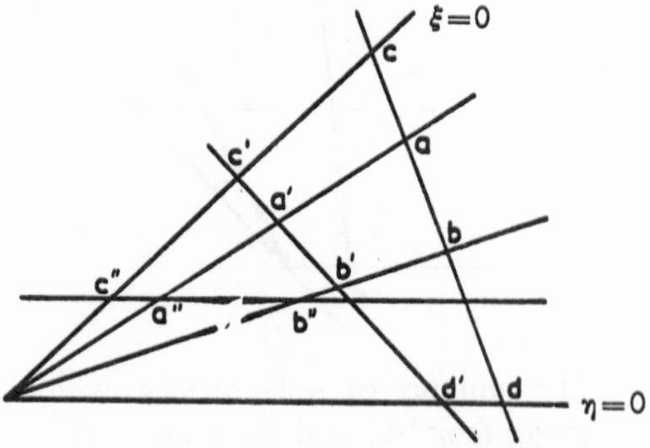


Fig. 7.5

In other words

Theorem [7.4]: *The cross-ratio is invariant under projection.*

Remark. In fig. 7.4b (abcd) is also called the *cross-ratio of the four corresponding lines* through p.

If a″ and b″ are such (fig. 7.5) that the line a″b″ is parallel to $\eta=0$, so that $\eta(a'') = \eta(b'')$, then the cross-ratio (7.6) with a″ for a and b″ for b becomes an ordinary ratio:

$$\lambda = (abcd) = \frac{\xi(a'')}{\xi(b'')} = \frac{a'' - c''}{b'' - c''}. \tag{7.8}$$

If we keep $\xi$, $\eta$ and b fixed and let x = a vary in the plane, then (7.6) defines a function (x =)a $\to \lambda$. In fig. 7.6 the level curves of this function are shown with their values. The function is not defined on $\eta^{-1}(0)$.

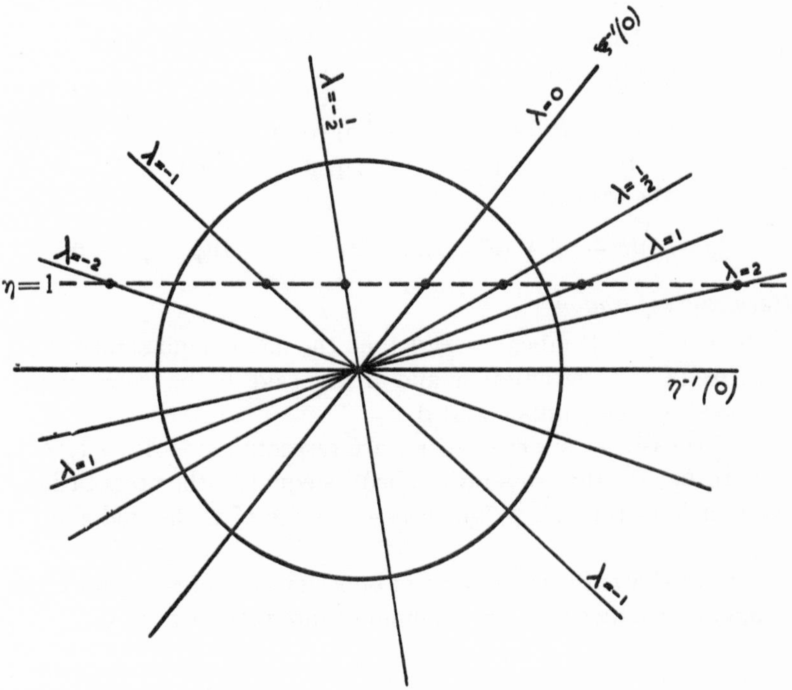


Fig. 7.6

Taking the letters a, b, c, d in the 24 possible different orders, we get 24 cross-ratios, which are not, however, all different. If (abcd) = $= \lambda$, then from the definition (7.5) it is obvious that (badc) = = (cdab) = $\lambda$ and (bacd) = (abdc) = $\lambda^{-1}$; also

$$(acbd) = \frac{a'' - b''}{c'' - b''} = \frac{(b'' - c'') - (a'' - c'')}{b'' - c''} = 1 - (abcd) = 1 - \lambda.$$

Repeated use of the permutations already considered yields

$$
\begin{aligned}
(\mathrm{abcd}) &= (\mathrm{badc}) = (\mathrm{cdab}) = (\mathrm{dcba}) = \lambda \\
(\mathrm{abdc}) &= (\mathrm{bacd}) = (\mathrm{cdba}) = (\mathrm{dcab}) = \lambda^{-1} \\
(\mathrm{acbd}) &= (\mathrm{bdac}) = (\mathrm{cadb}) = (\mathrm{dbca}) = 1 - \lambda \\
(\mathrm{acdb}) &= (\mathrm{bdca}) = (\mathrm{cabd}) = (\mathrm{dbac}) = (1 - \lambda)^{-1} \\
(\mathrm{adbc}) &= (\mathrm{bcad}) = (\mathrm{cbda}) = (\mathrm{dacb}) = (\lambda - 1)/\lambda \\
(\mathrm{adcb}) &= (\mathrm{bcda}) = (\mathrm{cbad}) = (\mathrm{dabc}) = \lambda/(\lambda - 1).
\end{aligned}
$$

PROBLEM (7.1). Prove that $(\mathrm{acbd}) + (\mathrm{abcd}) = 1$ by putting $\mathrm{a} = \mathrm{p} + \alpha\mathrm{q}$, $\mathrm{b} = \mathrm{p} + \beta\mathrm{q}$, $\mathrm{c} = \mathrm{p} + \gamma\mathrm{q}$, $\mathrm{d} = \mathrm{p} + \delta\mathrm{q}$, $\alpha, \beta, \gamma, \delta \in \mathbf{F}$, and using the identity

$$(\beta - \alpha)(\delta - \gamma) + (\gamma - \alpha)(\beta - \delta) + (\delta - \alpha)(\gamma - \beta) = 0.$$

*Harmonic separation*

Definition: If $(\mathrm{abcd}) = -1$ then the points (and similarly for lines or $(n-1)$-varieties) a and b are said to be *harmonically separated* by the points c and d.

In this case the six cross-ratios are respectively $-1, -1, 2, \frac{1}{2}, 2, \frac{1}{2}$. In fig. 7.7 the cross-ratio (abcd) is equal to the cross-ratio of the four lines through p, which is $-1$ since c″ is the midpoint of a″b″.

Fig. 7.8 shows the three pairs of opposite sides of the quadrangle a, b, c, d together with their points of intersection p, q, r.

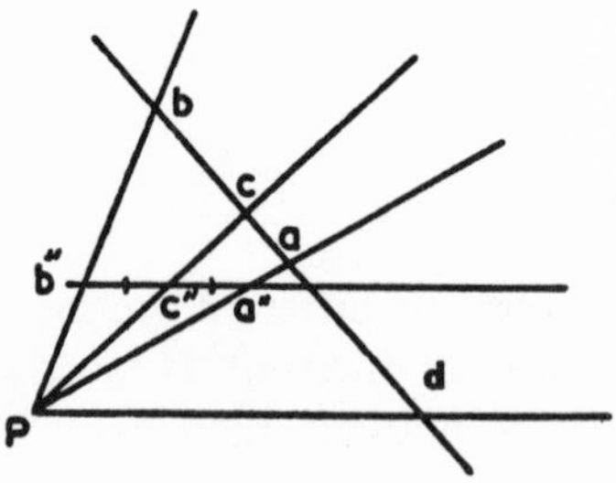


Fig. 7.7

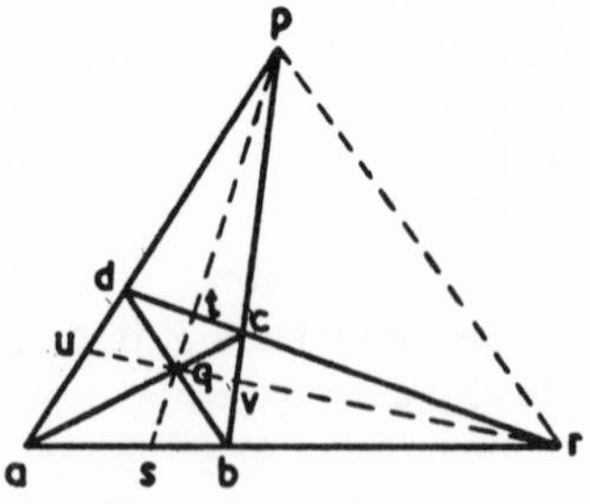


Fig. 7.8

The join of two of those points, p and q say, intersects the other two sides in points s and t, which are harmonically separated by p and q. For, in the figure we see:

$$\begin{aligned}
(\mathrm{pqts}) &= (\mathrm{pvcb}) \text{ (projection from r)}\\
(\mathrm{pvcb}) &= (\mathrm{puad}) \text{ ( ,, ,, q)}\\
(\mathrm{puad}) &= (\mathrm{pqst}) \text{ ( ,, ,, r).}
\end{aligned}$$

Hence $\lambda = (\mathrm{pqts}) = (\mathrm{pqst}) = \lambda^{-1}$, $\lambda^2 = 1$ and, since $\lambda \neq 1$, it follows that $\lambda = -1$.

Also (absr) $= -1$, by the remark after Ceva's theorem in this chapter.

Theorem [7.5]: *If* a, b, c, *and* d *are collinear and distinct, and if* m *is the midpoint of* a *and* b, *then the pair* a, b *separates harmonically the pair* c, d *if and only if* (b − m) *is the geometric mean of* (c − m) *and* (d − m):

$$(\mathrm{c}-\mathrm{m}) : (\mathrm{b}-\mathrm{m}) = (\mathrm{b}-\mathrm{m}) : (\mathrm{d}-\mathrm{m}), \qquad \mathrm{m} = \tfrac{1}{2}(\mathrm{a}+\mathrm{b}). \quad (7.9)$$

Fig. 7.9

Proof: Put $\mathrm{b} = \mathrm{m} + \mathrm{p}$, $\mathrm{a} = \mathrm{m} - \mathrm{p}$, $\mathrm{c} = \mathrm{m} + \mu\mathrm{p}$, $\mathrm{d} = \mathrm{m} + \nu\mathrm{p}$.
The points will be harmonic if

$$(\mathrm{abcd}) = \frac{\mathrm{a}-\mathrm{c}}{\mathrm{b}-\mathrm{c}} : \frac{\mathrm{a}-\mathrm{d}}{\mathrm{b}-\mathrm{d}} = \frac{-1-\mu}{1-\mu} : \frac{-1-\nu}{1-\nu} = -1$$

i.e. $\mu\nu = 1$.

(7.9) is equivalent to $\mu = \dfrac{1}{\nu}$, that is $\mu\nu = 1$.

Hence the two conditions are equivalent indeed.

Pappus's theorem [7.6]: *Let the points* $a_1$, $a_3$, $a_5$ *be on a line and the points* $a_2$, $a_4$, $a_6$ *be on another line intersecting the first one, and let the lines* $a_1a_2$ *and* $a_4a_5$ *be parallel and likewise the lines* $a_2a_3$ *and* $a_5a_6$. *Then the lines* $a_3a_4$ *and* $a_6a_1$ *are also parallel.*

Proof: If the vectors a and b are linearly independent and the vectors $\mathrm{b}-\mathrm{a}$ and $\mu\mathrm{b}-\lambda\mathrm{a}$ are linearly dependent (cf. fig. 7.10),

$$\mu\mathrm{b} - \lambda\mathrm{a} = \nu(\mathrm{b}-\mathrm{a}) \qquad (7.10)$$

then $\lambda = \mu = \nu$. For $(\mu - \nu)\mathrm{b} + (\nu - \lambda)\mathrm{a} = \mathrm{O}$, hence $\mu - \nu = \nu - \lambda = 0$.

Now take a representation of the plane such that the point of intersection of the lines $(\mathrm{a}_1\mathrm{a}_3\mathrm{a}_5)$ and $(\mathrm{a}_2\mathrm{a}_4\mathrm{a}_6)$ is represented by the vector O. We may then put (cf. fig. 7.11)

$$\mathrm{a}_1 = \mathrm{a},\ \mathrm{a}_3 = \lambda\mathrm{a},\ \mathrm{a}_5 = \mu\lambda\mathrm{a},\quad \mathrm{a}_2 = \mathrm{b},\ \mathrm{a}_4 = \lambda'\mu'\mathrm{b},\ \mathrm{a}_6 = \mu'\mathrm{b}.$$

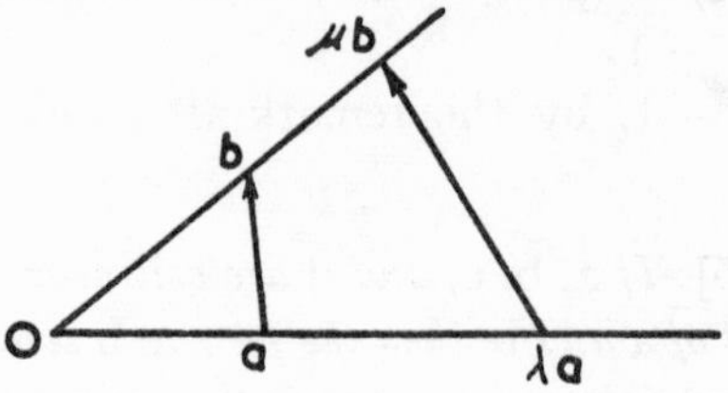

Fig. 7.10

Since the lines $\mathrm{a}_1\mathrm{a}_2$ and $\mathrm{a}_4\mathrm{a}_5$ are parallel, the vectors $\mathrm{a}_2 - \mathrm{a}_1 = \mathrm{b} - \mathrm{a}$ and $\mathrm{a}_4 - \mathrm{a}_5 = \lambda'\mu'\mathrm{b} - \mu\lambda\mathrm{a}$ are linearly dependent and hence, since a and b are independent, $\lambda'\mu' = \mu\lambda$.

Since the lines $\mathrm{a}_2\mathrm{a}_3$ and $\mathrm{a}_5\mathrm{a}_6$ are parallel, the vectors $\mathrm{a}_3 - \mathrm{a}_2 = \lambda\mathrm{a} - \mathrm{b}$ and $\mathrm{a}_5 - \mathrm{a}_6 = \mu\lambda\mathrm{a} - \mu'\mathrm{b}$ are linearly dependent and hence $\mu' = \mu$; it follows that $\lambda' = \lambda$.

$$\mathrm{a}_4 - \mathrm{a}_3 = \lambda\mu\mathrm{b} - \lambda\mathrm{a} = \lambda(\mu\mathrm{b} - \mathrm{a}) = \lambda(\mathrm{a}_6 - \mathrm{a}_1).$$

Hence the lines $\mathrm{a}_3\mathrm{a}_4$ and $\mathrm{a}_1\mathrm{a}_6$ are parallel [1]).

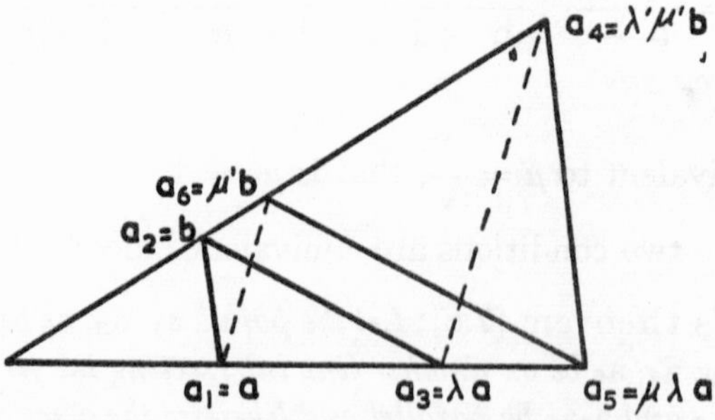

Fig. 7.11

[1]) **Remark: Analytic geometries can also be developed over skew-fields, where $\lambda\mu = \mu\lambda$ is not generally true. Pappus's theorem turns out to hold if and only if the field is commutative. For this reason Pappus's theorem is fundamental in synthetic projective geometry.**

PROBLEMS. (7.2). The two lines through the centre of a parallelogram parallel to the sides separate the diagonals harmonically.

(7.3). Consider fig. 7.8 as a figure in a plane in $A^3$. Take an $\mathscr{A}$-map onto $V^3$ such that the vector O is not in the image of the plane. Take a linear function $\varphi$ on $V^3$ with $\varphi(p) = \varphi(r) = 0$ and project with centre O the configuration onto the plane $\varphi = 1$. What configuration do you get? Use this to obtain another proof of $(pqts) = -1$.

(7.4). (Generalization of Menelaus's theorem). The points $b_i$, $i = 1, \cdots m$ are on the lines $a_i a_{i+1}$ respectively ($a_{m+1} = a_1$), in an $n$-dimensional affine space. If the points $b_i$ are all in a linear $(n-1)$-variety which contains none of the points $a_i$, then

$$\prod_{i=1}^{m} \frac{a_i - b_i}{a_{i+1} - b_i} = 1. \tag{7.11}$$

If, conversely, $m - 1$ of the points $b_i$ are in such an $(n-1)$-variety, and if (7.11) holds, then the $m$-th point also lies in the variety. Draw figures for the case $n = 3$, $m = 4$.

(7.5). If $a_1, \cdots a_4$ is a skew quadrangle in space, and $b_1, b_2, b_3, b_4$ are the midpoints of $a_1a_2$, $a_2a_3$, $a_3a_4$, $a_4a_1$, then the plane containing the points $b_1, b_2, b_3$ contains $b_4$ also. $b_1b_2b_3b_4$ is a parallelogram.

(7.6). (Converse of Pappus's theorem): If the points $a_1, a_3, a_5$ are collinear and if moreover

$a_1a_2$ is parallel to $a_4a_5$,
$a_2a_3$ ,, ,, ,, $a_5a_6$,
$a_3a_4$ ,, ,, ,, $a_6a_1$,

then the points $a_2, a_4, a_6$ are also collinear.

(7.7). The midpoints of the diagonals of the figure consisting of four mutually intersecting lines (the so-called complete quadrilateral) are collinear.

Solution: Take three of the sides as sides of a triangle abc and consider the fourth line as the zero-level of a linear function $\xi$. Let p, q, r be the points of intersection of the fourth line with the sides of the triangle (cf. fig. 7.12).

If $\xi(a) = \alpha$, $\xi(b) = \beta$, $\xi(c) = \gamma$, then it follows that

$$r = \frac{\alpha}{\alpha - \beta}\, b - \frac{\beta}{\alpha - \beta}\, a;$$

similar expressions for p and q are obtained by the cyclic permutations

$$\begin{array}{ccc} a & \to & b \\ \nwarrow & & \swarrow \\ & c & \end{array} \quad \text{and} \quad \begin{array}{ccc} p & \to & q \\ \nwarrow & & \swarrow \\ & r & \end{array}.$$

Then the midpoints of the diagonals are

$$\frac{a + p}{2} = \frac{\beta(a + c) - \gamma(a + b)}{2(\beta - \gamma)} \quad \text{etc. (cyclically).}$$

Hence

$$(\beta - \gamma)\,\frac{a + p}{2} + (\gamma - \alpha)\,\frac{b + q}{2} + (\alpha - \beta)\,\frac{c + r}{2} = 0,$$

and since the sum of the three coefficients equals zero, the assertion follows (cf. problem (4.4)).

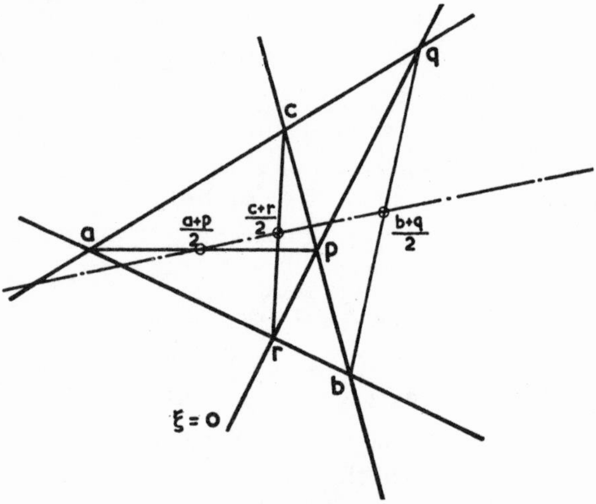


Fig. 7.12

# 8. A FINITE AFFINE PLANE

In the preceding chapters we used a field **F**, without specifying which field was meant by it, although in the figures we had in mind the field **R** of real numbers.

In order to emphasize that our theory is equally true for fields **F** other than **R**, we will now study an affine 2-dimensional space over a finite field **F**. Such a plane has a finite number of points and it will therefore be called a *finite affine plane*. Take for **F**, for example, the field $GF(5)$, that is the field consisting of the following 5 elements [1])

$0'$: the set of all integers which are multiples of 5
$1'$: the set of numbers $5n + 1$
$2'$: the set of numbers $5n + 2$
$3'$: the set of numbers $5n + 3$
$4'$: the set of numbers $5n + 4$.

Addition and multiplication of these elements $0', \cdots, 4'$ will be defined in the following tables, where the primes are omitted. Notice that these tables are obtained from the ordinary addition and multiplication of integers.

| | | | | | |
|---|---|---|---|---|---|
| 4 | 4 | 0 | 1 | 2 | 3 |
| 3 | 3 | 4 | 0 | 1 | 2 |
| 2 | 2 | 3 | 4 | 0 | 1 |
| 1 | 1 | 2 | 3 | 4 | 0 |
| 0 | 0 | 1 | 2 | 3 | 4 |
| + | 0 | 1 | 2 | 3 | 4 |

| | | | | | |
|---|---|---|---|---|---|
| 4 | 0 | 4 | 3 | 2 | 1 |
| 3 | 0 | 3 | 1 | 4 | 2 |
| 2 | 0 | 2 | 4 | 1 | 3 |
| 1 | 0 | 1 | 2 | 3 | 4 |
| 0 | 0 | 0 | 0 | 0 | 0 |
| × | 0 | 1 | 2 | 3 | 4 |

[1]). In the algebraic terminology $GF(5)$ ($GF$ actually means *Galois field*) is the field of residue classes modulo 5, or in other words, the *quotient* of the ring of integers modulo the ideal of the multiples of 5: $GF(5) = Z/(5)$. In this formula "(5)" may also be read as the equivalence relation "to differ by a multiple of 5".

Problem (8.1). Calculate from these tables

$2+2;\ 3+4;\ 3-1;\ 2-4;\ 2\times 2;\ 3\times 4;\ 4:2;\ 1:3;\ 2:3;$

$-1;\ -2;\ -3;\ -4;\ (3+4-\frac{2}{3})(1-\frac{3}{4}).$

The points of an affine plane over the field $GF(5)$ can be represented in a one-to-one way by the pairs of values assumed by a pair of coordinates (= linear functions) $(\xi, \eta)$. The plane has, therefore, 25 points. Any rectangle in fig. 8.1 represents a point corresponding to the values of the coordinates $\xi$ and $\eta$ which are printed in it.

| | | | | | |
|---|---|---|---|---|---|
| 4 | 0,4 | 1,4* | 2,4 | 3,4 | 4,4 |
| 3 | 0,3 | 1,3 | 2,3 | 3,3* | 4,3 |
| 2 | 0,2* | 1,2 | 2,2 | 3,2 | 4,2 |
| 1 | 0,1 | 1,1 | 2,1* | 3,1 | 4,1 |
| $\eta = 0$ | 0,0 | 1,0 | 2,0 | 3,0 | 4,0* |
| | $\xi = 0$ | 1 | 2 | 3 | 4 |

Fig. 8.1

Any line in the plane is obtained as "level-curve" of a linear non-constant function

$$\alpha\xi + \beta\eta + \gamma \qquad \alpha, \beta, \gamma \in \mathbf{F}.$$

The same system of level-curves will be obtained if $\gamma$ is subtracted. If $\beta$ or $\alpha$ is not zero, we may also multiply by $\beta^{-1}$ or $\alpha^{-1}$ respectively. Hence all lines can be obtained as level-curves of functions

$$\xi \text{ and } \eta + \alpha\xi \qquad \alpha \in \mathbf{F}.$$

In fig. 8.2 the values of these six functions on the 25 points are given thus indicating the lines (= level-curves). Any of the six five-columned sets is called an array and a line is a set of 5 points having the same value in one of the arrays. In fig. 8.1 the line $\eta + 3\xi = 2$ has been indicated by symbols *.

| $\xi$ | $\eta$ | $\eta+\xi$ | $\eta+2\xi$ | $\eta+3\xi$ | $\eta+4\xi$ |
|---|---|---|---|---|---|
| 01234 | 44444 | 40123 | 41302 | 42031 | 43210 |
| 01234 | 33333 | 34012 | 30241 | 31420 | 32104 |
| 01234 | 22222 | 23401 | 24130 | 20314 | 21043 |
| 01234 | 11111 | 12340 | 13024 | 14203 | 10432 |
| 01234 | 00000 | 01234 | 02413 | 03142 | 04321 |

Fig. 8.2

The plane has $6 \times 5 = 30$ lines, each consisting of five points. Any of the linear functions determines a set of 5 parallel lines. Lines represented by different arrays always have exactly one point of intersection. Through any two points there is exactly one line.

PROBLEMS. (8.2). Check for the points $(\xi, \eta) = (4, 2)$ and (3,4) the values of the function $\eta + 2\xi$ given in fig. 8.2.

(8.3). Determine the equation of the line through (1, 2) and (3, 1).

(8.4). Determine the point of intersection of the lines $\xi + \eta = 3$ and $\xi - \eta = 1$

a) from fig. 8.2.

b) by solving the two equations in the usual way.

Finite planes can be used to obtain solutions of the following problem. Let there be given a set of $n^2$ elements. A division of the $n^2$ elements into $n$ classes each containing $n$ elements, such that every element is contained in exactly one class, will be called a (special) *classification*. Two classifications are called orthogonal if any class of the first has one element in common with any class of the second. The problem is to obtain $k + 2$ *mutually orthogonal classifications* for some $k$. For $k = 0$ and arbitrary $n$ this is trivial. For $k = 1$, it is easy.

For $n^2 = 25$ a solution of this problem is obtained by taking the points of the above plane over $GF(5)$ as the elements, and the "level curves" (each consisting of five points) of a linear function as the classes of a classification. The six functions $\xi$, $\eta$, $\eta + \xi$, $\eta + 2\xi$, $\eta + 3\xi$, $\eta + 4\xi$ correspond to a set of six mutually orthogonal classifications. These are shown in fig. 8.2 where the classifications

$\xi$ and $\eta$ are represented as columns and rows of an array. An array $n \times n$ with a classification is called a *Latin square* if the classification is orthogonal to columns and orthogonal to rows. Two Latin squares are called *orthogonal* if they are orthogonal as classifications. In fig. 8.2 the functions $\eta + \xi, \eta + 2\xi, \eta + 3\xi$ and $\eta + 4\xi$ determine $k = 4$ mutually orthogonal Latin squares.

(8.5). Let $A^2$ and its coordinates $(\xi, \eta)$ be as defined in this chapter. The pairs $(\xi, \eta)$ form a mapping onto the vector space $V^2$ over the field $\mathbf{F} = GF(5)$.

a) Find in fig. 8.2 the line $a + \mu(b - a)$, $\mu \in \mathbf{F}$, if $a = (3, 1)$, $b = (2, 4)$.

b) Find the midpoint of a and b.

c) Find the medians of triangle abc and their point of intersection, if $c = (0, 4)$.

d) Find the cross-ratio of the collinear points $(0, 1)$, $(1, 2)$, $(2, 3)$ and $(3, 4)$.

e) Check Menelaus's theorem for an arbitrary triangle and line.

f) The points $(0, 0)$, $(0, 1)$, $(0, 2)$ and $(0, 4)$ are harmonic. Prove this.

g) Take a parallelogram and prove that the diagonals bisect each other.

(8.6). Investigate the affine plane over the field $\mathbf{F} = GF(3)$ having three elements, the field of residue classes of the integers modulo 3.

(8.7). Do the same if $\mathbf{F} = GF(2)$. (*N.B.* In all other chapters we shall not consider fields of characteristic 2, such as $GF(2)$).

(8.8). Do the same if $\mathbf{F} = GF(4)$ is the field having four elements $0$, $1$, $\omega$ and $\omega^2 = 1 + \omega$, with the following addition and multiplication tables

| | | | | |
|---|---|---|---|---|
| $\omega^2$ | $\omega^2$ | $\omega$ | 1 | 0 |
| $\omega$ | $\omega$ | $\omega^2$ | 0 | 1 |
| 1 | 1 | 0 | $\omega^2$ | $\omega$ |
| 0 | 0 | 1 | $\omega$ | $\omega^2$ |
| + | 0 | 1 | $\omega$ | $\omega^2$ |

| | | | | |
|---|---|---|---|---|
| $\omega^2$ | 0 | $\omega^2$ | 1 | $\omega$ |
| $\omega$ | 0 | $\omega$ | $\omega^2$ | 1 |
| 1 | 0 | 1 | $\omega$ | $\omega^2$ |
| 0 | 0 | 0 | 0 | 0 |
| $\times$ | 0 | 1 | $\omega$ | $\omega^2$ |

Take a parallelogram in this plane and prove that its diagonals are parallel.

*N.B.* $GF(4)$ is the quotient of the ring of the polynomials in $\omega$ with integral coefficients, modulo the ideal generated by the polynomials 2 and $1 + \omega + \omega^2$. $GF(4) = Z(\omega)/(2, 1 + \omega + \omega^2)$.

(8.9). Investigate the 3-dimensional affine space over the field $GF(5)$. How many points and planes are there in this space?

(8.10). The 4-dimensional space over the field $GF(2)$ has $2^4 = 16$ points. How many points has a hyperplane?

Divide in 15 different ways a set of 16 points $P_1, \cdots P_{16}$ into two sets of 8 each, such that any two sets corresponding to different divisions always have 4 points in common.

## 9. HOMOMORPHISMS OF VECTOR SPACES

Definition: A mapping $\sigma: A \to B$ of a vector space A into a vector space B is called *linear* if for every $a_1, a_2 \in A$, $\lambda \in \mathbf{F}$:

$$\sigma(\lambda a_1) = \lambda \cdot \sigma a_1 \tag{9.1}$$

$$\sigma(a_1 + a_2) = \sigma a_1 + \sigma a_2. \tag{9.2}$$

Repeated application of these formulas yields:

$$\sigma(\lambda_1 a_1 + \cdots + \lambda_n a_n) = \lambda_1 \sigma a_1 + \cdots + \lambda_n \sigma a_n. \tag{9.3}$$

A linear mapping $\sigma: A \to B$ is called a *homomorphism* or *linear transformation*. If A and B are the same space, it is also called an *endomorphism*.

*Some examples*

1°. A linear function $\varphi: V \to \mathbf{F}$ on a vector space is a homomorphism of V onto the field $\mathbf{F}$, considered as a 1-dimensional vector space. In this example, which has been amply discussed in chapter 5, the relations (9.1) and (9.2) are easily checked.

2°. If $\varphi_1, \cdots \varphi_m$ are linear functions on V, then the mapping defined by

$$a \to \{\varphi_1(a), \varphi_2(a), \cdots \varphi_m(a)\} \qquad \text{for } a \in V$$

is a homomorphism of V into the $m$-dimensional space $\mathbf{F}^m$. It may be a homomorphism-*onto* (also called an *epimorphism*) but this is not necessarily so, as may be seen by taking $\varphi_1 = \varphi_2$ or by taking for $\varphi_3$ the function zero.

3°. In ordinary plane geometry a rotation through a fixed angle about the origin gives a mapping for which (9.1) is evidently satisfied, whereas (9.2) holds since this mapping transforms parallelograms into parallelograms. Hence it is linear, and since A and B are the same space, it is an endomorphism.

4°. Geometrical multiplication of all vectors of a vector space A by a factor $\lambda \neq 0$. This endomorphism is simply denoted by $\lambda$, $\lambda$: A $\rightarrow$ A.

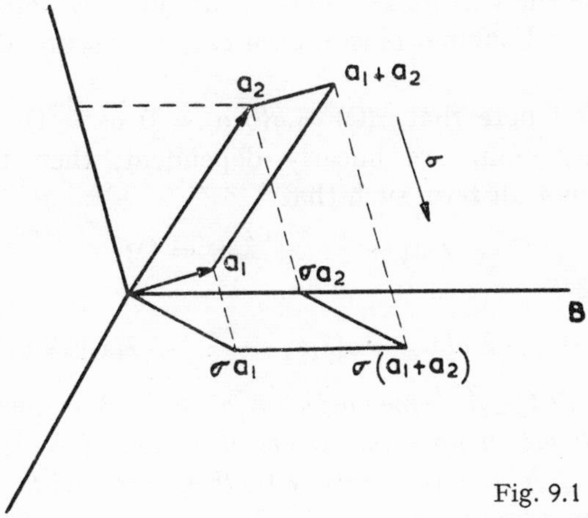


Fig. 9.1

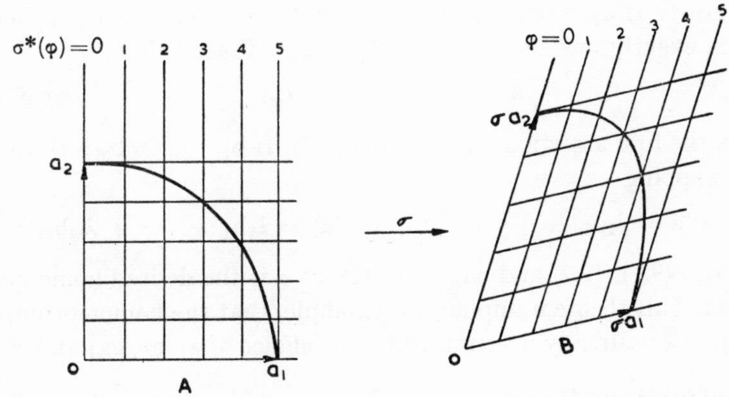


Fig. 9.2

5°. Fig. 9.1 shows a skew parallel projection of a 3-dimensional vectorspace A onto a 2-dimensional sub-space B. This, too, is a homomorphism (epimorphism) of A onto B $\subset$ A.

6°. In fig. 9.2 a homomorphism $\sigma$: A $\to$ B of two ordinary 2-dimensional vector spaces A and B is illustrated. In particular the image of a curve (circle segment) is drawn.

7°. An example of a map which is not a homomorphism is a translation (cf. p. 32).

Lemma: If the vectors $a_1, \cdots a_r \in A$ are linearly dependent and if $\sigma$: A $\to$ B is a homomorphism, then $\sigma a_1, \cdots \sigma a_r$ are also linearly dependent.

Proof: First note that $\sigma(O) = \sigma(0 \cdot a) = 0 \cdot \sigma a = O$.

Now, if $a_1, \cdots a_r$ are linearly dependent, then there exist $\lambda_1, \cdots \lambda_r \in \mathbf{F}$, not all zero, such that

$$\lambda_1 a_1 + \cdots + \lambda_r a_r = O;$$

hence

$$\lambda_1 \sigma(a_1) + \cdots + \lambda_r \sigma(a_r) = \sigma(\lambda_1 a_1 + \cdots + \lambda_r a_r) = \sigma(O) = O.$$

Theorem [9.1]: *A homomorphism* $\sigma$: A $\to$ B *is completely determined by its action upon the vectors of a basis of* A. *If* $a_1, \cdots a_m$ *form a basis of* A *and* $b_1, \cdots b_m \in B$, *then there exists exactly one homomorphism* $\sigma$ *for which* $\sigma a_i = b_i$, $i = 1, \cdots m$.

Proof: If $a_1, \cdots a_m$ form a basis of A, then for any $a \in A$ there exists exactly one set of scalars $\lambda_1, \cdots \lambda_m \in \mathbf{F}$ such that

$$a = \lambda_1 a_1 + \cdots + \lambda_m a_m. \tag{9.4}$$

Thus the first assertion follows from (9.3). If $b_1, b_2, \cdots b_m \in B$, then the mapping

$$\sigma: a = \lambda_1 a_1 + \cdots + \lambda_m a_m \to \sigma(a) = \lambda_1 b_1 + \cdots + \lambda_m b_m$$

satisfies (9.1), (9.2) and $\sigma a_i = b_i$. Hence $\sigma$ is the desired homomorphism. This theorem implies, for example, that the homomorphism in fig. 9.2 is already determined by the choice of $a_1$, $a_2$, $\sigma a_1$ and $\sigma a_2$.

Definition: If $\sigma$: A $\to$ B is a homomorphism, then $\sigma$A is called the *image*, $\sigma^{-1}(O)$ the *kernel*, A the *source* and the dimension of $\sigma$A the *rank* of $\sigma$.

Theorem [9.2]: *The kernel* $\sigma^{-1}(O)$ *and the image* $\sigma$A *of a homomorphism* $\sigma$: A $\to$ B *are linear subspaces of* A *and* B *respectively. The sum of the dimensions of kernel and image is equal to the dimension of the source*: *dim* $\sigma^{-1}(\mathrm{O})$ + *dim* $\sigma(\mathrm{A})$ = *dim* A.

$$\text{dim kernel} + \text{dim image} = \text{dim source.}$$

Proof: If $a_1$ and $a_2$ are vectors in the kernel $\sigma^{-1}(\mathrm{O})$, and $\lambda \in \mathbf{F}$, then

$$\sigma(\lambda a_1) = \lambda\sigma a_1 = \mathrm{O} \text{ and } \sigma(a_1 + a_2) = \sigma a_1 + \sigma a_2 = \mathrm{O} + \mathrm{O} = \mathrm{O}.$$

Hence $\lambda a_1$ and $a_1 + a_2$ are also contained in $\sigma^{-1}(\mathrm{O})$, and thus the kernel is a linear subspace of A (cf. chapter 3).

If

$$b_1 = \sigma a_1 \in \sigma\mathrm{A}, \quad b_2 = \sigma a_2 \in \sigma\mathrm{A}, \quad \lambda \in \mathbf{F}$$

then

$$\lambda b_1 = \lambda\sigma a_1 = \sigma(\lambda a_1) \in \sigma\mathrm{A}$$

and

$$b_1 + b_2 = \sigma a_1 + \sigma a_2 = \sigma(a_1 + a_2) \in \sigma\mathrm{A}$$

so that as well as $b_1$ and $b_2$, also $\lambda b_1$ and $b_1 + b_2$ are contained in the image $\sigma\mathrm{A} \subset \mathrm{B}$. Thus the image $\sigma\mathrm{A}$ is a linear subspace of B. This proves the first part of the theorem.

Let the dimensions of A and $\sigma^{-1}(\mathrm{O})$ be $m$ and $m - r$ respectively. Take a basis $a_{r+1}, \cdots a_m$ of $\sigma^{-1}(\mathrm{O})$ and complete it to a basis $a_1, \cdots a_m$ of A. Then

$$\sigma a_i = \mathrm{O} \text{ for } i > r.$$

We define

$$\sigma a_i = b_i \text{ for } i \leqslant r.$$

The vectors $b_1, \cdots b_r$ form a set of generators of $\sigma\mathrm{A}$, since for arbitrary $a \in \mathrm{A}$ we have

$$\sigma a = \sigma(\lambda_1 a_1 + \cdots + \lambda_m a_m) = \lambda_1 b_1 + \cdots + \lambda_r b_r. \qquad (9.5)$$

Indeed they form a basis. For suppose that $\lambda_1, \cdots \lambda_r \in \mathbf{F}$ and

$$\lambda_1 b_1 + \cdots + \lambda_r b_r = \mathrm{O}.$$

Then

$$\lambda_1\sigma a_1 + \cdots + \lambda_r\sigma a_r = \sigma(\lambda_1 a_1 + \cdots + \lambda_r a_r) = \mathrm{O},$$

$$\lambda_1 a_1 + \cdots + \lambda_r a_r \in \sigma^{-1}(\mathrm{O}).$$

Since $a_{r+1}, \cdots a_m$ is a basis of $\sigma^{-1}(O)$, there exist scalars $\lambda_{r+1}, \cdots \lambda_m$ such that

$$\lambda_1 a_1 + \cdots + \lambda_r a_r = \lambda_{r+1} a_{r+1} + \cdots + \lambda_m a_m$$

and because of the independence of $a_1, \cdots a_m$ this implies that $\lambda_1 = \lambda_2 = \cdots = \lambda_r = 0$. This means that the dimension of $\sigma A$ is equal to $r$, which proves the theorem.

PROBLEM (9.1). The vector spaces A and B over the real numbers have bases $a_1$, $a_2$, $a_3$ and $b_1$, $b_2$ respectively. Consider the homomorphism determined by $\sigma a_1 = b_1$, $\sigma a_2 = b_2$, $\sigma a_3 = b_1 + b_2$.
Determine $\sigma(a_1 + a_2 + a_3)$, $\sigma A$, $\sigma^{-1}(O)$ and the rank of $\sigma$, and verify theorem [9.2] for this case. Illustrate the answer by a drawing. Answer the same questions for the homomorphism $\rho$ determined by

$$\rho a_1 = \rho a_2 = \rho a_3 = b_1.$$

If B is a subspace of A then we can define the following relation, an equivalence, which will also be denoted by B. Two vectors $a, a' \in A$ are said to be equivalent if $a' - a \in B$. Since B is a vector space it follows immediately that $a \sim a$; $a' \sim a$ if $a \sim a'$; and $a \sim a''$ if $a \sim a'$ and $a' \sim a''$, implying that the relation is in fact an equivalence.

We note furthermore that: If $\lambda \in \mathbf{F}$, $a \sim a'$ so that $a' - a \in B$, then $\lambda a' - \lambda a = \lambda(a' - a) \in B$ and $\lambda a' \sim \lambda a$. Moreover, if $a \sim a'$, $b \sim b'$ so that $a' - a \in B$, $b' - b \in B$, then also $(a' + b') - (a + b) \in B$ and $a' + b' \sim a + b$.

Let the element of the quotient set A/B represented by $a \in A$ be denoted by $\{a\}$.

Now define the following vector space structure in the quotient set A/B:

$$\lambda\{a\} = \{\lambda a\}, \quad \{a\} + \{b\} = \{a + b\}.$$

From the remarks we have just made it follows that this definition of multiplication by scalars and addition in A/B is independent of the special choice of the representatives a and b. It may be left to the reader to check that axioms $A_3, \cdots A_9$ hold. *In the sequel* A/B *will always be the quotient space with this vector space structure.* The mapping which associates to $a \in A$ its class $\{a\}$ is a *homomorphism-*

*onto*, $\sigma$: A $\rightarrow$ A/B, with kernel B. For the dimensions we then have, by theorem [9.2],

$$\text{rank } \sigma = \dim A/B = \dim A - \dim B.$$

Now consider the sequence

$$O \rightarrow B \rightarrow A \rightarrow A/B \rightarrow O.$$

The arrows in O $\rightarrow$ B $\rightarrow$ A should be interpreted as the homomorphisms "identity mapping into", the arrow in A/B $\rightarrow$ O as the homomorphism onto the zero vector. Then for any of the spaces in this sequence it is true that the image of the preceding homomorphism is the kernel of the following. A sequence of homomorphisms with this property is said to be *exact*. Exact sequences are an important tool in mathematics. Discussion is however beyond the scope of this book.

## *The vector space Hom*(A, B)

Let $\sigma$ and $\rho$ be two homomorphisms of A into B, and let $\lambda \in \mathbf{F}$. We now consider the following *mappings* of A into B

$$a \rightarrow \lambda\sigma a \text{ and } a \rightarrow \sigma a + \rho a \text{ for } a \in A.$$

Both mappings are homomorphisms themselves! For, if $a_1$, $a_2$, a $\in$ A and $\mu \in \mathbf{F}$, then the images of the vectors $\mu a$ and $a_1 + a_2$ are respectively

$$\lambda\sigma(\mu a) = \lambda\mu\sigma a = \mu(\lambda\sigma a), \quad \lambda\sigma(a_1 + a_2) = \lambda(\sigma a_1 + \sigma a_2) = \lambda\sigma a_1 + \lambda\sigma a_2$$

and

$$\sigma(\mu a) + \rho(\mu a) = \mu\sigma a + \mu\rho a = \mu(\sigma a + \rho a)$$

$$\sigma(a_1 + a_2) + \rho(a_1 + a_2) = (\sigma a_1 + \rho a_1) + (\sigma a_2 + \rho a_2).$$

The newly constructed homomorphisms are denoted by $\lambda\sigma$ and $\sigma + \rho$. They may be defined by the formulas

$$(\lambda\sigma)a = \lambda\sigma(a) \text{ and } (\sigma + \rho)(a) = \sigma(a) + \rho(a).$$

Note that

$$\sigma + \rho = \rho + \sigma. \tag{9.6}$$

*Thus the operations of addition and multiplication by field elements are defined in the set of homomorphisms* A $\rightarrow$ B.

Theorem [9.3]: *With these definitions of addition and multipli-*

*cation by scalars the homomorphisms of the vector space* A *into the vector space* B *form another vector space, the dimension of which is equal to the product mn of the dimensions m and n of* A *and* B. *This vector space is called Hom*(A, B).

Proof: The validity of properties $A_3, \cdots A_8$ of chapters 3 follows immediately by substitution.

Now let $\mathrm{a}_1, \cdots \mathrm{a}_m$ form a basis of A and $\mathrm{b}_1, \cdots \mathrm{b}_n$ a basis of B. An arbitrary homomorphism is determined by $mn$ scalars $\sigma_{ji}$, $i = 1, \cdots m; j = 1, \cdots n$, as is seen from the mapping

$$\sigma: \begin{cases} \mathrm{a}_1 \to \sigma_{11}\mathrm{b}_1 + \sigma_{21}\mathrm{b}_2 + \cdots + \sigma_{n1}\mathrm{b}_n \in \mathrm{B} \\ \mathrm{a}_2 \to \sigma_{12}\mathrm{b}_1 + \sigma_{22}\mathrm{b}_2 + \cdots + \sigma_{n2}\mathrm{b}_n \in \mathrm{B} \\ \cdot \quad \cdot \quad \cdot \quad \cdots \quad \cdot \quad \cdot \\ \mathrm{a}_m \to \sigma_{1m}\mathrm{b}_1 + \sigma_{2m}\mathrm{b}_2 + \cdots + \sigma_{nm}\mathrm{b}_n \in \mathrm{B}. \end{cases} \tag{9.7}$$

Let $\varepsilon_{ji}$ designate the homomorphism mapping $\mathrm{a}_i$ into $\mathrm{b}_j$ and mapping all other vectors $\mathrm{a}_k$, $k \neq i$, into the zero vector of B. There are $mn$ different $\varepsilon_{ji}$ for $i = 1, \cdots m; j = 1, \cdots n$. Clearly $\sum_{i,j} \sigma_{ji}\varepsilon_{ji}$ is also a homomorphism, the action of which upon $\mathrm{a}_1, \cdots \mathrm{a}_m$ is the same as that of $\sigma$. Hence it *is* $\sigma$:

$$\sigma = \textstyle\sum_{i,j} \sigma_{ji}\varepsilon_{ji}. \tag{9.8}$$

The homomorphisms $\varepsilon_{ji}$ are thus a set of generators for Hom(A, B). Suppose now that $\sigma$ in (9.8) is the trivial homomorphism, mapping any vector into the zero vector of B. Then the image $\sigma\mathrm{a}_i$ of $\mathrm{a}_i$ is also the zero vector:

$$\mathrm{O} = \sigma\mathrm{a}_i = \textstyle\sum_j \sigma_{ji}\varepsilon_{ji}\mathrm{a}_i = \sum_j \sigma_{ji}\mathrm{b}_j.$$

Since $\mathrm{b}_1, \cdots \mathrm{b}_n$ are independent, $\sigma_{ji} = 0$ for $j = 1, \cdots n$, and this is true for $i = 1, \cdots m$. The $mn$ homomorphisms $\varepsilon_{ji}$ form therefore a basis of the $mn$-dimensional vector space Hom(A, B).

PROBLEMS. (9.2). In the ordinary plane (of chapter 1) with origin O we draw two perpendicular vectors $\mathrm{a}_1$ and $\mathrm{a}_2$ of equal length and consider the following homomorphisms of the vector space with basis $\mathrm{a}_1$ and $\mathrm{a}_2$ into or onto itself.

$\sigma$: rotation through an angle of 90°. This can be defined as the homomorphism having the action: $\sigma(\mathrm{a}_1) = \mathrm{a}_2$, $\sigma(\mathrm{a}_2) = -\mathrm{a}_1$;

$\varepsilon$: the identity, i.e. the homomorphism mapping any vector to itself;

$\rho$: the homomorphism with the action $\rho(a_1) = 2a_1$, $\rho(a_2) = a_2$.

Now determine the geometrical meaning of each of the following homomorphisms:

$$\sigma + \varepsilon, \ \rho + \varepsilon, \ \rho - \varepsilon, \ 3\sigma, \ 2\varepsilon, \ \sigma - \rho, \ -\rho, \ 3\sigma + 4\varepsilon - 2\rho.$$

(9.3). The vector space of all homomorphisms $V \to \mathbf{F}$ has already been considered. Prove that it is the dual space $V^*$ that has been mentioned at the end of chapter 5.

*Composition (multiplication) of homomorphisms*

Let $\sigma: A \to B$ and $\rho: B \to C$ be homomorphisms of vector spaces and consider the mapping of A into C associating to $a \in A$ the vector $\rho(\sigma a) \in C$. Application of the definition shows that this mapping is also a homomorphism. It is called the *product* of $\sigma$ by $\rho$ and is denoted by $\rho\sigma: A \to C$. Observe that in the product $\rho\sigma$ the mapping $\sigma$ acts first and $\rho$ subsequently. If $\tau: C \to D$ is another homomorphism then $(\tau\rho)\sigma$ and $\tau(\rho\sigma)$ also are homomorphisms. They are identical, for the image of $a \in A$ under $(\rho\sigma)$ is $\rho(\sigma a)$; under $\tau(\rho\sigma)$ it is $\tau(\rho(\sigma a))$; under $\sigma$: $\sigma a$; under $(\tau\rho)\sigma$: $\tau(\rho(\sigma a))$.

Hence we have the *associative law of multiplication of homomorphisms*:

$$(\tau\rho)\sigma = \tau(\rho\sigma). \tag{9.9}$$

Note that the product $\rho\sigma$ of two homomorphisms can only be defined if the image of $\sigma$ is contained in the source of $\rho$.

If the homomorphisms $\sigma, \tau: A \to B$; $\rho: B \to C$ are given, then for arbitrary $a \in A$ we have

$$\rho\{\sigma a + \tau a\} = \rho\sigma(a) + \rho\tau(a)$$

and hence we have the right-distributive law for homomorphisms:

$$\varrho(\sigma + \tau) = \varrho\sigma + \varrho\tau. \tag{9.10}$$

Similarly if $\rho: A \to B$; $\sigma, \tau: B \to C$, the left-distributive law is obtained:

$$(\sigma + \tau)\rho = \sigma\rho + \tau\rho. \tag{9.11}$$

A homomorphism $\sigma$: A $\to$ B which is a one-to-one mapping onto B is called an *isomorphism*. The homomorphism $\sigma$: A $\to$ B mapping A onto B is an isomorphism if and only if $\sigma^{-1}(O) = O$. For in that case, whenever $\sigma a_1 = \sigma a_2 = b$, we have $\sigma a_1 - \sigma a_2 = \sigma(a_1 - a_2) = O$, and hence $a_1 - a_2 = O$, $a_1 = a_2$. On the other hand, if the homomorphism is one-to-one, $\sigma^{-1}(O)$ must clearly be O.

Furthermore, if $a_1 = \sigma^{-1}(b_1)$, $a_2 = \sigma^{-1}(b_2)$, then

$$\sigma(\lambda_1 a_1 + \lambda_2 a_2) = \lambda_1 \sigma a_1 + \lambda_2 \sigma a_2 = \lambda_1 b_1 + \lambda_2 b_2.$$

Hence

$$\sigma^{-1}(\lambda_1 b_1 + \lambda_2 b_2) = \lambda_1 a_1 + \lambda_2 a_2 = \lambda_1 \sigma^{-1}(b_1) + \lambda_2 \sigma^{-1}(b_2)$$

which means that $\sigma^{-1}$ is also a homomorphism (indeed an isomorphism) of $\sigma$(A) onto A. Note that $\sigma^{-1}\sigma$ = the identity mapping of A onto itself, and $\sigma\sigma^{-1}$ is the identity mapping of B onto itself.

A homomorphism $\sigma$: A $\to$ A of A into itself has already been called an endomorphism. An *isomorphism* of A *onto* itself is called an *automorphism*. An endomorphism which is not an automorphism is called *singular*.

Theorem [9.4]: *If $\sigma$ and $\tau$ are isomorphisms-onto, $\sigma$: A $\to$ B and $\tau$: B $\to$ C, then*

$$(\tau\sigma)^{-1} = \sigma^{-1}\tau^{-1}. \tag{9.12}$$

*This is particularly true for automorphisms*: A = B = C.

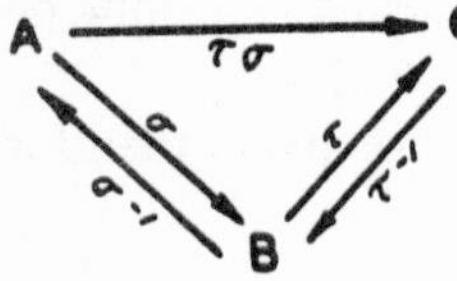

Fig. 9.3

Proof: (cf. fig. 9.3) For any a $\epsilon$ A we have

$$(\sigma^{-1}\tau^{-1})(\tau\sigma)a = \sigma^{-1}(\tau^{-1}\tau)\sigma a = \sigma^{-1}\sigma a = a;$$

hence $(\sigma^{-1}\tau^{-1})(\tau\sigma)$ is the identity and (9.12) holds by definition of its left-hand side.

Problem (9.4). Determine the geometrical meaning of any of the following endomorphisms, if $a_1$, $a_2$, $\sigma$, $\varepsilon$, $\rho$, have the same meaning as in problem (9.2):

$$\sigma\varepsilon,\ \varepsilon\rho,\ \sigma\sigma = \sigma^2,\ \sigma^4,\ \sigma^5,\ \sigma\rho,\ \rho\sigma,\ \sigma(\rho - \varepsilon),$$

$$(\rho - \varepsilon)\sigma(\rho - \varepsilon),\ \sigma(\rho - \varepsilon)^2,\ \sigma^{-1},\ \sigma^{-1}\rho\sigma.$$

Theorem [9.5]: *The automorphisms of a vector space* A *form a group under multiplication. It is called the linear group and is usually denoted by* $Gl(n, \mathbf{F})$, *where* $n$ *is the dimension of* A *and* $\mathbf{F}$ *is the field.*

Proof: The theorem follows immediately from the following definition of a group:

Definition: A *group* is a set $G$ of elements with a mapping of $G \times G$ onto $G$ with the following properties (the image of the pair $(\sigma, \rho)$ is written as $\sigma\rho$ and is called the product of $\sigma$ and $\rho$):

1. There exists an element $\varepsilon \in G$, the *unit element*, such that for any $\sigma \in G$

$$\varepsilon\sigma = \sigma\varepsilon = \sigma.$$

2. To any element $\sigma \in G$ there belongs exactly one element $\sigma^{-1} \in G$ such that

$$\sigma^{-1}\sigma = \sigma\sigma^{-1} = \varepsilon.$$

3. If $\sigma, \rho, \tau \in G$ then

$$(\sigma\rho)\tau = \sigma(\rho\tau) \qquad \text{(associative law)}.$$

In the case of the automorphisms of A considered as elements of $G$, $\varepsilon$ is the identity and $\sigma^{-1}$ is the inverse of $\sigma$. The associative law is expressed by (9.9).

PROBLEMS. (9.5). A vector space is an *Abelian* (= commutative) group, if addition of vectors is chosen as group multiplication.

(9.6). If $\sigma$ is as defined in problem (9.2), then the automorphism $\sigma, \sigma^2, \sigma^3$, and $\sigma^4$ form a group under multiplication.

(9.7). Prove that rank $\sigma\tau \leqslant$ rank $\sigma$ and $\leqslant$ rank $\tau$.

Theorem [9.6]: *The endomorphisms of a vector space* A *form a ring.*

This follows immediately from the definition of a ring:

Definition: A *ring* is a set $M$ of elements with *two* mappings of $M \times M$ into $M$, called sum and product, with the following properties:

$R1$. $M$ is a group with respect to *addition.*
$R2$. This group is commutative, $\sigma + \rho = \rho + \sigma$.
$R3$. Multiplication is associative.
$R4$. Multiplication is left- and right-distributive.

Remark. In this connection we may also recall the definition of a field:

Definition: A *field* is a ring whose non-zero elements form an Abelian group under multiplication.

*The dual homomorphism of the dual vector spaces*

Let a fixed homomorphism $\sigma$: A $\to$ B be given and let $\psi$: B $\to \mathbf{F}$ be a homogeneous linear function on B. $\psi$ may then be considered as a homomorphism. Now consider the homomorphism $\psi\sigma$: A $\to \mathbf{F}$, which is also a linear function. The linear functions on B(or A) form the dual vector space B* (or A*). The mapping $\sigma^*$ which maps $\psi \in$ B* to $\psi\sigma \in$ A* is a homomorphism since for any $\lambda \in \mathbf{F}$, $\psi_1, \psi_2 \in$ B* we have

$$\sigma^*(\lambda\psi_1) = (\lambda\psi_1)\sigma = \lambda(\psi_1\sigma) = \lambda\sigma^*\psi_1$$

$$\sigma^*(\psi_1 + \psi_2) = (\psi_1 + \psi_2)\sigma = \psi_1\sigma + \psi_2\sigma = \sigma^*\psi_1 + \sigma^*\psi_2.$$

$\sigma^*$ is said to be dual to $\sigma$. $\sigma^*\psi = \psi\sigma$ is called the *dual image* of $\psi$ under $\sigma$.

Fig. 9.2, page 59, shows a linear function $\varphi$ and its image function $\sigma^*\varphi = \varphi\sigma$ on two-dimensional vector spaces.

Theorem [9.7]: *The homomorphism* $\sigma$: A $\to$ B *and the dual homomorphism* $\sigma^*$: B* $\to$ A* *have the same rank.*

Proof: Let the rank of $\sigma$ be $r$. In the $m$-dimensional space A take a basis $a_1, \cdots a_m$ such that $a_{r+1}, \cdots a_m$ generate the subspace $\sigma^{-1}(O)$. In the $n$-dimensional space B take a basis $b_1, \cdots b_n$ such that (this is possible!, cf. [9.2])

$$\sigma(a_i) = b_i \text{ for } i \leqslant r.$$

Let in A* and B* the corresponding cobases consist of the linear functions $\varphi_1, \cdots \varphi_m$ and $\psi_1, \cdots \psi_n$ respectively.

Then we have

$$\varphi_i(a_j) = \delta_{ij};\ \psi_i(b_j) = \delta_{ij}(= 0\ i \neq j;\ = 1\ i = j).$$

The space $\sigma^*$B* is generated by the functions $\sigma^*\psi_i$, $i = 1, \cdots n$.

Now

$$(\sigma^*\psi_i)a_j = \psi_i(\sigma a_j) = \begin{cases} 0 & \text{for } i > r \\ \psi_i(b_j) = \varphi_i(a_j) & \text{for } i \leqslant r, \end{cases}$$

in other words
$$\sigma^*\psi_i = 0 \qquad i > r$$
$$= \varphi_i \qquad i \leqslant r.$$

Hence the space $\sigma^*B^*$ is already generated by the functions $\varphi_1, \cdots \varphi_r$, which are independent. The rank of $\sigma^*$ is the dimension of $\sigma^*B^*$, and so it is $r$.

Theorem [9.8]: *Let the dual homomorphisms of*

$\sigma: A \to B$ *and* $\tau: B \to C$ *be* $\sigma^*: B^* \to A^*$ *and* $\tau^*: C^* \to B^*$

*respectively. Then the dual homomorphism of* $\tau\sigma: A \to C$ *is*

$$(\tau\sigma)^* = \sigma^*\tau^*: C^* \to A^*. \tag{9.13}$$

Proof: We first give the scheme

$$A \xrightarrow{\sigma} B \xrightarrow{\tau} C, \quad A \xrightarrow{\tau\sigma} C \qquad A^* \xleftarrow{\sigma^*} B^* \xleftarrow{\tau^*} C^*, \quad A^* \xleftarrow{\sigma^*\tau^*} C^*.$$

If $\chi \in C^*$, $a \in A$, then

$$\{(\tau\sigma)^*\chi\}a = \chi(\tau\sigma)a = (\chi\tau)\sigma a = \sigma^*(\chi\tau)a = \sigma^*\tau^*\chi a,$$

and hence

$$(\tau\sigma)^*\chi = \sigma^*\tau^*\chi \text{ and } (\tau\sigma)^* = \sigma^*\tau^*.$$

*The inner product of vectors with respect to a basis.* We have seen that to any vector space V there belongs a dual space V* of the same dimension. Furthermore to a given basis $a_1, \cdots a_m$ there belongs a cobasis of linear functions $\varphi_1, \cdots \varphi_m$ defined by

$$\varphi_i(a_j) = \delta_{ij}.$$

An important isomorphism of V onto V* is the isomorphism $^t$ which acts according to the law

$$^t\colon\ a_i \to {}^ta_i = \varphi_i.$$

The inverse of this is also denoted by $^t$ (cf. chapter 5):

$$^t\colon\ \varphi_i \to {}^t\varphi_i = a_i = {}^{tt}a_i.$$

This isomorphism is determined by the basis $a_1, \cdots a_m$. The image of an arbitrary vector

$$a = \lambda_1 a_1 + \cdots + \lambda_m a_m$$

under $^t$ is called the *transposed of* a *with respect to that basis.* It is

$$^t a = \lambda_1 \varphi_1 + \lambda_2 \varphi_2 + \cdots + \lambda_m \varphi_m.$$

If a, b $\epsilon$ V then $^t a(b)$, or shorter $^t ab$ is a scalar: if

$$a = \lambda_1 a_1 + \cdots + \lambda_m a_m, \quad b = \mu_1 a_1 + \cdots + \mu_m a_m,$$

$$^t ab = \lambda_1 \varphi_1(b) + \cdots + \lambda_m \varphi_m(b) = \lambda_1 \mu_1 + \lambda_2 \mu_2 + \cdots + \lambda_m \mu_m. \quad (9.14)$$

(9.14) is called the *inner product* of a and b with respect to the basis $a_1, \cdots a_m$. Note that

$$^t a_i a_j = \delta_{ij}.$$

Problem (9.8). Let the vectors a and b form the independent basis of a 2-dimensional vector space. Investigate the automorphism $\sigma$ with the action

$$\sigma(a) = a + b, \quad \sigma(a + b) = b.$$

Prove that $\sigma^6$ is the identical automorphism. Do you see any relation with the regular hexagon?

Calculate the inner product with respect to the basis a, b, of the vectors $2a + 3b$ and $3a - b$.

(9.9). Let V be the vector space of polynomials in x of degree $< n$. (Cf. problem (3.10) p. 12.) The differential operators

$$\frac{d}{dx} \text{ and } \frac{d^2}{dx^2} + 3\frac{d}{dx}$$

define endomorphisms of V.

# 10. MATRICES

In this chapter we shall consider the *homomorphisms of vector spaces* $\mathbf{F}^m$. We will thus give a more explicit treatment of the homomorphisms of arbitrary vector spaces, since any $m$-dimensional vector space $V^m$ is isomorphic to an $m$-dimensional vector space $\mathbf{F}^m$. We recall that such an isomorphism is given by $m$ linearly independent linear functions on $V^m$ (cf. (5.8)).

In this chapter a *vector* in $\mathbf{F}^m$ will be a *column* of $m$ scalars:

$$\mathrm{x} = \begin{bmatrix} \xi_1(\mathrm{x}) \\ \xi_2(\mathrm{x}) \\ \cdot \\ \cdot \\ \cdot \\ \xi_m(\mathrm{x}) \end{bmatrix}. \tag{10.1}$$

*As basis we shall always take the vectors*

$$\mathrm{e}_1 = \begin{bmatrix} 1 \\ 0 \\ 0 \\ \cdot \\ \cdot \\ 0 \end{bmatrix}, \ \mathrm{e}_2 = \begin{bmatrix} 0 \\ 1 \\ 0 \\ \cdot \\ \cdot \\ 0 \end{bmatrix}, \ \cdots, \ \mathrm{e}_m = \begin{bmatrix} 0 \\ 0 \\ 0 \\ \cdot \\ \cdot \\ 1 \end{bmatrix}. \tag{10.2}$$

These vectors will be called the *standard basis vectors* in $\mathbf{F}^m$.

The mapping $\mathrm{x} \to \xi_i(\mathrm{x})$ is a linear function on $\mathbf{F}^m$ which we denote by $\xi_i$. It is the $i$-th vector of *the* cobasis in the dual vector space, since

$$\xi_i(\mathrm{e}_j) = \delta_{ij}$$

(cf. p. 26 for $\delta_{ij}$).

An arbitrary linear function $\varphi$ on $\mathbf{F}^m$ is a linear combination o these cobasis vectors:

$$\varphi(\mathrm{x}) = \alpha_1\xi_1(\mathrm{x}) + \cdots + \alpha_m\xi_m(\mathrm{x}) \quad \alpha_1, \cdots \alpha_m \in \mathbf{F}. \tag{10.3}$$

We represent this function of x by the *row* of scalars

$$\varphi = (\alpha_1, \alpha_2, \cdots \alpha_m). \tag{10.3'}$$

The transposed of the vector $\mathrm{e}_i$ is the linear function $\xi_i$. The *transposed* of

$$\mathrm{a} = \begin{bmatrix} \alpha_1 \\ \alpha_2 \\ \cdot \\ \cdot \\ \cdot \\ \alpha_m \end{bmatrix} \tag{10.4}$$

is the linear function (10.3), i.e. the row (10.3′). The value assumed by this function $\varphi = {}^t\mathrm{a}$ on the vector (10.1) is the *inner product* of a and x with respect to the basis (10.2):

$$\alpha_1\xi_1(\mathrm{x}) + \alpha_2\xi_2(\mathrm{x}) + \cdots + \alpha_m\xi_m(\mathrm{x}) = {}^t\mathrm{a}\mathrm{x} = \varphi(\mathrm{x}). \tag{10.5}$$

By theorem [9.1], a homomorphism $\sigma\colon \mathbf{F}^m \to \mathbf{F}^n$ is unambiguously determined by its action upon the basis vectors:

$$\sigma\mathrm{e}_1 = \mathrm{s}_1 = \begin{bmatrix} \sigma_{11} \\ \sigma_{21} \\ \cdot\cdot \\ \sigma_{n1} \end{bmatrix}, \sigma\mathrm{e}_2 = \mathrm{s}_2 = \begin{bmatrix} \sigma_{12} \\ \sigma_{22} \\ \cdot\cdot \\ \sigma_{n2} \end{bmatrix}, \cdots \sigma\mathrm{e}_m = \mathrm{s}_m = \begin{bmatrix} \sigma_{1m} \\ \sigma_{2m} \\ \cdot\cdot \\ \sigma_{nm} \end{bmatrix}. \tag{10.6}$$

This homomorphism may be denoted by the following array of scalars $\sigma_{ij}(1 \leqslant i \leqslant n,\ 1 \leqslant j \leqslant m)$, and such an array of $n$ rows and $m$ columns is called a *matrix* ($n \times m$-matrix):

$$\sigma = \begin{bmatrix} \sigma_{11} & \sigma_{12} & \cdot & \cdot & \sigma_{1m} \\ \sigma_{21} & \sigma_{22} & \cdot & \cdot & \sigma_{2m} \\ \cdot & \cdot & \cdot & \cdot & \cdot \\ \sigma_{n1} & \sigma_{n2} & \cdot & \cdot & \sigma_{nm} \end{bmatrix}. \tag{10.7}$$

From theorem [9.1] we obtain

Theorem [10.1]: *The homomorphisms $\sigma\colon \mathbf{F}^m \to \mathbf{F}^n$ are in one-to-one correspondence with the matrices with $m$ columns and $n$ rows.*

The image of (10.4) under the homomorphism (10.7) is

$$\sigma \mathrm{a} = \sigma(\alpha_1 \mathrm{e}_1 + \alpha_2 \mathrm{e}_2 + \cdots + \alpha_m \mathrm{e}_m) = \alpha_1 \sigma \mathrm{e}_1 + \cdots + \alpha_m \sigma \mathrm{e}_m = \\ = \alpha_1 \mathrm{s}_1 + \cdots + \alpha_m \mathrm{s}_m$$

$$\sigma \mathrm{a} = \begin{bmatrix} \sigma_{11} & \sigma_{12} & \cdots & \sigma_{1m} \\ \cdots & \cdots & \cdots & \cdots \\ \sigma_{n1} & \sigma_{n2} & \cdots & \sigma_{nm} \end{bmatrix} \begin{bmatrix} \alpha_1 \\ \alpha_2 \\ \cdot \\ \cdot \\ \alpha_m \end{bmatrix} = \begin{bmatrix} \sigma_{11}\alpha_1 + \sigma_{12}\alpha_2 + \cdots + \sigma_{1m}\alpha_m \\ \cdots \quad \cdots \quad \cdots \quad \cdots \\ \sigma_{n1}\alpha_1 + \sigma_{n2}\alpha_2 + \cdots + \sigma_{nm}\alpha_m \end{bmatrix}. \tag{10.8}$$

It is a column of scalars which are the inner products of the *rows* of $\sigma$ and the vector a.

Definition: The $\lambda$-multiple, the sum and the product of matrices is the matrix-representation of the $\lambda$-multiple, the sum and the product of the homomorphisms represented by the matrices. With these conventions the theorems of chapter 9 can be carried over to matrices, and we shall do so.

But first we shall give formal expressions for the above matrix operations.

The $\lambda$-multiple ($\lambda \in \mathbf{F}$) of $\sigma$ is the homomorphism transforming the vector $\mathrm{e}_i$ into $\lambda \mathrm{s}_i$. It can therefore be represented by the matrix

$$\lambda \begin{bmatrix} \sigma_{11} & \sigma_{12} & \cdot & \cdot & \sigma_{1m} \\ \cdots & \cdots & \cdot & \cdot & \cdots \\ \sigma_{n1} & \sigma_{n2} & \cdot & \cdot & \sigma_{nm} \end{bmatrix} = \begin{bmatrix} \lambda\sigma_{11} & \lambda\sigma_{12} & \cdot & \cdot & \lambda\sigma_{1m} \\ \cdots & \cdots & \cdot & \cdot & \cdots \\ \lambda\sigma_{n1} & \lambda\sigma_{n2} & \cdot & \cdot & \lambda\sigma_{nm} \end{bmatrix}. \tag{10.9}$$

The *sum* of two homomorphisms $\sigma$ and $\rho\colon \mathbf{F}^m \to \mathbf{F}^n$ transforms the vector $\mathrm{e}_i \in \mathbf{F}^m$ into $\sigma \mathrm{e}_i + \rho \mathrm{e}_i$, so that

$$\begin{bmatrix} \sigma_{11} & \sigma_{12} & \cdot & \cdot & \sigma_{1m} \\ \cdots & \cdots & \cdot & \cdot & \cdots \\ \sigma_{n1} & \sigma_{n2} & \cdot & \cdot & \sigma_{nm} \end{bmatrix} + \begin{bmatrix} \rho_{11} & \rho_{12} & \cdot & \cdot & \rho_{1m} \\ \cdots & \cdots & \cdot & \cdot & \cdots \\ \rho_{n1} & \rho_{n2} & \cdot & \cdot & \rho_{nm} \end{bmatrix} =$$

$$\begin{bmatrix} \sigma_{11} + \rho_{11} & \sigma_{12} + \rho_{12} & \cdots & \sigma_{1m} + \rho_{1m} \\ \cdots & \cdots & \cdots & \cdots \\ \sigma_{n1} + \rho_{n1} & \sigma_{n2} + \rho_{n2} & \cdots & \sigma_{nm} + \rho_{nm} \end{bmatrix}. \tag{10.10}$$

The product of two homomorphisms $\sigma\colon \mathbf{F}^m \to \mathbf{F}^n$ and $\rho\colon \mathbf{F}^n \to \mathbf{F}^p$ maps the vector $\mathrm{e}_i \in \mathbf{F}^m$ to the image of $\sigma \mathrm{e}_i$ under $\rho$ (cf. 10.8), that is, to the vector

$$\rho(\sigma \mathrm{e}_i) = \begin{bmatrix} \rho_{11} & \cdot\cdot & \rho_{1n} \\ \cdot\cdot & \cdot\cdot & \cdot\cdot \\ \rho_{p1} & \cdot\cdot & \rho_{pn} \end{bmatrix} \begin{bmatrix} \sigma_{11} & \cdot\cdot & \sigma_{1m} \\ \cdot\cdot & \cdot\cdot & \cdot\cdot \\ & & \\ \sigma_{n1} & \cdot\cdot & \sigma_{nm} \end{bmatrix} \mathrm{e}_i = \begin{bmatrix} \rho_{11} & \cdot\cdot & \rho_{1n} \\ \cdot\cdot & \cdot\cdot & \cdot\cdot \\ \rho_{p1} & \cdot\cdot & \rho_{pn} \end{bmatrix} \begin{bmatrix} \sigma_{1i} \\ \cdot \\ \cdot \\ \sigma_{ni} \end{bmatrix} =$$

$$= \begin{bmatrix} \rho_{11}\sigma_{1i}+\rho_{12}\sigma_{2i} & + \cdot\cdot + & \rho_{1n}\sigma_{ni} \\ \cdots\cdots & \cdot\cdot & \cdots \\ \rho_{p1}\sigma_{1i}+\rho_{p2}\sigma_{2i} & + \cdot\cdot + & \rho_{pn}\sigma_{ni} \end{bmatrix}. \qquad (10.11)$$

The *product* $\rho\sigma$ of the matrices

$\sigma$ having the scalar $\sigma_{ji}$ in the $i$-th column and the $j$-th row and $\rho$ having the scalar $\rho_{kj}$ in the $j$-th column and the $k$-th row

has the scalar

$$\sum_{j=1}^{n} \rho_{kj}\sigma_{ji} = \rho_{k1}\sigma_{1i} + \rho_{k2}\sigma_{2i} + \cdots + \rho_{kn}\sigma_{ni} \qquad (10.11)$$

in its $i$-th column and $k$-th row, $i = 1, \cdots m$; $k = 1, \cdots p$. This scalar is the inner product of the $k$-th row of $\rho$ and the $i$-th column of $\sigma$.

Schematically:

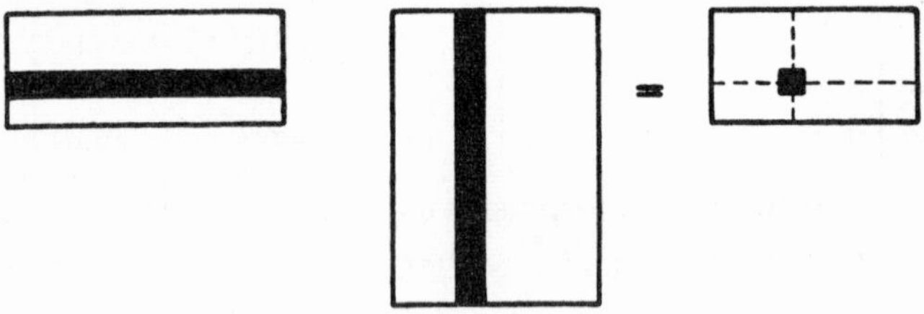

Fig. 10.1

*The column vectors of an $n \times m$-matrix* generate a subspace $\sigma(\mathbf{F}^m)$ in $\mathbf{F}^n$, the *dimension* of which is the rank $r$ of $\sigma$. $r$ is also called the *rank of the matrix*. By theorem [9.2] the vectors which are mapped to the zero vector form a space of dimension (dim $\mathbf{F}^m$) — — (rank $\sigma$) $= m - r$.

If $m = n$, the matrix, which is then called a *square matrix*, represents an endomorphism $\sigma$: $\mathbf{F}^m \rightarrow \mathbf{F}^m$. By theorem [9.6] all square matrices with $m$ rows form a ring. The endomorphism is also an isomorphism, hence an *automorphism,* if $\sigma^{-1}(O) = O$. This is the case if and only if the *rank* of $\sigma$ is equal to the number of columns, $r = m$. Theorem [9.5] then implies: *The square matrices $m \times m$ of rank $m$ form the linear group $Gl(m, \mathbf{F})$ under multiplication.*

Square matrices $m \times m$ of rank $< m$ are called *singular.*

The identity $\varepsilon$: $\mathbf{F}^m \to \mathbf{F}^m$ transforms any of the standard basis vectors to itself, and can therefore be represented by

$$\varepsilon = \begin{bmatrix} 1 & 0 & \cdots & 0 \\ 0 & 1 & \cdots & 0 \\ \cdot & \cdot & \cdots & \cdot \\ 0 & 0 & \cdots & 1 \end{bmatrix}. \tag{10.12}$$

This matrix is called the *unit matrix $m \times m$.* It is the unit element of the group $Gl(m, \mathbf{F})$.

If $\sigma$ is a matrix and $\sigma^{-1}\sigma = \sigma\sigma^{-1} = \varepsilon$, then $\sigma^{-1}$ is called the *inverse matrix.* By theorem [9.4] we have for square matrices $\sigma$ and $\tau$ (of rank $m$) which admit inverses,

$$(\tau\sigma)^{-1} = \sigma^{-1}\tau^{-1}.$$

The expressions (10.4) and (10.3′) can also be considered as matrices, having one column and one row respectively, and representing homomorphisms of type $\mathbf{F}^1 \to \mathbf{F}^m$ and $\mathbf{F}^m \to \mathbf{F}^1$ respectively. Equation (10.8) can then be considered as the product of the homomorphism (10.4) by the homomorphism (10.7).

Finally we consider the homomorphism $(\mathbf{F}^n)^* \to (\mathbf{F}^m)^*$, which is the dual of a given homomorphism $\sigma$: $\mathbf{F}^m \to \mathbf{F}^n$. If $\psi \in (\mathbf{F}^n)^*$ is an arbitrary linear function on $\mathbf{F}^n$, then the *dual image* of $\psi$ is the function associating to an arbitrary vector $\mathrm{a} \in \mathbf{F}^m$ the value $\psi\{\sigma \mathrm{a}\}$. If $\eta_1, \cdots \eta_n$ form a cobasis of $(\mathbf{F}^n)^*$ and $\psi$ is the function

$$\psi = \beta_1\eta_1 + \cdots + \beta_n\eta_n \qquad \beta_1, \cdots \beta_n \in \mathbf{F}$$

then the function (= homomorphism) $\psi$ is represented by the matrix = row (cf. (10.3′))

$$\psi = (\beta_1, \cdots \beta_n)$$

and *the image function* $\in (\mathbf{F}^m)^*$ by the matrix product $\psi\sigma$.

$\psi$ and $\psi\sigma$ can also be denoted by the transposed ${}^t\psi$ and ${}^t(\psi\sigma)$ i.e. by columns instead of rows. If in particular $\psi$ is the $j$-th vector of the cobasis $\eta_j \in (\mathbf{F}^n)^*$, then

$$ {}^t(\eta_j\sigma) = \begin{bmatrix} \sigma_{j1} \\ \sigma_{j2} \\ \cdot\cdot \\ \sigma_{jm} \end{bmatrix} $$

and, more generally,

$$ {}^t(\psi\sigma) = \begin{bmatrix} \sigma_{11} & \sigma_{21} & \cdot\cdot & \sigma_{n1} \\ \sigma_{12} & \sigma_{22} & \cdot\cdot & \sigma_{n2} \\ \cdot\cdot & \cdot\cdot & \cdot\cdot & \cdot\cdot \\ \cdot\cdot & \cdot\cdot & \cdot\cdot & \cdot\cdot \\ \sigma_{1m} & \sigma_{2m} & \cdot\cdot & \sigma_{nm} \end{bmatrix} \begin{bmatrix} \beta_1 \\ \beta_2 \\ \cdot \\ \cdot \\ \cdot \\ \beta_n \end{bmatrix}. \tag{10.13} $$

The matrix obtained from $\sigma$ by putting the scalar which is in the $i$-th row and $j$-th column into the $j$-th row and $i$-th column of a new matrix, is called the *transposed* matrix, designated by ${}^t\sigma$. It is a generalization of the transposition of matrices of one row or one column that has already been introduced. The matrix ${}^t\sigma$ occurs in (10.13), which can now be written as

$$ {}^t(\psi\sigma) = {}^t\sigma {}^t\psi. \tag{10.14} $$

For a given choice of basis and cobasis of scalar spaces the dual homomorphism of $\sigma$ is represented by an (ordinary) matrix-left-multiplication by the transposed matrix ${}^t\sigma$.

From theorem [9.7] we then have

Theorem [10.2]: *The rank of a matrix is equal to the rank of the transposed matrix.*

In other words: *the space generated by the columns of a matrix has the same dimension as the space generated by the rows of that matrix.*

If $\rho$ and $\sigma$ are homomorphisms and matrices as in (10.11) and if $\psi \in (\mathbf{F}^p)^*$, then the function $\psi\rho$ is the dual image of $\psi$ in $(\mathbf{F}^n)^*$ and $\psi\rho\sigma$ is the dual image of $\psi$ in $(\mathbf{F}^m)^*$.

If these functions are denoted by their transposed, we have:

$$ {}^t\psi,\ {}^t(\psi\rho) = {}^t\rho {}^t\psi \text{ and } {}^t\{\psi(\rho\sigma)\} = {}^t(\rho\sigma){}^t\psi. $$

The last expression represents the dual image to ${}^t\rho{}^t\psi$ under the dual homomorphism ${}^t\sigma$. For matrices we have then

$${}^t(\rho\sigma){}^t\psi = {}^t\sigma{}^t\rho{}^t\psi \text{ for any } \psi$$

and

$${}^t(\rho\sigma) = {}^t\sigma{}^t\rho. \qquad (10.15)$$

(10.15) expresses theorem [9.8] in the case of homomorphisms of scalar spaces.

PROBLEMS. (10.1). The following is known about the action of a homomorphism $\sigma$: A $\to$ B:

$$\begin{bmatrix}2\\2\\0\end{bmatrix} \to \begin{bmatrix}4\\6\end{bmatrix}; \quad \begin{bmatrix}2\\0\\6\end{bmatrix} \to \begin{bmatrix}8\\6\end{bmatrix}; \quad \begin{bmatrix}1\\1\\1\end{bmatrix} \to \begin{bmatrix}3\\3\end{bmatrix}.$$

Use the definition of homomorphism to determine successively the image of

$$\begin{bmatrix}4\\4\\0\end{bmatrix}, \begin{bmatrix}1\\0\\3\end{bmatrix}, \begin{bmatrix}0\\-1\\2\end{bmatrix}, \begin{bmatrix}0\\2\\6\end{bmatrix}, \begin{bmatrix}0\\0\\1\end{bmatrix}, \begin{bmatrix}0\\1\\0\end{bmatrix} \text{ and } \begin{bmatrix}1\\0\\0\end{bmatrix},$$

and give the matrix belonging to $\sigma$.

(10.2). Calculate

$$\sigma\begin{bmatrix}3\\0\\0\\2\end{bmatrix} \text{ and } \sigma\begin{bmatrix}1\\1\\1\\1\end{bmatrix} \text{ if } \sigma = \begin{bmatrix}2 & 1 & 0 & 0\\1 & 1 & 1 & 1\\0 & -1 & 1 & 1\end{bmatrix}.$$

(10.3). Calculate the homomorphism (product of two matrices) $\sigma = \begin{bmatrix}1\\4\\2\end{bmatrix}[1 \; 3 \; 0]$, and determine the rank of $\sigma$.

(10.4). Let $\sigma = \begin{bmatrix}1 & 2 & -5 & -1\\2 & 4 & -10 & -2\\-1 & -2 & 5 & 1\end{bmatrix}$.

Determine the transposed matrix ${}^t\sigma$ and calculate the rank of $\sigma$ and of ${}^t\sigma$.

(10.5). If $\sigma = \begin{bmatrix} 1 & -1 \\ 1 & 0 \end{bmatrix}$, calculate $\sigma^6$. What relation exists between this problem and problem (9.8)? [$\sigma^2 = \sigma \cdot \sigma$; $\sigma^{k+1} = \sigma \cdot \sigma^k$ for integral $k$].

(10.6). Determine the scalars $a$, $b$, $c$ such that the following matrices have rank 2:

$$\begin{bmatrix} 1 & 1 & a^2 & 1 \\ 0 & -2 & 3 & 1 \\ 0 & 0 & -a & c-1 \end{bmatrix}, \begin{bmatrix} 1 & 1 & 2 & -5 \\ 0 & 2 & 8 & b \\ 2 & 3 & a & 13 \end{bmatrix}, \begin{bmatrix} 1 & 2 & a & 3 \\ -1 & a & 2 & 1 \\ 2 & 1 & -3 & b \end{bmatrix}.$$

(10.7). A homomorphism has the following action:

$$\sigma \begin{bmatrix} 1 \\ 1 \\ 1 \end{bmatrix} = \begin{bmatrix} 1 \\ 0 \\ 0 \end{bmatrix}, \sigma \begin{bmatrix} -1 \\ 0 \\ 1 \end{bmatrix} = \begin{bmatrix} 0 \\ 1 \\ 0 \end{bmatrix}, \sigma \begin{bmatrix} 0 \\ -2 \\ 1 \end{bmatrix} = \begin{bmatrix} 0 \\ 0 \\ 1 \end{bmatrix}.$$

Give the matrix representation of the inverse mapping $\sigma^{-1}$.

(10.8). $\sigma = \begin{bmatrix} 1 & 1 \\ 0 & 1 \end{bmatrix}$. Calculate $\sigma^k$ for every integral $k$. Also calculate $({}^t\sigma)^k$ for every integral $k$.

(10.9). Answer the same questions if

$$\sigma = \begin{bmatrix} 0 & 1 & 0 & 0 \\ 0 & 0 & 1 & 0 \\ 0 & 0 & 0 & 1 \\ 1 & 0 & 0 & 0 \end{bmatrix}.$$

Also calculate $\sigma + \sigma^2 + \sigma^3 + \sigma^4$ and the rank of this matrix.

(10.10). The set **C** of all matrices of type

$$\sigma = \begin{bmatrix} \alpha & -\beta \\ \beta & \alpha \end{bmatrix}, \ \alpha \text{ and } \beta \text{ real}$$

forms a commutative *group* under addition; after omitting the element 0 it also forms a commutative group under multiplication (cf. theorem [9.5] and problem (9.5)). It forms a *ring* (cf. theorem [9.6]), and because of the group-property of multiplication, this ring is by definition a *field*.

Putting

$$\begin{bmatrix} 1 & 0 \\ 0 & 1 \end{bmatrix} = \underline{1} \quad \text{and} \begin{bmatrix} 0 & -1 \\ 1 & 0 \end{bmatrix} = \underline{i}$$

it may be seen that **C** is isomorphic to the field of complex numbers ($\underline{i}^2 = -\underline{1}$). Finally calculate ${}^t\sigma\sigma$.

(10.11). The matrices $\begin{bmatrix} \cos\alpha & -\sin\alpha \\ \sin\alpha & \cos\alpha \end{bmatrix}$, $\alpha$ real, form a group under multiplication (geometrically these matrices may be interpreted as rotations about a point in a plane; algebraically (cf. the preceding problem) they can be interpreted as the complex numbers of absolute value 1). Calculate ${}^t\sigma\sigma$.

(10.12) The set **K** of all matrices of type

$$q = \begin{bmatrix} \alpha & -\beta & -\gamma & \delta \\ \beta & \alpha & -\delta & -\gamma \\ \gamma & \delta & \alpha & \beta \\ -\delta & \gamma & -\beta & \alpha \end{bmatrix}$$

$\alpha, \beta, \gamma, \delta$ real, forms a field in which multiplication is not commutative. It is called the skewfield of *quaternions*. If $\underline{e}$ is the unit matrix and $\underline{i}, \underline{j}, \underline{k}$ are matrices such that $q = \alpha\underline{e} + \beta\underline{i} + \gamma\underline{j} + \delta\underline{k}$ then $-\underline{j}\underline{i} = \underline{i}\underline{j} = \underline{k}$ (cyclically) and $\underline{i}^2 = \underline{j}^2 = \underline{k}^2 = -\underline{e}$.

An equivalent definition of quaternions is to define them as the matrices

$$\begin{bmatrix} A & -C \\ \bar{C} & \bar{A} \end{bmatrix}$$

with $A = \alpha\underline{1} + \beta\underline{i}$, $C = \gamma\underline{1} + \delta\underline{i}$, $\bar{A} = \alpha\underline{1} - \beta\underline{i}$ is the complex conjugate of $A$, $\bar{C}$ is the complex conjugate of $C$.

(10.13). Let **F** be the field $GF(5)$ with the five elements 0, 1, 2, 3, 4 (cf. chapter 8). Calculate all integral powers of the matrix

$$\sigma = \begin{bmatrix} 1 & 2 \\ 3 & 4 \end{bmatrix}.$$

(10.14). The set $D$ of all matrices of type

$$\begin{bmatrix} \alpha & \beta \\ 0 & \alpha \end{bmatrix}, \qquad \alpha, \beta \text{ real}$$

forms a ring. The elements of this ring are called the *dual numbers*.

If we put

$\begin{bmatrix} 1 & 0 \\ 0 & 1 \end{bmatrix} = \underline{1}$ and $\begin{bmatrix} 0 & 1 \\ 0 & 0 \end{bmatrix} = \varepsilon$, then for any $\alpha, \beta, \gamma, \delta \in \mathbf{R}$ we have $(\alpha + \beta\varepsilon)(\gamma + \delta\varepsilon) = \alpha\gamma + (\alpha\delta + \beta\gamma)\varepsilon$ (we omitted the $\underline{1}$).

If $\alpha = \gamma = 0$ then the product is the matrix $\underline{0} = \begin{bmatrix} 0 & 0 \\ 0 & 0 \end{bmatrix}$.

(10.15). If $\sigma = \begin{bmatrix} 4 & 7 \\ 1 & 2 \end{bmatrix}$, calculate $\sigma^{-1}$.

(10.16). $\sigma = \frac{1}{\sqrt{6}} \begin{bmatrix} 1 & -2 & 1 \\ \sqrt{2} & \sqrt{2} & \sqrt{2} \\ -\sqrt{3} & 0 & \sqrt{3} \end{bmatrix}$ Calculate ${}^t\sigma$, ${}^t\sigma\sigma$, $\sigma^{-1}$ and prove that for two arbitrary column vectors a and b:

$$^t(\sigma a)(\sigma b) = {}^t ab.$$

(10.17)*. The square matrices of scalars $\alpha_{ij}$ $i, j = 1, \cdots n$ with $\alpha_{ij} = 0$ for $i > j$, form a ring. Those matrices of this ring of which none of the elements $\alpha_{ii}$ $(i = 1, \cdots n)$ is zero, form a group under multiplication.

(10.18)*. We consider $n \times n$-matrices with real elements. Let $M$ be a set of such matrices. Then prove that the set of all matrices $\sigma$ with the property

$$\sigma\mu = \mu\sigma \text{ for every } \mu \in M$$

is a group under addition, and is, indeed, a ring. Determine this ring in the case that $M$ is the set of *all* real $n \times n$-matrices.

(10.19). Solve the $3 \times 3$-matrix $\sigma$ when

$$\begin{bmatrix} 1 & 5 & 0 \\ 2 & 4 & 3 \\ 3 & 1 & 1 \end{bmatrix} = \begin{bmatrix} 5 & 0 & 1 \\ 4 & 3 & 2 \\ 1 & 1 & 3 \end{bmatrix} \sigma.$$

(10.20). $s_1, \cdots s_n$ are $n$ columns of $n$ scalars forming a basis of $\mathbf{F}^n$. Solve the $n \times n$-matrix $\sigma$ from the matrix-equation

$$(s_{j_1} s_{j_2} \cdots s_{j_n}) = (s_1 s_2 \cdots s_n) \cdot \sigma$$

if $(j_1, j_2, \cdots j_n)$ can be obtained from $(1, 2, \cdots n)$ by a sequence of interchanges.

# 11. SETS OF LINEAR EQUATIONS

The set

$$\begin{aligned} \sigma_{11}\xi_1 + \cdots + \sigma_{1m}\xi_m &= 0 \\ \sigma_{21}\xi_1 + \cdots + \sigma_{2m}\xi_m &= 0 \\ \cdots\cdots\cdots&\cdots\cdots\cdots \\ \sigma_{n1}\xi_1 + \cdots + \sigma_{nm}\xi_m &= 0 \end{aligned} \tag{11.1}$$

with known scalars $\sigma_{ij}$ and unknowns $\xi_1, \cdots \xi_m$ is called a set of $n$ homogeneous linear equations in $m$ unknowns. The problem is to solve these equations. This problem can be reformulated as follows: find the kernel $\sigma^{-1}(\mathrm{O})$ of the homomorphism $\sigma$: $\mathbf{F}^m \to \mathbf{F}^n$ with matrix

$$\sigma = \begin{bmatrix} \sigma_{11} & \cdot\cdot & \sigma_{1m} \\ \sigma_{21} & \cdot\cdot & \sigma_{2m} \\ \cdot & \cdot\cdot & \cdot \\ \sigma_{n1} & \cdot\cdot & \sigma_{nm} \end{bmatrix}. \text{ If we write } \begin{bmatrix} \xi_1 \\ \xi_2 \\ \cdot \\ \xi_m \end{bmatrix} = \mathrm{x}$$

then $\sigma^{-1}(\mathrm{O})$ consists of all x which satisfy

$$\sigma(\mathrm{x}) = \mathrm{O}. \tag{11.1'}$$

This condenses the set of equations (11.1) to one equation in the unknown vector x.

If $r$ is the rank of the matrix $\sigma$, then $m - r$ is the dimension of $\sigma^{-1}(\mathrm{O})$: *The solutions of* (11.1) *form an* $(m - r)$*-dimensional subspace of* $\mathbf{F}^m$. If $r = m$ then there is exactly one solution, viz.

$$\xi_1 = \xi_2 = \cdots = \xi_m = 0.$$

The set

$$\begin{matrix} \sigma_{11}\xi_1 + \cdots + \sigma_{1m}\xi_m = \alpha_1 \\ \cdot\cdot \quad \cdots \quad \cdot\cdot \quad \cdot \\ \sigma_{n1}\xi_1 + \cdots + \sigma_{nm}\xi_m = \alpha_n \end{matrix}, \text{ or, more briefly, } \sigma\mathrm{x} = \mathrm{a}, \tag{11.2}$$

with known scalars $\sigma_{ij}$, $\alpha_j$ and unknowns $\xi_1, \cdots \xi_m$ is called *a set of n non-homogeneous linear equations in m unknowns.* (11.1) is called the corresponding homogeneous set. There are two cases to be distinguished:

I. The vector a, that is, the column of scalars $\alpha_1, \cdots \alpha_n$, lies in $\sigma(\mathbf{F}^m)$. Then there is a solution. The ranks of the following matrices are equal since their columns generate the same space of dimension $r$:

$$\sigma = \begin{bmatrix} \sigma_{11} & \cdot\cdot & \sigma_{1m} \\ \cdot & \cdot\cdot & \cdot \\ \sigma_{n1} & \cdot\cdot & \sigma_{nm} \end{bmatrix} \quad \text{and} \quad \begin{bmatrix} \sigma_{11} & \cdot\cdot & \sigma_{1m} & \alpha_1 \\ \cdot & \cdot\cdot & \cdot & \cdot \\ \sigma_{n1} & \cdot\cdot & \sigma_{nm} & \alpha_n \end{bmatrix}.$$

The second matrix is also called the *augmented matrix.*

If y is a solution of (11.2), i.e. $\sigma y = a$, and x is a solution of (11.1), i.e. $\sigma x = O$, then $y + x$ is also a solution of (11.2), since $\sigma(y + x) = \sigma y + \sigma x = a + O = a$, and conversely any two solutions of (11.2) differ by a solution of (11.1). In other words: if y is a particular solution of (11.2), then all solutions form the set $y + \sigma^{-1}(O)$, which is a linear $(m - r)$-variety.

II. The vector a does not lie in $\sigma(\mathbf{F}^m)$. Then there is no solution. The columns of the augmented matrix span a space which contains the space spanned by the columns of $\sigma$ as a proper subspace, i.e. the spaces are not identical. The ranks of the matrices are different.

This proves:

Theorem [11.1]: *The equations* (11.2) *have no solution if the rank $r$ of the matrix $\sigma$ differs from the rank of the augmented matrix. If the ranks are both equal to $r$ then the solutions form a linear $(m - r)$-variety in $\mathbf{F}^m$.*

Theorem [11.2]: *If the number of equations in* (11.2) *and the number of unknowns are both equal to the rank of the matrix $\sigma$, $n = m = r$, then* (11.2) *has exactly one solution.*

If a consistent set (11.2) is given, and its rank $r$ is less than the number of equations, then there exists a row of the augmented matrix, the $i$-th say, which depends linearly on the other rows. Then there exist scalars $\gamma_k$ such that

$$\sigma_{ij} = \sum_{k \neq i} \gamma_k \sigma_{kj}, \quad \alpha_i = \sum_{k \neq i} \gamma_k \alpha_k$$

hence

$$\textstyle\sum_j \sigma_{ij}\xi_j - \alpha_i = \displaystyle\sum_{k \neq i} \gamma_k \{\textstyle\sum_j \sigma_{kj}\xi_j - \alpha_k\}.$$

Thus the $i$-th equation of (11.2) will be satisfied by the scalars $\xi_1, \cdots \xi_m$ as soon as the other equations are satisfied. Hence the $i$-th equation gives no new information and can be deleted.

Repeating this procedure, $n - r$ equations can be deleted. The remaining $r$ equations are independent, and the remaining matrix as well as the remaining augmented matrix has rank $r$. We therefore restrict ourselves to the case $n = r$.

The matrix $\sigma$ has $n = r$ independent columns, which form a basis of $\mathbf{F}^n$. After rearrangement if necessary, we may assume that they are the first $n$ columns. Instead of (11.2) we now write

$$\begin{array}{ccccccccccc} \sigma_{11}\xi_1 & + & \cdots & + & \sigma_{1n}\xi_n & = & \alpha_1 & - & \sigma_{1n+1}\xi_{n+1} - \cdots - \sigma_{1m}\xi_m \\ \cdot\cdot & & \cdots & & \cdot\cdot & & \cdot & & \cdot\cdot \quad \cdots \quad \cdot\cdot \\ \sigma_{n1}\xi_1 & + & \cdots & + & \sigma_{nn}\xi_n & = & \alpha_n & - & \sigma_{nn+1}\xi_{n+1} - \cdots - \sigma_{nm}\xi_m. \end{array} \tag{11.3}$$

By theorem [11.2] substitution of arbitrary values for $\xi_{n+1}, \cdots \xi_m$ yields one solution of the set of equations (11.3).

The problem of the practical solution of (11.2) is now reduced to the case $m = n = \text{rank}\ \sigma$:

$$\begin{array}{ccccccc} \sigma_{11}\xi_1 & + & \cdots & + & \sigma_{1n}\xi_n & = & \alpha_1 \\ \cdot\cdot & & \cdots & & \cdot\cdot & & \cdot \\ \sigma_{n1}\xi_1 & + & \cdots & + & \sigma_{nn}\xi_n & = & \alpha_n \end{array} \qquad \begin{array}{l} \text{more briefly: } \sigma \mathrm{x} = \mathrm{a} \\ \text{rank } \sigma = n. \end{array} \tag{11.4}$$

Since $\sigma$ has rank $n$, it is an automorphism, and it has an inverse $\sigma^{-1}$. From $\sigma\mathrm{x} = \mathrm{a}$ it follows that $\sigma^{-1}\sigma\mathrm{x} = \sigma^{-1}\mathrm{a}$. Hence a formula for the solution of (11.4) is

$$\mathrm{x} = \sigma^{-1}\mathrm{a}.$$

Another expression for the solution will be given in chapter 13 (determinants).

In order to solve (11.4) in practice, one proceeds as follows.

By means of one of the $n$ equations, express one of the unknowns in terms of the others. The other $n - 1$ equations can then be replaced by $n - 1$ equations in $n - 1$ unknowns. Repeating this process with $n - 1$ instead of $n$, and then $n - 2, \cdots 2$ instead of $n$, we eventually have one equation in one unknown, which can be trivially solved. Back-substitution then yields the values of the other unknowns.

PROBLEMS. (11.1). Determine all solutions of the following sets of equations in real numbers:

$$\text{(a)}\quad \begin{aligned} \xi_1 + 2\xi_2 - \xi_3 &= -1 \\ 2\xi_1 - \xi_2 + \xi_3 &= 9 \\ \xi_1 \qquad - 4\xi_3 &= -5 \end{aligned} \qquad \text{(b)}\quad \begin{aligned} \xi_1 + \xi_2 + \xi_3 &= 2 \\ 2\xi_1 - 2\xi_2 + 3\xi_3 &= 1 \\ 3\xi_1 - \xi_2 + 4\xi_3 &= 3. \end{aligned}$$

(11.2). Do the same in complex numbers:

$$\begin{aligned} (1 + i)\xi_1 + i\xi_2 &= 1 + 3i \\ (2 - i)\xi_1 - 5\xi_2 &= 5. \end{aligned}$$

(11.3). Do the same in integers mod. 5 (cf. chapter 8):

$$\begin{aligned} \xi_1 + 2\xi_2 + 4\xi_3 &= 1 \\ 2\,\xi_1 - 3\xi_2 + \xi_3 &= -4 \\ -\xi_1 - 4\xi_2 + 2\xi_3 &= 1. \end{aligned}$$

# 12. FUNCTIONS OF SEVERAL VARIABLES. DETERMINANT

In chapter 2, p. 6 we introduced the notion of a function on a set $A$ as a mapping of the set $A$ into some field $\mathbf{F}$. From now on we shall also consider *functions of several variables.*

Definition: A function of $n$ variables on a set $A$ is a function on $A \times A \times \cdots \times A$ ($n$ times); i.e. a mapping associating an element $f(a_1, a_2, \cdots a_n) \in \mathbf{F}$ to any $n$-tuple $(a_1, a_2, \cdots a_n)$ of elements of $A$.

It follows that a function in the previous sense might also be called a function of one variable.

In the future we shall often encounter the following situation. A function $f$ of $n$ variables on a set $A$ is given and we study for example the function of two variables $f': (a_1, a_n) \to f(a_1, \cdots a_n)$. In such a case we shall, of course, assume that $a_2, \cdots a_{n-1}$ have fixed values, and each set of values of $a_2, \cdots a_{n-1}$ gives another function $f'$.

Another important way of reducing the number of variables of a function of several variables is given in the following definition.

Definition: The *diagonal* of a function $f$ of $n$ variables is the function $f^{\cdot}: a \to f(a, a, \cdots a)$. If a function of several variables is denoted by some symbol ($f$, for example), then its diagonal will be denoted by the same symbol followed by a dot ($f^{\cdot}$).

As preparation for the notions that will be introduced in this chapter, we consider two vectors a and b with initial point O in the ordinary plane of chapter 1. We denote the area of the parallelogram with sides a and b by $I$(a, b). Now we define a function $\psi$ of two variables which are vectors, as follows: $\psi$(a, b) $= I$(a, b) if rotation from a to b through the smaller angle is clock-wise; $\psi$(a, b) $= - I$(a, b) if this rotation is counter-clock-wise; $\psi$(a, b)$=0$ if a and b are linearly dependent. Observe that $I$(a, b)$=|\psi$(a, b)$|$. For fixed b the function a $\to \psi$(a, b) is a homogeneous linear function, since for an arbitrary real number $\lambda$ and arbitrary vectors a and a' we have, as may be seen from the plane figure 12.1:

$$\psi(a + a', b) = \psi(a, b) + \psi(a', b) \tag{12.1}$$

$$\psi(\lambda a, b) = \lambda\psi(a, b), \text{ also for } \lambda = 0 \text{ and } -1! \tag{12.2}$$

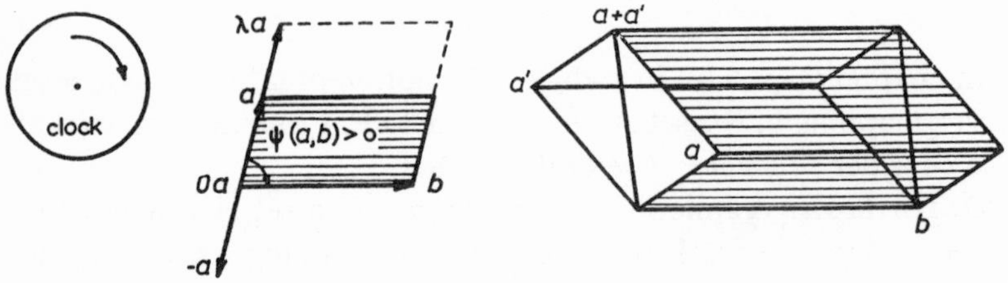


Fig. 12.1

Similarly for constant a the function $b \to \psi(a, b)$ is a linear function.

Definition: A function $\varphi$ of $r$ variables on a vector space V over **F** and with values in **F** is called a multilinear (or $r$-linear) function if each of the functions $x_i \to \varphi(x_1, \cdots x_r)$ ($x_j$ fixed for $j \neq i$) is linear.

The function is said to be *antisymmetric* if

$$\varphi(x_1, \cdots x_r) = -\varphi(y_1, \cdots y_r)$$

whenever the sequence of vectors $y_1, \cdots y_r$ can be obtained from the sequence $x_1, \cdots x_r$ by interchanging two of the vectors. The function $\psi$ we just discussed is multilinear (bilinear) and antisymmetric as well. Indeed, from (12.1) and (12.2) follows:

$$0 = \psi(a + b, a + b) = \psi(a, a) + \psi(a, b) + \psi(b, a) + \psi(b, b) =$$
$$= \psi(a, b) + \psi(b, a). \tag{12.3}$$

Another, similar, example of a multilinear antisymmetric function can be obtained as follows. Take three vectors a, b, c with initial point O in the three dimensional space of chapter 1. Let $I$(a, b, c) be the volume of the parallelopiped having a, b, c as edges, and $I = 0$ if a, b, c are linearly dependent. Let $\psi(a, b, c) = I(a, b, c)$ if rotation from a to b through the smaller angle is clock-wise if looked at from c. Put $\psi(a, b, c) = -I(a, b, c)$ if this is not the case. As before it is easily checked that the function $\psi$ is multilinear and antisymmetric.

After this introduction we now treat multilinear antisymmetric functions without any appeal to geometrical intuition.

Theorem [12.1]: *If $\varphi$ is an r-linear function on the vector space* V *over* **F** *and values in* **F**, *then the following three conditions are equivalent:*

(1) *$\varphi$ is antisymmetric;*

(2) $\varphi(x_1, \cdots x_r) = 0$ *whenever two of the vectors* $x_1, \cdots x_r \in V$ *are equal;*

(3) $\varphi(x_1, \cdots x_r) = 0$ *whenever* $x_1, \cdots x_r$ *are linearly dependent.*

Proof: The second condition is an immediate consequence of (1) as well as of (3). Now assume (2). Consider the function of two variables $\varphi'$: $(x_p, x_q) \to \varphi(x_1, \cdots x_r)$ ($x_i$ fixed for $i \neq p, q$). This is a bilinear function. For this we have already proved $\varphi'(a, b) = - \varphi'(b, a)$ (cf. (12.3)). Hence (1) follows from (2), and the two are then equivalent. We finally prove that (3) follows from (2). Therefore, let (2) again be satisfied, and let $x_1, \cdots x_r$ be linearly dependent. Then, after rearranging if necessary, there exist $\lambda_2, \cdots \lambda_r \in \mathbf{F}$ such that

$$x_1 = \lambda_2 x_2 + \cdots + \lambda_r x_r, \quad \lambda_i \in \mathbf{F}.$$

But then

$$\varphi(x_1, x_2, \cdots x_r) = \varphi(\lambda_2 x_2 + \cdots + \lambda_r x_r, \ x_2, \cdots x_r) =$$
$$= \lambda_2 \varphi(x_2, x_2, \cdots x_r) + \cdots + \lambda_r \varphi(x_r, x_2, \cdots x_r) = 0.$$

In the following we need the notion of *permutation*. A permutation is a one-to-one mapping of a finite set onto itself. When $\pi$ is a permutation of the set $(a_1, \cdots a_n)$, then the sequence $\pi(a_1), \cdots \pi(a_n)$ will also be called a *permutation* of the sequence $a_1, \cdots a_n$. Thus 4, 2, 3, 1 is a permutation of 1, 2, 3, 4. Composition (cf. chapter 2) of permutations is possible, and if we take this composition as multiplication, the permutations form a group. A permutation which maps all elements but two to themselves, is called an interchange (of these two elements). Any permutation of $n$ elements $a_1, \cdots a_n$ can be obtained as a product of interchanges, which for example are such that the partial product of the first $k$ interchanges (in the formula below read from right to left) map $a_1, \cdots a_k$ into their finally required image elements, and this for $k = 1, \cdots n - 1$.

Theorem [12.2]: *If* $\sigma$ *is a permutation of a finite set, and* $\tau_i$, $i = 1, \cdots m$, $\tau'_j$, $j = 1, \cdots m'$ *are interchanges such that*

$$\sigma = \tau_m \tau_{m-1} \cdots \tau_1 = \tau'_{m'} \tau'_{m'-1} \cdots \tau'_1$$

*then either both* $m$ *and* $m'$ *are even or both are odd; or, equivalently,* $(-1)^m = (-1)^{m'}$.

This theorem makes possible the following *definition*: A permutation is said to be even or odd if it can be obtained as a composition of an even or an odd number of interchanges respectively. The number $\varepsilon(\sigma) = (-1)^m = (-1)^{m'}$ is then equal to $+1$ or $-1$ respectively.

Proof of the theorem: We number the elements of the finite set by the natural numbers $1, 2, \cdots n$, and then represent them by these numbers. Let $\sigma$ be a permutation and $\sigma^{-1}(i) = j_i$, or $\sigma(j_i) = i$. We shall denote this permutation $\sigma$ by the sequence.

$$(\sigma^{-1}(1), \sigma^{-1}(2), \cdots \sigma^{-1}(n)) = (j_1, j_2, \cdots j_n).$$

A number pair $(j_p, j_q)$ with $p < q$ will be called an *inversion* of the permutation $\sigma$ when $j_p > j_q$. Let $N(j_1, \cdots j_n)$ denote the number of inversions of $\sigma$. Then $N(1, 2, \cdots n) = 0$. Interchanging two adjacent elements in the sequence $j_1, \cdots j_n$ increases or decreases $N(j_1, \cdots j_n)$ by just 1. An interchange of two arbitrary elements, the $p$-th and the $q$-th say, can be brought about by an odd number, namely $2(q - p) - 1$ of such interchanges of adjacent elements. Hence: interchanging any two elements in the sequence $(j_1, \cdots j_n)$ changes the sign of the function value of

$$(-1)^{N(j_1, \cdot\cdot j_n)}.$$

Therefore, since the permutation $\sigma$ can be composed of $m$ interchanges, we have

$$(-1)^{N(j_1, \cdot\cdot j_n)} = (-1)^m. \tag{12.4}$$

For a given permutation $\sigma$ of the numbers $1, 2, \cdots n$, the left-hand member is independent of the number $m$, and the theorem follows: $(-1)^m = (-1)^{m'}$. The right-hand member however, is independent of the way the elements have been ordered. It follows that the number $\varepsilon(\sigma) = \varepsilon(j_1, \cdots j_n) = (-1)^{N(j_1, \cdots j_n)} = (-1)^m$ is completely determined by $\sigma$; hence $\varepsilon$ is a function of $\sigma$ only ,and in particular does not depend on the numbering at the beginning of this proof.

Theorem [12.3]: *If* V *is an n-dimensional vector space over* **F**, *then there exists exactly one n-linear antisymmetric function* $\varphi$ *on* V *which assumes a given value* $\lambda \in \mathbf{F}$ *on a given basis* $a_1, \cdots a_n$ *of* V.

Proof: We first show the uniqueness of the function $\varphi$ for given $a_1, \cdots a_n$ and $\lambda$; i.e. we show that if a $\varphi$ exists, its values are completely determined.

Let $x_1, \cdots x_n \in V$ and

$$x_i = \sum_{k=1}^{n} \sigma_{ki} a_k.$$

Then because of the multilinearity of $\varphi$ we have

$$\varphi(x_1, \cdots x_n) = \varphi(\Sigma \sigma_{j_1 1} a_{j_1}, \cdots \Sigma \sigma_{j_n n} a_{j_n}) =$$

$$= \Sigma \sigma_{j_1 1} \sigma_{j_2 2}, \cdots \sigma_{j_n n} \varphi(a_{j_1}, \cdots a_{j_n}).$$

In the second member of this equality the summations are over $j_1, \cdots j_n$ each of which runs from 1 to $n$; in the third member the summation is over $j_1, \cdots j_n$, each running from 1 to $n$.

Now consider the expression $\varphi(a_{j_1}, \cdots a_{j_n})$ occurring in the equality above. It is zero whenever two of $a_{j_1}, \cdots a_{j_n}$ are equal. If no two of them are equal, $j_1, \cdots j_n$ can be obtained from $1, \cdots n$ by a permutation. If this permutation is an interchange of two elements then

$$\varphi(a_{j_1}, \cdots a_{j_n}) = -\varphi(a_1, \cdots a_n) = -\lambda.$$

Therefore, if the permutation can be obtained from $m$ such interchanges, we have

$$\varphi(a_{j_1}, \cdots a_{j_n}) = (-1)^m \varphi(a_1, \cdots a_n) = (-1)^{N(j_1, \cdots j_n)} \cdot \lambda.$$

If we now define $\varepsilon(j_1, \cdots j_n) = \varepsilon(\sigma) = (-1)^{N(j_1, \cdots j_n)}$ when $j_1, \cdots j_n$ are obtained from $1, \cdots n$ by the permutation $\sigma$, and $\varepsilon(j_1, \cdots j_n) = 0$

whenever two of $j_1, \cdots j_n$ are equal, then the function $\varphi$, if it exists, must satisfy

$$\varphi(x_1, \cdots x_n) = \Sigma \sigma_{j_1 1}\, \sigma_{j_2 2}, \cdots \sigma_{j_n n} \cdot \varepsilon(j_1, j_2, \cdots j_n) \cdot \varphi(a_1, \cdots a_n) \quad \text{with } \varphi(a_1, \cdots a_n) = \lambda. \tag{12.5}$$

To prove the *existence* of $\varphi$ it is sufficient to prove that the function $\varphi$ defined by (12.5) has the required properties.

If $x_i = a_i$, $i = 1, \cdots n$ we have $\sigma_{j_i i} = \delta_{j_i i}$ (for def. cf. p. 26). Substitution yields $\varphi(a_1, \cdots a_n) = \lambda$ as required.

For a particular $i$, the function $x_i \rightarrow \varphi(x_1, \cdots x_n)$ ($x_j$ fixed for $j \neq i$) is easily seen to be linear if we carry out the substitutions $x_i = \nu u_i$ and $x_i = u_i + v_i$. Since this is the case for $i = 1, \cdots n$, the function $\varphi$ is $n$-linear.

We finally have to show that $\varphi$ is antisymmetric. By theorem [12.1] it is sufficient to show that $\varphi(x_1, \cdots x_n) = 0$ if two of $x_1, \cdots x_n$ are equal. So suppose $x_p = x_q$. Then also $\sigma_{rp} = \sigma_{rq}$ for $r = 1, \cdots n$. Now consider the terms of the sum in (12.5). We need only consider those terms for which the value of $\varepsilon$ is not zero, i.e. for which $j_1, \cdots j_n$ is a permutation of $1, \cdots n$. These terms can be grouped into pairs such that the terms of any pair have all indices equal, except $j_p$ and $j_q$ which are interchanged. But the values of $\varepsilon$ in the terms of such a pair are opposite, and, since $\sigma_{rp} = \sigma_{rq}$ for all $r$, the other factors of the two terms are identical. Hence their sum is zero, and therefore $\varphi(x_1, \cdots x_n)$ being a sum of zero contributions, is itself zero. This completes the proof.

For the case $n = 2$, (12.5) becomes

$$\begin{aligned} \varphi(x_1, x_2) &= \varphi(\sigma_{11}a_1 + \sigma_{21}a_2, \sigma_{12}a_1 + \sigma_{22}a_2) = \\ &= \sigma_{11}\varphi(a_1, \sigma_{12}a_1 + \sigma_{22}a_2) + \sigma_{21}\varphi(a_2, \sigma_{12}a_1 + \sigma_{22}a_2) \\ &= \sigma_{11}\sigma_{12}\varphi(a_1, a_1) + \sigma_{11}\sigma_{22}\varphi(a_1, a_2) + \sigma_{21}\sigma_{12}\varphi(a_2, a_1) + \sigma_{21}\sigma_{22}\varphi(a_2, a_2) \\ &= \sigma_{11}\sigma_{22}\varphi(a_1, a_2) + \sigma_{21}\sigma_{12}\varphi(a_2, a_1) \\ &= (\sigma_{11}\sigma_{22} - \sigma_{21}\sigma_{12})\varphi(a_1, a_2). \end{aligned}$$

PROBLEM (12.1). For the case $n = 3$ show similarly

$$\varphi(x_1, x_2, x_3) = (\sigma_{11}\sigma_{22}\sigma_{33} - \sigma_{11}\sigma_{32}\sigma_{23} - \sigma_{21}\sigma_{12}\sigma_{33} - \sigma_{31}\sigma_{22}\sigma_{13} + \sigma_{21}\sigma_{32}\sigma_{13} + \sigma_{31}\sigma_{12}\sigma_{23})\varphi(a_1, a_2, a_3).$$

From (12.5) we see that $\varphi$ is identically zero as soon as $\varphi$ assumes the value zero on some basis of V. Furthermore we notice that the coefficient of $\varphi(a_1, \cdots a_n)$ is independent of $\varphi$. Hence if $\psi$ and $\varphi$ are $n$-linear antisymmetric functions, not identically zero, then for two bases $(y_1, \cdots y_n)$ and $(z_1, \cdots z_n)$ we always have

$$\frac{\psi(y_1, \cdots y_n)}{\varphi(y_1, \cdots y_n)} = \frac{\psi(z_1, \cdots z_n)}{\varphi(z_1, \cdots z_n)}. \tag{12.5'}$$

In other words: The ratio of two $n$-linear antisymmetric functions on an $n$-dimensional vector space is a constant.

Now consider an $n$-linear antisymmetric function $\varphi$, which is not the trivial function zero, and an endomorphism $\sigma$: V $\to$ V. Let $\varphi_\sigma$ be the function associating to $(y_1, \cdots y_n)$ the value $\varphi(\sigma y_1, \cdots \sigma y_n)$. This function $\varphi_\sigma$ is also $n$-linear and has the value zero as soon as two of $y_1, \cdots y_n$ are equal. It is therefore an $n$-linear antisymmetric function on V, and it is identically zero only if the rank of $\sigma$ is less than $n$. The number

$$\frac{\varphi(\sigma y_1, \cdots \sigma y_n)}{\varphi(y_1, \cdots y_n)}, \tag{12.6}$$

a quotient of values of two linear antisymmetric functions as in (12.5′), is then independent of the basis $y_1, \cdots y_n$ and this holds for any rank of $\sigma$. Again from (12.5′), when $y_1, \cdots y_n$ are fixed, the value of (12.6) does not change either if $\varphi$ is replaced by, say, $\psi$. This value depends therefore on $\sigma$ only, and is called the *determinant of the endomorphism* $\sigma$, denoted by det $\sigma$ or $|\sigma|$:

$$\frac{\varphi(\sigma y_1, \cdots \sigma y_n)}{\varphi(y_1, \cdots y_n)} = \det \sigma = |\sigma|. \tag{12.6'}$$

If we now put $y_i = a_i$, $\sigma y_i = x_i = \sum_{j=1}^{n} \sigma_{ji} a_j$ for $i = 1, \cdots n$, then by (12.5):

$$\det \sigma = \sum \sigma_{j_1 1} \sigma_{j_2 2} \cdots \sigma_{j_n n} \cdot \varepsilon(j_1, \cdots j_n). \tag{12.7}$$

Theorem [12.4]: *If* $\sigma$ *and* $\tau$ *are endomorphisms* V $\to$ V, *then*

$$\det(\sigma\tau) = \det \sigma \cdot \det \tau$$

$$\det(\text{identity}) = 1; \ \det(\sigma^{-1}) = (\det \sigma)^{-1}.$$

Proof: If the rank of $\sigma$ or $\tau$ is less than $n$, then the rank of $\sigma\tau$ is less than $n$ also, and $\det(\sigma\tau) = 0 = \det\sigma\cdot\det\tau$. If not, then for a basis $y_1, \cdots y_n \in V$ and a non-trivial $n$-linear antisymmetric function $\varphi$, it follows from (12.6) that

$$0 \neq \varphi(\sigma\tau y_1, \cdots \sigma\tau y_n) = \det(\sigma\tau)\cdot\varphi(y_1, \cdots y_n) =$$
$$= (\det\sigma)\cdot\varphi(\tau y_1, \cdots \tau y_n) = \det\sigma\cdot\det\tau\cdot\varphi(y_1, \cdots y_n)$$

implying the first assertion. The other assertions are trivial consequences of the first one.

Definition: The determinant of an endomorphism $\sigma\colon \mathbf{F}^n \to \mathbf{F}^n$ is also called the *determinant of the matrix* representing this endomorphism.

The determinant of the matrix (10.7) with $m = n$ is then given by (12.7) and is denoted by

$$\begin{vmatrix} \sigma_{11} & \sigma_{12} & \cdots & \sigma_{1n} \\ \cdots & \cdots & \cdots & \cdots \\ & & & \\ \cdots & \cdots & \cdots & \cdots \\ \sigma_{n1} & \sigma_{n2} & \cdots & \sigma_{nn} \end{vmatrix}.$$

If we consider an $n \times n$-matrix as an $n$-tuple of column vectors, then a matrix actually is an element of $\mathbf{F}^n \times \mathbf{F}^n \times \cdots \times \mathbf{F}^n$ ($n$ times). In this way a function $f$ of $n$ variables on $\mathbf{F}^n$ is also a function on the set of $n \times n$-matrices, and conversely. Since the same could and will be done with rows instead of columns, we shall say that $f$ is a *function on the columns of the matrices*. Similarly we shall use *functions on the rows of matrices*.

Theorem [12.5]: *The determinant of an $n \times n$-matrix $\sigma$ is the value of that $n$-linear antisymmetric function on the columns of $n \times n$-matrices which assumes the value 1 for the unit matrix.*

Proof: Substitute in (12.6) for $y_1, \cdots y_n$ the columns of the unit matrix and for $\varphi$ the function mentioned in the theorem.

Theorem [12.6]: *If $\sigma$ is a square matrix and ${}^t\sigma$ its transposed, then*

$$\det\sigma = \det{}^t\sigma. \tag{12.8}$$

Proof: Det $\sigma$ is a sum of terms of type

$$\sigma_{j_1 1}\sigma_{j_2 2} \cdots \sigma_{j_n n}\, \varepsilon(j_1, \cdots j_n). \tag{12.9}$$

If in a term like (12.9) two indices $j_r$ and $j_s$ happen to be equal, then this term vanishes. If the value $i$ occurs exactly once among $j_1, \cdots j_n$, then the function mapping the $i$-th row of $\sigma$ to the expression in (12.9) is linear, and this is true for $i = 1, \cdots n$ if two indices $j_r$ and $j_s$ in this term are equal. Consequently, by summation, the determinant is an $n$-linear function on the rows of $n \times n$-matrices, and is antisymmetric since det $\sigma = 0$ as soon as the rank of $\sigma$ is less than $n$.

If follows that the function $\det^t$: $\sigma \to \det({}^t\sigma)$ is multilinear and antisymmetric in the columns of matrices, and it clearly assumes the value 1 on the unit matrix. Hence, by theorem [12.5], det $\sigma =$ $=$ det ${}^t\sigma$.

Since the dual of a homomorphism of vector spaces is expressed by the transposed matrix, we have also obtained:

Theorem [12.7]: *The determinant of an endomorphism is equal to the determinant of the dual endomorphism.*

The following theorem will now be clear:

Theorem [12.8]: *The determinant of a square matrix is zero if and only if the columns (or rows) are linearly dependent. Interchange of two columns or rows in a matrix yields the opposite value for the determinant. Adding a multiple of a column (row) to another column (row) does not change the value of the determinant.*

*Development of the determinant of an $n \times n$-matrix according to a row (column)*

Let $s_j$ be the $j$-th column of an $n \times n$-matrix $\sigma$; $\sigma_{kj}$ be its $k$-th element. As always the $i$-th standard basis vector in the space of columns of $n$ elements is denoted by $e_i$. We now decompose the vector $s_j$ into two components:

$$s_j = \sigma_{ij}e_i + (s_j - \sigma_{ij}e_i) = u_j + v_j.$$

Note that the column $v_j = s_j - \sigma_{ij}e_i = s_j - u_j$ has zero as $i$-th element whereas $u_j$ can have a non-zero element only on that place (this element may be zero as well). Because of the multilinearity of the determinant, $\det \sigma = \det(s_1, \cdots s_n) = \det(u_1 + v_1, \cdots u_n + v_n)$ is equal to a sum of determinants of type:

$$\det(w_1, w_2, \cdots w_n), \ w_j = u_j \text{ or } v_j, \ j = 1, \cdots n.$$

If $w_j = v_j$ for $j = 1, \cdots n$ then the $i$-th row of the matrix consists of zeros only, and the determinant is zero. Also if $w_j = u_j$ for more than one of the values $j = 1, \cdots n$, the determinant is zero, since then two columns are dependent. Hence there remain only the matrices with $w_j = u_j = \sigma_{ij} e_i$ for exactly one of the $j = 1, \cdots n$.

From the matrix in which $w_j = u_j$ a matrix of type

$$\begin{bmatrix} \sigma_{ij} & 0 \cdots\cdots 0 \\ 0 & \\ \cdot & \\ \cdot & A_{ij} \\ \cdot & \\ 0 & \end{bmatrix} \tag{12.10}$$

can be obtained by $j - 1$ interchanges of neighbouring columns and $i - 1$ interchanges of neighbouring rows. In the empty square of this matrix we have the matrix $A_{ij}$, obtained from $\sigma$ by omitting the $i$-th row and $j$-th column. If we consider the set of all matrices of this type, with a fixed value for $\sigma_{ij}$, then the determinant is again multilinear and antisymmetric in the columns of the matrices $A_{ij}$, and when $A_{ij}$ is the unit matrix, it is equal to $\sigma_{ij}$.

Hence, by theorem [12.5] the determinant of (12.10) is equal to

$$\sigma_{ij} \det A_{ij}$$

and because of the $(i - 1) + (j - 1)$ adjacent interchanges its contributions to $\det \sigma$ is

$$\sigma_{ij}(-1)^{i+j} \det A_{ij}.$$

(Some authors call $(-1)^{i+j} \det A_{ij}$ the *co-factor* of $\sigma_{ij}$).

This yields the *formula* for the development of $\det \sigma$ according to the $i$-th row:

$$\det \sigma = \sum_{j=1}^{n} \sigma_{ij}(-1)^{i+j} \det A_{ij}. \tag{12.11}$$

Example: Development of a determinant according to the first row.

$$\begin{vmatrix} 1 & 0 & 3 \\ 4 & 2 & 8 \\ 1 & 5 & 1 \end{vmatrix} = \begin{vmatrix} 1 & 0 & 0 \\ 0 & 2 & 8 \\ 0 & 5 & 1 \end{vmatrix} + \begin{vmatrix} 0 & 0 & 0 \\ 4 & 0 & 8 \\ 1 & 0 & 1 \end{vmatrix} + \begin{vmatrix} 0 & 0 & 3 \\ 4 & 2 & 0 \\ 1 & 5 & 0 \end{vmatrix} =$$

$$1. \begin{vmatrix} 2 & 8 \\ 5 & 1 \end{vmatrix} + 0 + (-1)^2 \cdot 3 \cdot \begin{vmatrix} 4 & 2 \\ 1 & 5 \end{vmatrix} = (2 - 40) + 3(20 - 2) = 16.$$

PROBLEMS. (12.2). A two-dimensional vector space over the real numbers has basis $a_1, a_2$. Let $b = 2a_2 - \frac{1}{2}a_1$. Consider the endomorphism mapping $a_1, a_2$ into respectively $a_1, b$; $a_2, a_1$; $a_1+2a_2, 2a_1$; $-a_1, -a_2$; $-a_2, a_1$; $a_1+a_2, a_2-a_1$; $b, 2b$. Determine in each of these cases the determinant of the endomorphism.

(12.3). $a_1, a_2, a_3$ form a basis of a real vector space. Find the determinant of the endomorphisms with the following properties

$$\begin{aligned} &(a_1, a_2, a_3) \longrightarrow (3a_1, 5a_2, -2a_3) \\ &(a_1, a_2, a_3) \longrightarrow (a_3, a_2, a_1) \\ &(a_1, a_2, a_3) \longrightarrow (a_2 + a_3, a_3 + a_1, a_1 + a_2) \\ &(a_2 + a_3, a_3 + a_1, a_1 + a_2) \rightarrow (a_1, a_2, a_3) \\ &(a_1, a_2, a_3) \longrightarrow (a_2 - a_3, a_3 - a_1, a_1 - a_2). \end{aligned}$$

(12.4). Find all even permutations of (1 2 3 4).

(12.5). Determine the number of inversions in (2 4 6 1 3 5).

(12.6). Calculate the following determinant by development according to the last column

$$\begin{vmatrix} 3 & 0 & 2 & 0 \\ 2 & 4 & 5 & 1 \\ 4 & 1 & 1 & 0 \\ 1 & 2 & 2 & 0 \end{vmatrix}.$$

(12.7). If $a_1, \cdots a_n$ is a basis of $V^n$, $(j_1, \cdots j_n)$ is a permutation of $(1, \cdots n)$, and $\sigma$ is the automorphism with the action $\sigma a_i = a_{j_i}$, $i = 1, \cdots n$, then the determinant of $\sigma$ is $+1$ or $-1$ according as the permutation is even or odd.

(12.8). If $\sigma$ and $\tau$ are $n \times n$-matrices of rank $n$, then

$$\det(\tau^{-1}) = (\det \tau)^{-1}$$
$$\det(\tau\sigma\tau^{-1}) = \det \sigma$$
$$\det(\sigma^k) = (\det \sigma)^k \text{ for all integral } k.$$

(12.9). Calculate the following determinants:

$$\begin{vmatrix} 3 & 1 & 2 \\ 0 & 2 & 9 \\ 0 & 0 & 5 \end{vmatrix}; \quad \begin{vmatrix} 1 & 1 \\ \alpha & \beta \end{vmatrix}; \quad \begin{vmatrix} 1 & 1 & 1 \\ \alpha & \beta & \gamma \\ \alpha^2 & \beta^2 & \gamma^2 \end{vmatrix}; \quad \begin{vmatrix} \alpha & \beta \\ \gamma & \delta \end{vmatrix}; \quad \begin{vmatrix} \sigma_{11} & \sigma_{12} & \sigma_{13} \\ \sigma_{21} & \sigma_{22} & \sigma_{23} \\ \sigma_{31} & \sigma_{32} & \sigma_{33} \end{vmatrix}.$$

(12.10). Do the same for

$$\begin{vmatrix} 2 & 1 & 1 & 1 & 1 \\ 1 & 2 & 1 & 1 & 1 \\ 1 & 1 & 2 & 1 & 1 \\ 1 & 1 & 1 & 2 & 1 \\ 1 & 1 & 1 & 1 & 2 \end{vmatrix}; \quad \begin{vmatrix} 0 & \alpha \\ -\alpha & 0 \end{vmatrix}; \quad \begin{vmatrix} 0 & \alpha & \beta \\ -\alpha & 0 & \gamma \\ -\beta & -\gamma & 0 \end{vmatrix}.$$

(12.11). A matrix $\sigma$ is called *antisymmetric* if ${}^t\sigma = -\sigma$.
Theorem: *The determinant of an antisymmetric matrix with an odd number of rows and columns is zero.*

(12.12). A real matrix $\sigma$ is called *orthogonal* if ${}^t\sigma = \sigma^{-1}$. The determinant of an orthogonal matrix is $+1$ or $-1$. Cf. problem (10.16). The orthogonal matrices form a group under multiplication, the *orthogonal group*.

(12.13)*. (*O. Bottema*, Wisk. Genootschap, Nieuwe opgaven vol. XX no. 125.) If $\sigma$ and $\tau$ are orthogonal matrices with odd numbers of rows and columns then $\det(\sigma - \tau)(\sigma + \tau) = 0$.

(12.14)*. A matrix $\sigma$ of complex numbers is called *unitary* if ${}^t\bar{\sigma} = \sigma^{-1}$. The absolute value of the determinant of a unitary matrix is 1. ($\bar{\sigma}$ is obtained from $\sigma$ by replacing each element of $\sigma$ by its complex conjugate). The unitary matrices form a group under multiplication, the *unitary group*.

(12.15)*. If $\sigma$ and $\tau$ are unitary matrices with an odd number of rows and columns $n$ then

$$i \det(\bar{\sigma} - \bar{\tau}) \det(\sigma + \tau)$$

is real. The coefficient of $i$ is real if the number of rows and columns is even.

(12.16). A matrix $\sigma$ of complex numbers is called *hermitian* if $\bar{\sigma} = {}^t\sigma$. If $\sigma$ is hermitian, and $\tau$ is unitary, then $\tau^{-1}\sigma\tau$ is also hermitian.

(12.17). Let $(j_0, \cdots j_n)$ be a permutation of $(0, \cdots n)$; let $a_0, \cdots a_n$ be points in an $n$-dimensional space, and suppose that they are not contained in a hyperplane. Then the determinant of the endomorphism mapping $a_i - a_0$ into $a_{j_i} - a_{j_0}$ for $i = 1, \cdots n$ is equal to $+ 1$ or $- 1$ according as the permutation is even or odd.

(12.18). If the elements $\omega_{ij}$ of the matrix $\omega$ are the cofactors of the matrix $\sigma$, and $I$ is the unit matrix, then $\sigma \cdot {}^t\omega = (\det \sigma).I$. If $\sigma$ is non-singular then $\sigma^{-1} = (\det \sigma)^{-1}\,{}^t\omega$, which is a useful formula for calculating the inverse matrix of $\sigma$ for small values. ${}^t\omega$ is called the *adjoint* matrix of $\sigma$.

# 13. APPLICATIONS OF DETERMINANTS. VOLUME

*The equation of the line through two points.* The points in a two-dimensional affine space $A$ are represented in a one-to-one way by the pairs of values of two independent linear functions $\xi_1, \xi_2$. The pairs $(\xi_1, \xi_2)$ form a vector space. Three points $(\alpha_1, \alpha_2)$, $(\beta_1, \beta_2) \neq (\alpha_1, \alpha_2)$, and $(\gamma_1, \gamma_2)$ are on a line if and only if

$$(\gamma_1, \gamma_2) - (\alpha_1, \alpha_2) = (\gamma_1 - \alpha_1, \gamma_2 - \alpha_2)$$

and

$$(\beta_1, \beta_2) - (\alpha_1, \alpha_2) = (\beta_1 - \alpha_1, \beta_2 - \alpha_2)$$

are linearly dependent, that is, by theorem [12.8], if

$$\begin{vmatrix} \gamma_1 - \alpha_1 & \gamma_2 - \alpha_2 \\ \beta_1 - \alpha_1 & \beta_2 - \alpha_2 \end{vmatrix} = 0.$$

This is the case if and only if

$(\gamma_1 - \alpha_1, \gamma_2 - \alpha_2, 0)$, $(\beta_1 - \alpha_1, \beta_2 - \alpha_2, 0)$ and $(\alpha_1, \alpha_2, 1)$ are linearly dependent, that is if

$$\begin{vmatrix} \gamma_1 - \alpha_1 & \gamma_2 - \alpha_2 & 0 \\ \beta_1 - \alpha_1 & \beta_2 - \alpha_2 & 0 \\ \alpha_1 & \alpha_2 & 1 \end{vmatrix} = 0$$

or

$$\begin{vmatrix} \gamma_1 & \gamma_2 & 1 \\ \beta_1 & \beta_2 & 1 \\ \alpha_1 & \alpha_2 & 1 \end{vmatrix} = 0.$$

The line through the points $(\alpha_1, \alpha_2)$ and $(\beta_1, \beta_2)$ therefore consists of the points $(\xi_1, \xi_2)$ satisfying the equation

$$\begin{vmatrix} \xi_1 & \xi_2 & 1 \\ \alpha_1 & \alpha_2 & 1 \\ \beta_1 & \beta_2 & 1 \end{vmatrix} = 0.$$

PROBLEM (13.1). Let $\xi_1, \cdots \xi_n$ be coordinates in an $n$-dimensional affine space, let $a_1, \cdots a_r$ be points of this space, and let the scalars $\xi_i(a_j)$ be represented by $\alpha_{ij}$. Then prove that the $r$ points are in a linear $(r - 2)$-variety if and only if the matrix

$$\begin{bmatrix} \alpha_{11} & \cdots & \alpha_{n1} & 1 \\ \cdots & \cdots & \cdots & \cdots \\ \alpha_{1r} & \cdots & \alpha_{nr} & 1 \end{bmatrix}$$

has rank different from $r$. If $r = n + 1$, this matrix is square, and the condition is the vanishing of its determinant.

*Three concurrent lines in A.* Let $\xi_1$ and $\xi_2$ again be coordinates for $A$. Three lines are the zero level curves of linear functions

$$\alpha_1\xi_1 + \alpha_2\xi_2 + \alpha_3, \ \beta_1\xi_1 + \beta_2\xi_2 + \beta_3 \text{ and } \gamma_1\xi_1 + \gamma_2\xi_2 + \gamma_3$$

where $\alpha_1, \cdots \gamma_3$ are constants. The lines are called concurrent if they have a point in common or are parallel, i.e. if the three linear functions are linearly dependent, which means that $(\alpha_1, \alpha_2, \alpha_3)$, $(\beta_1, \beta_2, \beta_3)$ and $(\gamma_1, \gamma_2, \gamma_3)$ are linearly dependent (cf. problem (6.6)). The lines are concurrent if and only if

$$\begin{vmatrix} \alpha_1 & \beta_1 & \gamma_1 \\ \alpha_2 & \beta_2 & \gamma_2 \\ \alpha_3 & \beta_3 & \gamma_3 \end{vmatrix} = 0.$$

*Volume of parallelopiped and simplex.* We restrict ourselves to *real* spaces. By a *measure*, sometimes called *area* or *volume*, on a point set $A$ is meant a function $I$, associating a non-negative number $I(G)$ to any $G$ of a collection of subsets of $A$, and having the property:

$$\text{If } G_1 \cap G_2 = 0, \text{ then } I(G_1 \cup G_2) = I(G_1) + I(G_2). \quad (13.1)$$

We shall give formulas for the volume of a parallelopiped (*par.*, for short) and simplex. In the following the reader is again recommended to consider first the cases $n = 2$ and $n = 3$, before considering the general case.

Definition: By a *par.* in an $n$-dimensional real affine space $A$ with $\mathscr{A}$-map $\kappa\colon A \to V$ the following point set is meant:

$$u + \textstyle\sum_{i=1}^{n} \lambda_i b_i \quad 0 < \lambda_i < 1; \ u, b_i \in V. \quad (13.2)$$

In agreement with the beginning of chapter 12 we define the volume of the par. as $|\varphi(b_1, \cdots b_n)|$, where $\varphi$ is an $n$-linear anti-symmetric function. If $a_1, \cdots a_n$ is a basis of V, $\sigma$ an endomorphism

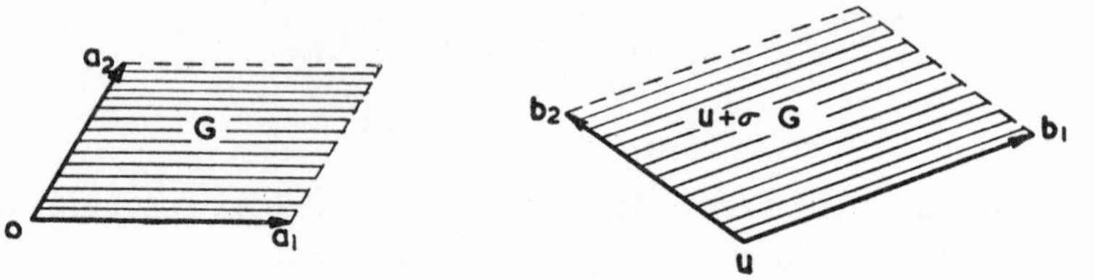


Fig. 13.1

with the action $\sigma a_i = b_i$, $G$ the point set $\sum_{i=1}^n \lambda_i a_i \; 0 < \lambda_i < 1$, then the set mentioned in (13.2) is the set $u + \sigma G$. The volume should satisfy (cf. the beginning of chapter 12)

$$I(u + \sigma G) = |\det \sigma| \cdot I(G) \tag{13.3}$$

for any $G$ in the collection of subsets. That this indeed does determine a measure, we only assert, but we shall not prove it. Note that the volume of the par. is independent of the order of $b_1, \cdots b_n$ (cf. problem (12.7)), and that it does not change under a translation of the par.

In order to determine the volume completely, a unit has still to be chosen, and this can be done, for example, by requiring that $I(G) = 1$.

If $V = \mathbf{R}^n$, we choose $a_i$ equal to the $i$-th standard basis vector $e_i$ in $\mathbf{R}^n$, $b_i = \sigma e_i = \sum_{j=1}^n \sigma_{ji} e_j$ and $I(G) = 1$; then *the volume of the par. is*

$$I(u + \sigma G) = |\det \sigma| = \left\{ \text{absolute value of} \begin{vmatrix} \sigma_{11} & \cdots & \sigma_{1n} \\ \cdots & \cdots & \cdots \\ \sigma_{n1} & \cdots & \sigma_{nn} \end{vmatrix} \right\}. \tag{13.4}$$

If the set of functions $\xi_1, \cdots \xi_n$ is a cobasis of $a_1, \cdots a_n$, then $G$ can also be defined as the point set for which

$$0 < \xi_j < 1 \quad j = 1, \cdots n.$$

We shall now determine the formula for the volume of a simplex, starting from the formulas (13.1) and (13.3) and using the fact that the volume of any point set lying in a linear $(n-1)$-variety is zero, and thus can be neglected.

Definition: An *n-simplex* (with $n+1$ vertices; for example $n = 2$: triangle, $n = 3$: tetrahedron) is a point set

$$S\colon \mathrm{u} + \textstyle\sum_{i=1}^{n} \mu_i \mathrm{c}_i,\ 0 < \mu_i,\ \sum_{i=1}^{n} \mu_i < 1;\ \mathrm{u}, \mathrm{c}_i \in \mathrm{V}.$$

If we introduce the vectors $\mathrm{b}_i$ by

$$\mathrm{b}_1 = \mathrm{c}_1,\ \ \mathrm{b}_i = \mathrm{c}_i - \mathrm{c}_{i-1} \qquad\qquad i = 2, \cdots n$$

$S$ can be written as

$$\mathrm{u} + \textstyle\sum_{i=1}^{n} \lambda_i \mathrm{b}_i,\ \ 0 < \lambda_{k+1} < \lambda_k < 1,\ \ k = 1, \cdots n-1. \qquad (13.5)$$

We now consider the par.

$$\mathrm{u} + \textstyle\sum_{i=1}^{n} \lambda_i \mathrm{b}_i,\ \ 0 < \lambda_i < 1.$$

The volume of it is known ((13.3) or (13.4)).

If we remove from this par. the $(n-1)$-varieties consisting of the points for which $\lambda_i = \lambda_j$ for any pair $i, j$ with $i \neq j$, the volume of the point set does not change, but the point set itself separates into n! simplices, namely

$$\mathrm{u} + \textstyle\sum_{i=1}^{n} \lambda_{j_i} \mathrm{b}_i,\ \ 0 < \lambda_{j_{k+1}} < \lambda_{j_k} < 1,\ \ k = 1, \cdots n-1 \qquad (13.6)$$

with $(j_1, \cdots j_n)$ a permutation of $(1, \cdots n)$ (cf. fig. 13.2 and 13.3). The simplex (13.5) can be obtained from (13.6) by the endomorphism sending $\mathrm{b}_i$ into $\mathrm{b}_{j_i}$, which is therefore a permutation of the basis $\mathrm{b}_1, \cdots \mathrm{b}_n$. We now recall that (13.3) is valid for simplices also. This proves that any of the $n$! simplices (13.6) has the same volume as (13.5) since $|\varphi(\mathrm{b}_1, \cdots \mathrm{b}_n)|$ is invariant under interchange of two elements and therefore under a

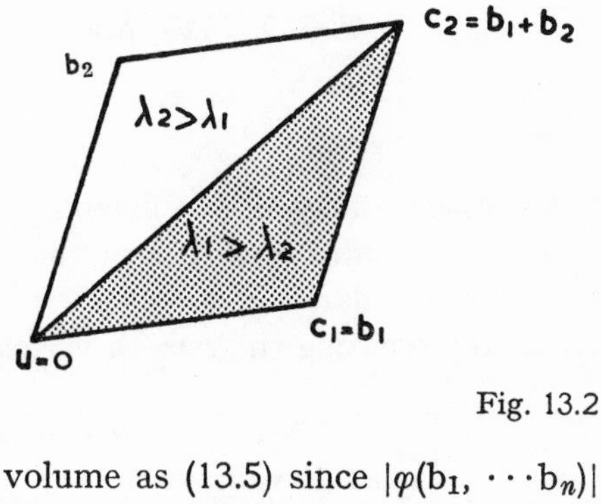


Fig. 13.2

permutation of $b_1, \cdots b_n$. All simplices together have the volume (13.4). Hence *the volume of the simplex* $S$ (13.5) is:

$$I(S) = \frac{1}{n!}\,|\det \sigma| = \frac{1}{n!}\left\{\text{absolute value of} \begin{vmatrix} \sigma_{11} & \cdots & \sigma_{1n} \\ \cdot\cdot & & \cdot\cdot \\ \sigma_{n1} & \cdots & \sigma_{nn} \end{vmatrix}\right\}.$$

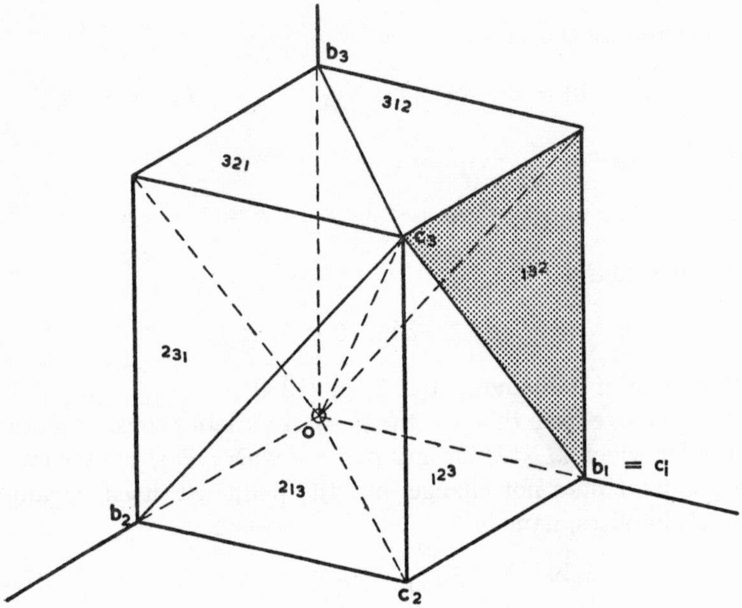


U = O, 123 means $\lambda_1 > \lambda_2 > \lambda_3$, etc.

Fig. 13.3

A simplex $S$ may also be given by its $n + 1$ vertices, represented by $n + 1$ columns of $n$ scalars, the $j$-th column of which consists, say, of the scalars $\alpha_{ij}$; $i = 1, \cdots n$ $(j = 0, \cdots n)$. Subtracting the vector representing the zero-th vertex, we find

$$I(S) = \frac{1}{n!}\left\{\text{absolute value of} \begin{vmatrix} \alpha_{11}-\alpha_{10} & \alpha_{12}-\alpha_{10} & \cdots & \alpha_{1n}-\alpha_{10} \\ \cdots\cdots & \cdots\cdots & & \cdots\cdots \\ \alpha_{n1}-\alpha_{n0} & \alpha_{n2}-\alpha_{n0} & \cdots & \alpha_{nn}-\alpha_{n0} \end{vmatrix}\right\}$$

or, in another formulation (cf. problem (13.1)):

$$I(S) = \frac{1}{n!}\left\{\text{absolute value of} \begin{vmatrix} \alpha_{10} & \alpha_{11} & \cdots & \alpha_{1n} \\ \cdot\cdot & \cdot\cdot & & \cdot\cdot \\ \alpha_{n0} & \alpha_{n1} & \cdots & \alpha_{nn} \\ 1 & 1 & & 1 \end{vmatrix}\right\}.$$

From the last formula it is apparent that $I(S)$ is independent of the order of the vertices of the simplex. It therefore depends on the point set $S$ only.

*Orientation*: A basis of $n$ vectors in an $n$-dimensional vector space $V^n$ is called an *n-frame*. Two $n$-frames $(a_1, \cdots a_n)$ and $(b_1, \cdots b_n)$ in a real space $V^n$ are called *orientation-equivalent* if the determinant of the automorphism $\sigma$ with the action $\sigma a_i = b_i$ for $i = 1, \cdots n$, is positive. It may be left to the reader to show that this relation between $n$-frames is a proper equivalence (cf. chapter 2), i.e. reflexive, symmetric and transitive. The $n$-frames which are not equivalent to a given $n$-frame are mutually equivalent. Thus there are only two equivalence classes. Each is called an *orientation* in $V^n$. Sometimes one of the orientations is called the positive one, the other the negative one.

PROBLEMS. (13.2). If $a_1$, $a_2$ form a basis of a real two-dimensional vector space, then the 2-frames $(a_1, a_2)$, $(-a_1, -a_2)$, $(-a_2, a_1)$, $(a_2, -a_1)$, $(a_1 + a_2, a_2)$, $(3a_1 - 4a_2, 2a_2)$ have the same orientation; $(a_2, a_1)$, $(-a_2, -a_1)$, $(-a_1, a_2)$ have the other orientation. In fig. 13.4 the latter orientation is clockwise.

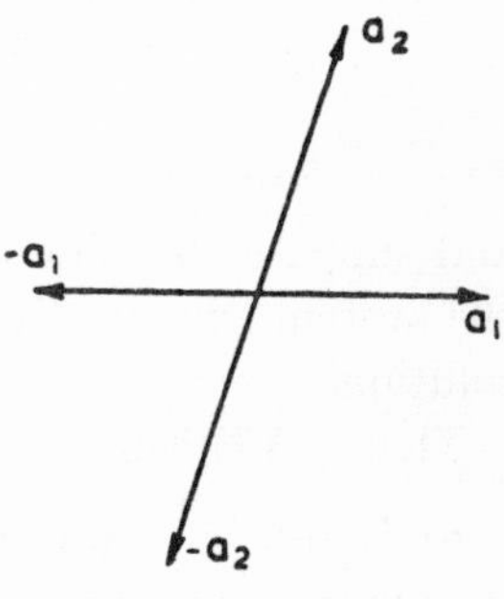

Fig. 13.4

(13.3). If $a_1$, $a_2$, $a_3$ form a basis of a real three-dimensional vector space, then the 3-frames $(a_1, a_2, a_3)$, $(a_2, a_3, a_1)$, $(a_3, a_1, a_2)$, $(5a_1, 2a_2, a_3)$, $(a_1 + a_2 + a_3, a_2, a_3)$, $(-a_1, -a_2, a_3)$ have the same orientation, whereas $(a_1, a_3, a_2)$, $(-a_1, -a_2, -a_3)$, $(a_3, a_2, a_1)$ have the other orientation.

Also the $n$-simplices in a real affine $n$-space with ordered vertices can be divided into two orientation classes. Two simplices $(a_0, \cdots a_n)$

and $(b_0, \cdots b_n)$ will be said to have the same orientation if the $n$-frames $(a_1 - a_0, \cdots a_n - a_0)$ and $(b_1 - b_0, \cdots b_n - b_0)$ have the same orientation.

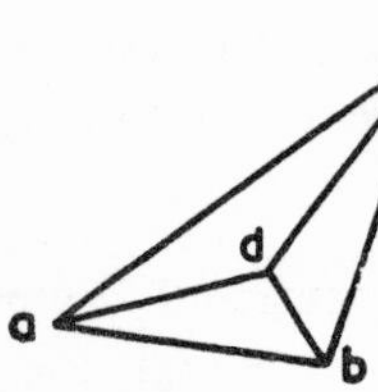


Fig. 13.5

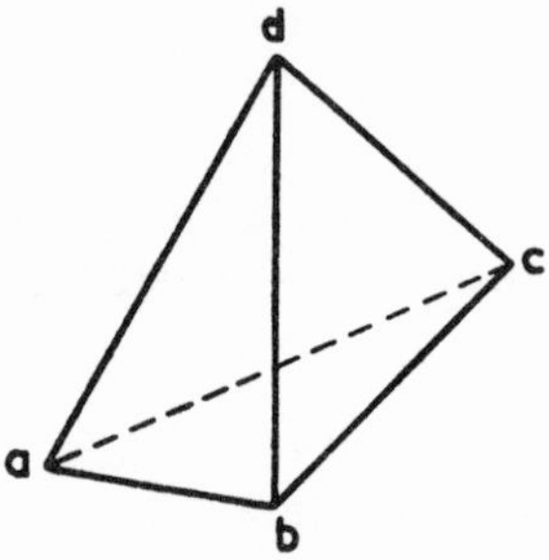


Fig. 13.6

(13.4). In the plane figure 13.5 the triangles abc, bca, abd, bcd, adc, dca have the same orientation, and acb, cba, cda, cbd have the other orientation. In the stereometrical fig. 13.6 abcd, bcad, cdab, cabd have the same orientation, bacd, acbd have the other orientation.

*Cramer's rule for solving linear equations.* Let the following system of $n$ linear equations with $n$ unknowns be given

$$\begin{matrix} \sigma_{11}\xi_1 + \cdots + \sigma_{1n}\xi_n = \alpha_1 \\ \cdots \qquad \cdots \qquad \cdot \\ \sigma_{n1}\xi_1 + \cdots + \sigma_{nn}\xi_n = \alpha_n \end{matrix}, \text{ more briefly: } \sigma x = a \qquad (13.7)$$

and suppose that $\det \sigma \neq 0$. Then, as we have seen in chapter 11, the system has exactly one solution. Let $\xi_1, \cdots \xi_n$ also denote this solution.

Then (13.7) can be rewritten as

$$\begin{matrix} \sigma_{11}\xi_1 + \cdots + (\sigma_{1i}\xi_i - \alpha_1) + \cdots + \sigma_{1n}\xi_n = 0 \\ \cdots\cdots\cdots\cdots\cdots\cdots\cdots\cdots\cdots\cdots \\ \sigma_{n1}\xi_1 + \cdots + (\sigma_{ni}\xi_i - \alpha_n) + \cdots + \sigma_{nn}\xi_n = 0 \end{matrix} \qquad i = 1, \cdots n.$$

Hence the columns of the following matrix are linearly dependent:

$$\begin{bmatrix} \sigma_{11} & \sigma_{1i}\xi_i - \alpha_1 & \sigma_{1n} \\ \cdots & \cdots & \cdots \\ \sigma_{n1} & \sigma_{ni}\xi_i - \alpha_n & \sigma_{nn} \end{bmatrix},$$

and its determinant is therefore zero. Since the determinant is multilinear in the columns of the matrix, we may write

$$\det \sigma \cdot \xi_i - \det \sigma_i = 0,$$

where $\sigma_i$ is the matrix obtained from $\sigma$ by substituting for the $i$-th column the column of scalars $\alpha_1, \cdots \alpha_n$. Hence

$$\xi_i = \frac{\det \sigma_i}{\det \sigma}. \tag{13.8}$$

This formula for the solution of a set of linear equations is called *Cramer's rule.*

PROBLEMS. (13.5). Use Cramer's rule to solve problems (11.1)–(11.3).

(13.6). The lines $\varphi_1, \varphi_2, \varphi_3$ respectively pass through the vertices a, b, c of triangle abc. The lines $\psi_1, \psi_2, \psi_3$ parallel to $\varphi_1, \varphi_2, \varphi_3$ respectively, pass through the midpoints of the opposite sides.

(a) $\varphi_1, \varphi_2, \varphi_3$ are concurrent if and only if $\psi_1, \psi_2, \psi_3$ are concurrent.

(b) If $\varphi_1, \varphi_2, \varphi_3$ have a point p in common, then $\psi_1, \psi_2, \psi_3$ have a point q in common, and p, q and the centroid of triangle abc are collinear (take for example the altitudes of a triangle abc in the ordinary plane).

Hint: choose two of the coordinates suitably.

# 14. QUADRATIC AND SYMMETRIC BILINEAR FUNCTIONS

A. *Functions on a vector space*

If $\xi_1$ and $\xi_2$ are independent linear functions on a two-dimensional vector space V, then some examples of quadratic functions on V are those which map $x \in V$ to

$$\{\xi_1(x)\}^2, \ \{\xi_1(x)\}^2 + \{\xi_2(x)\}^2, \ \xi_1(x)\xi_2(x), \ \{\xi_1(x)\}^2 - \{\xi_2(x)\}^2$$

or, in a shorter notation,

$$\xi_1^2, \xi_1^2 + \xi_2^2, \xi_1\xi_2, \xi_1^2 - \xi_2^2.$$

In fig. 14.1 some level curves are shown of the (real) functions $\xi_1$ and $\xi_2$, which can be considered as coordinates, and also some level curves of each of the above quadratic functions. Introducing new linear functions $\eta_1$ and $\eta_2$ by the formulas

$$\eta_1 = \xi_1 + \xi_2, \quad \eta_2 = \xi_1 - \xi_2$$

we have $\xi_1^2 - \xi_2^2 = \eta_1\eta_2$ which transforms the last of the above quadratic functions into one like the second-last.

The level curves in the cases $\xi_1^2 + \xi_2^2$ and $\xi_1^2 - \xi_2^2$ are called ellipses and hyperbolas respectively. If $\xi_1 = 0$ and $\xi_2 = 0$ are perpendicular, and $|\xi_1|$ and $|\xi_2|$ are just the distances from the point $(\xi_1, \xi_2)$ to $\xi_1 = 0$ and $\xi_2 = 0$ in ordinary geometry, then the level curves of $\xi_1^2 + \xi_2^2$ are circles (cf. fig. 14.1, third figure).

Beside the quadratic function $\xi_1^2 + \xi_2^2$ we also consider the function $\varphi$: $(x, y) \to \xi_1(x)\xi_1(y) + \xi_2(x)\xi_2(y)$, which is bilinear on V. The given quadratic function is the diagonal of $\varphi$: $\xi_1^2 + \xi_2^2 = \varphi^{\cdot}$. In theorem [14.2] we shall prove that the diagonals of the bilinear functions are just the quadratic functions (we remind the reader that quadratic functions on vector spaces were supposed to be homogeneous).

Let V now be an $n$-dimensional vector space over **F**. A function $\varphi$ of two variables on V is said to be *symmetric* if for all x, y $\epsilon$ V

$$\varphi(\mathrm{x}, \mathrm{y}) = \varphi(\mathrm{y}, \mathrm{x}) \tag{14.1}$$

and *antisymmetric* if

$$\varphi(\mathrm{x}, \mathrm{y}) = -\,\varphi(\mathrm{y}, \mathrm{x}). \tag{14.1'}$$

Any function $\varphi$ of two variables is the sum of a symmetric and an antisymmetric function, for

$$\varphi(\mathrm{x}, \mathrm{y}) = \tfrac{1}{2}\{\varphi(\mathrm{x}, \mathrm{y}) + \varphi(\mathrm{y}, \mathrm{x})\} + \tfrac{1}{2}\{\varphi(\mathrm{x}, \mathrm{y}) - \varphi(\mathrm{y}, \mathrm{x})\}. \tag{14.2}$$

The first term of this sum is called the symmetric part of $\varphi$.

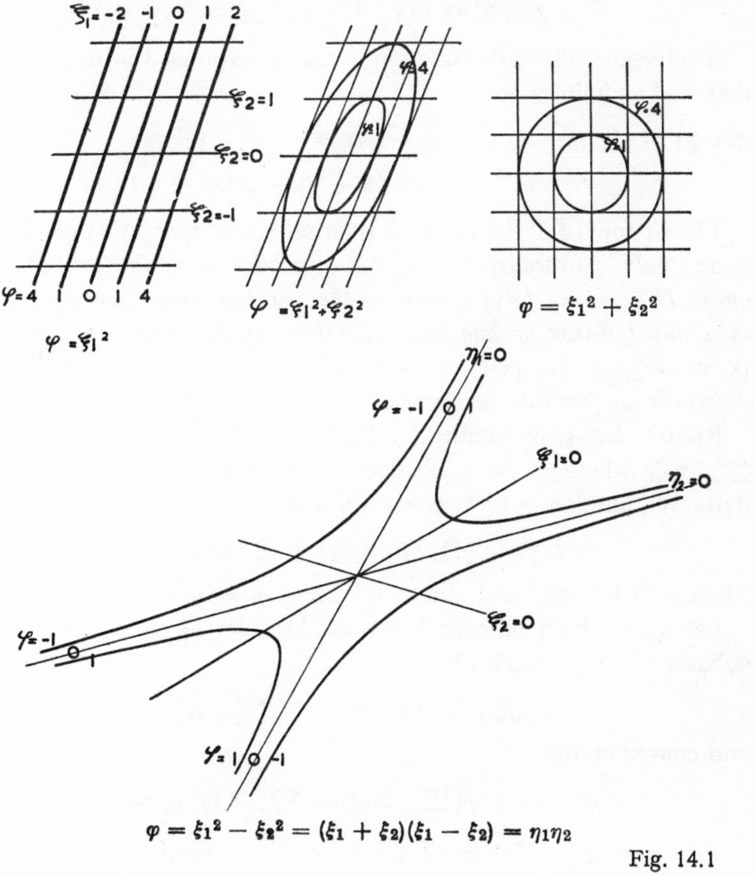


Fig. 14.1

As the reader may easily verify, a function of two variables and its symmetric part have the same diagonal. Hence, a function is not determined by its diagonal. The following theorem, however, says that a *bilinear symmetric* function is determined by its diagonal.

Theorem [14.1]: *If the bilinear symmetric functions* $\varphi$ *and* $\psi$ *have the same diagonal then they are identical.*

Proof: Under the given assumptions the function $\chi = \varphi - \psi$ is bilinear and symmetric, and $\chi(x, x) = 0$ for all $x \in V$. Then for all $x, y \in V$ we have

$$0=\chi(x+y, x+y)=\chi(x, x)+\chi(x, y)+\chi(y, x)+\chi(y, y)=2\chi(x, y)$$

$$\chi(x, y) = \varphi(x, y) - \psi(x, y) = 0.$$

A bilinear symmetric function $\varphi$ can be expressed in terms of its diagonal as follows:

$$\varphi(x, y) = \tfrac{1}{2}\{\varphi(x + y, x + y) - \varphi(x, x) - \varphi(y, y)\} =$$

$$= \tfrac{1}{2}\{\varphi^{\cdot}(x + y) - \varphi^{\cdot}(x) - \varphi^{\cdot}(y)\}. \qquad (14.3)$$

Theorem [14.2]: *A function* $\psi$ *on the vector space* V *is quadratic if and only if it occurs as diagonal of a bilinear symmetric function on* V. *If* $\xi_1, \cdots \xi_n$ *form a basis of the space of linear function on* V *then any bilinear or quadratic function can be written in the form* $(x, y) \to \sum_{i,j=1}^{n} \alpha_{ij}\xi_i(x)\xi_j(y)$, *or* $x \to \sum_{i,j=1}^{n} \alpha_{ij}\xi_i(x)\xi_j(x)$ *respectively. The bilinear function is symmetric if and only if* $\alpha_{ij} = \alpha_{ji}$.

Proof: Let $\psi$ be quadratic. Then by definition $\psi$ has the form $\sum_{i=1}^{k} \eta_i\zeta_i$, where $\eta_i$ and $\zeta_i$ are linear functions on V. Using (14.3) we define a function $\varphi$ of two variables by

$$\varphi(x, y) = \tfrac{1}{2}\{\sum \eta_i(x)\zeta_i(y) + \sum \eta_i(y)\zeta_i(x)\}.$$

Then $\varphi$ is bilinear and symmetric, and $\varphi^{\cdot} = \psi$.

Let now $\varphi$ be a bilinear function. Also, let $a_1, \cdots a_n \in V$ be the cobasis of $\xi_1, \cdots \xi_n \in V^*$. Then

$$x = \sum_{i=1}^{n} \xi_i(x)a_i \text{ and } y = \sum_{i=1}^{n} \xi_i(y)a_i,$$

and consequently,

$$\varphi(x, y) = \varphi(\sum_{i=1}^{n} \xi_i(x)a_i, \sum_{j=1}^{n} \xi_j(y)a_j) =$$

$$= \sum_{i,j=1}^{n} \xi_i(x)\xi_j(y)\varphi(a_i, a_j) = \sum_{i,j=1}^{n} \alpha_{ij}\xi_i(x)\xi_j(y)$$

with $\alpha_{ij} = \varphi(a_i, a_j)$. If $\varphi$ is symmetric, then

$$\alpha_{ij} = \varphi(a_i, a_j) = \varphi(a_j, a_i) = \alpha_{ji}.$$

If, conversely, $\alpha_{ij} = \alpha_{ji}$ then

$$\varphi(x, y) - \varphi(y, x) = \sum_{i \neq j} \alpha_{ij}\{\xi_i(x)\xi_j(y) - \xi_i(y)\xi_j(x)\}$$
$$= \sum_{i \neq j} (\alpha_{ij} - \alpha_{ji})\xi_i(x)\xi_j(y) = 0.$$

Finally, if $\psi$ is the diagonal of $\varphi$, then $\psi = \sum_{i=1}^{k} \alpha_{ij}\xi_i\xi_j$, which is quadratic by definition.

Main Theorem on quadratic functions on a vector space $V^n$ [14.3]: *If* $\varphi^\cdot: V^n \to \mathbf{F}$ *is a quadratic function on the n-dimensional vector space* $V^n$ *over* $\mathbf{F}$, *then there exists a basis* $\xi_1, \cdots \xi_n$ *of the linear functions on* $V^n$ *such that*

$$\varphi^\cdot = \sum_{i=1}^{r} \lambda_i \xi_i^2 \qquad 0 \neq \lambda_i \in \mathbf{F}. \tag{14.4}$$

The number $r$ is independent of the choice of $\xi_1, \cdots \xi_n$ and is called the *rank* of $\varphi^\cdot$. $\varphi^\cdot$ is called *singular* if $r < n$.

Proof: Let $\varphi$ be the bilinear symmetric function of which $\varphi^\cdot$ is the diagonal. We choose successively vectors $a_1, a_2, \cdots a_n$ of a basis of V in the following way: $a_j$ ($j = 1, 2, \cdots n$) shall be such that

$$\varphi(a_i, a_j) = 0 \quad \text{for } i < j \tag{14.5}$$

and if possible, such that in addition

$$\varphi(a_j, a_j) \neq 0. \tag{14.6}$$

Let $r$ be the greatest value of the index $j$ such that (14.6) is satisfied. Then

$$\varphi(a_j, a_j) = \lambda_j \begin{cases} \neq 0 \text{ for } j \leqslant r \\ = 0 \text{ for } j > r. \end{cases} \tag{14.7}$$

If $\zeta_1, \cdots \zeta_n$ is the cobasis of $a_1, \cdots a_n$, i.e. $\zeta_i(a_j) = \delta_{ij}$, then for all $x \in V$ it follows that

$$x = \sum_{i=1}^{n} \zeta_i(x) \cdot a_i;$$

then, just as in the proof of theorem [14.2]:

$$\varphi^\cdot(x) = \varphi(x, x) = \varphi\{\sum_{i=1}^{n} \zeta_i(x)a_i, \sum_{j=1}^{n} \zeta_j(x)a_j\}$$
$$= \sum_{i,j=1}^{n} \zeta_i(x)\zeta_j(x)\varphi(a_i, a_j),$$

which, in connection with (14.5) and (14.7), is equal to

$$\Sigma_{j=1}^{r} \lambda_j \zeta_j^2(\mathrm{x}) \qquad \lambda_i \neq 0 \text{ for } i = 1, \cdots r.$$

Then (14.4) follows by putting $\xi_i = \zeta_i$.

For the bilinear symmetric function $\varphi$ we have

$$\varphi(\mathrm{x}, \mathrm{y}) = \Sigma_{i=1}^{r} \lambda_i \xi_i(\mathrm{x}) \xi_i(\mathrm{y}) \quad \lambda_i \neq 0 \quad i = 1, \cdots r.$$

This implies that a vector y satisfies $\varphi(\mathrm{x}, \mathrm{y}) = 0$ for all $\mathrm{x} \in \mathrm{V}$ if and only if $\xi_i(\mathrm{y}) = 0$ for $i = 1, \cdots r$. These vectors y therefore form an $(n - r)$-dimensional space, and *this characterizes the rank* $r$ *independently of the representation* (14.4) *of* $\varphi$.

Continuation of the Main Theorem [14.3′]: *If* **F** *is the field* **C** *of complex numbers, then a choice of the cobasis is possible such that* $\varphi^{\cdot}$ *has the normal form*:

$$\varphi^{\cdot} = \Sigma_{i=1}^{r} \xi_i^2. \tag{14.4'}$$

*If* **F** *is the field* **R** *of real numbers then a choice is possible such that*

$$\varphi^{\cdot} = \Sigma_{i=1}^{p} \xi_i^2 - \Sigma_{i=p+1}^{p+q} \xi_i^2, \quad p + q = r. \tag{14.4''}$$

*Here the numbers* $p$, $q$ *and* $p + q = r$ *are independent of the choice of the coordinates.*

$q$ is called the *index of inertia* of $\varphi^{\cdot}$, and the last line of the theorem represents the *theorem of inertia.*

Proof: If $\mathbf{F} = \mathbf{C}$ then (14.4′) follows from the proof of (14.4) by putting

$$\xi_i = \sqrt{\lambda_i}\zeta_i.$$

If $\mathbf{F} = \mathbf{R}$ and if after possible rearrangement $\lambda_1, \cdots \lambda_p$ are positive, $\lambda_{p+1}, \cdots \lambda_r$ negative, then (14.4″) follows by putting

$$\xi_i = \sqrt{\lambda_i}\zeta_i \qquad i = 1, \cdots p$$

$$\xi_j = \sqrt{-\lambda_j}\zeta_j \quad j = p+1, \cdots r.$$

Now let $\mathrm{P}^p$ and $\mathrm{Q}^{n-p}$ be the subspaces of dimensions $p$ and $n - p$, with equations $\xi_i = 0$ for $i > p$ and $\xi_i = 0$ for $i \leqslant p$ respectively. These subspaces have the property that for any non-zero vectors $\mathrm{a} \in \mathrm{P}^p$, $\mathrm{b} \in \mathrm{Q}^{n-p}$ the relations $\varphi^{\cdot}(\mathrm{a}) > 0$, $\varphi^{\cdot}(\mathrm{b}) \leqslant 0$ hold. Suppose that another representation (14.4″) with $\xi_i'$, $p_1$, $q_1$ instead of $\xi_i$, $p$, $q$ were possible. We already know that $p + q = p_1 + q_1 = r$. Suppose that $p_1 > p$. Then there would be a space $P_1^{p_1}$ of dimension $p_1$ such that for any non-zero vector $a \in P_1^{p_1}$, $\varphi^{\cdot}(a) > 0$. $P_1^{p_1}$ and $Q^{n-p}$ together span a space of dimension at most $n$. The second dimension theorem of chapter 5 then implies that $P_1^{p_1} \cap Q^{n-p}$ is a space of dimension at least $p_1 + (n - p) - n = p_1 - p > 0$, and the vectors $c \neq 0$ in this space satisfy

$$\varphi^{\cdot}(c) > 0 \text{ and } \varphi^{\cdot}(c) \leqslant 0,$$

which is a contradiction. Hence $p_1 > p$ is impossible. But similarly, $p_1 < p$ is impossible too, so that $p_1 = p$, which proves the theorem of inertia.

If $\xi_1, \cdots \xi_n$ are expressed in terms of a given basis $\eta_1, \cdots \eta_n$ then these expressions for $\xi_1, \cdots \xi_n$ are *linear forms* in $\eta_1, \cdots \eta_n$. In this case the assertion is called the theorem of inertia for *quadratic forms.* (14.4′) and (14.4″) are called the *normal forms* of the quadratic form.

Application: Let $\sum_{i,j=1}^{n} f_{ij}\eta_i\eta_j$ be an ordinary homogeneous quadratic form with real coefficients in the symbols $\eta_1, \cdots \eta_n$. This may be interpreted as a quadratic function on a vector space V if $\eta_1, \cdots \eta_n$ are considered as the functions (coordinates) of a cobasis of V. The main theorem then implies that there exist linear forms

$$\xi_i = \sum_{j=1}^{n} \gamma_{ij}\eta_j$$

such that

$$\sum_{i,j=1}^{n} f_{ij}\eta_i\eta_j = \sum_{i=1}^{p} \xi_i^2 - \sum_{j=p+1}^{p+q} \xi_j^2$$

where $p$ and $q$ are determined by the given function.

Definitions: A real quadratic form is called

| | |
|---|---|
| *positive definite* | if $p = r = n$ |
| *negative definite* | if $q = r = n$ |
| *semi-definite* (positive) | if $q = 0$ |
| (negative) | if $p = 0$ |
| *indefinite* | if $p > 0$ and $q > 0$ |
| *singular* | if $r < n$ |
| *non-singular* | if $r = n$. |

PROBLEM (14.1). Any real quadratic function $\varphi^{\cdot}$ on a two-dimensional real vector space can be written in one of the forms

$$0,\ \xi_1^2,\ -\xi_1^2,\ \xi_1^2 + \xi_2^2,\ -(\xi_1^2 + \xi_2^2) \text{ or } \xi_1^2 - \xi_2^2.$$

In fig. 14.1 some level curves of such functions are drawn. The following names are assigned to the non-empty level curves: *ellipse* if it is a non-zero-level curve of a non-singular definite quadratic function; *hyperbola* if it is a non-zero-level curve of a non-singular indefinite quadratic function. The zero-level curve of a non-singular definite function is a point, that of a non-singular indefinite function is a pair of intersecting lines. The non-zero-level curves of a singular function are pairs of parallel lines, while the zero-level curve is a single line. All level curves of quadratic functions on two-dimensional spaces are called *conic sections*.

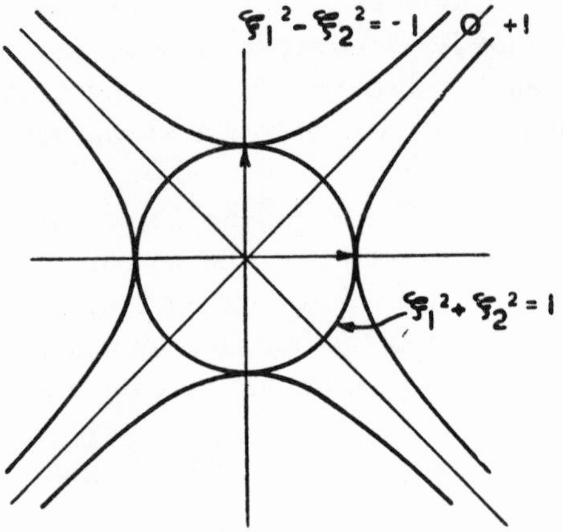


Fig. 14.2

In fig. 14.2 a representation has been chosen such that the basis having $\xi_1$, $\xi_2$ as cobasis, consists of two perpendicular vectors of equal length.

By the main theorem any real quadratic function $\varphi^{\cdot}$ on a real three-dimensional vector space can be written in one of the following forms. In parentheses the names of the non-empty level sets when $\varphi^{\cdot} \neq 0$ are given: $\pm\, \xi_1^2$ (pair of planes); $\pm\, (\xi_1^2 + \xi_2^2)$ (elliptic cylinder); $\xi_1^2 - \xi_2^2$ (hyperbolic cylinder); $\pm\, (\xi_1^2 + \xi_2^2 + \xi_3^2)$

(ellipsoid); $\pm(\xi_1^2 + \xi_2^2 - \xi_3^2)$ (hyperboloid). If in this last case the level set has the equation

$$\xi_1^2 + \xi_2^2 - \xi_3^2 = -\alpha^2 < 0 \text{ or } \xi_1^2 + \xi_2^2 + \alpha^2 = \xi_3^2$$

then there exists a subspace (plane), namely $\xi_3 = 0$, containing no point of the hyperboloid. The hyperboloid contains with x also the point $-$ x, and consists of two parts: that for which $\xi_3 > 0$ and that for which $\xi_3 < 0$. The hyperboloid is therefore called *hyperboloid of two sheets.*

If the level set has the equation

$$\xi_1^2 + \xi_2^2 - \xi_3^2 = \alpha^2 > 0, \text{ and if } \beta_1\xi_1 + \beta_2\xi_2 + \beta_3\xi_3 = 0$$

is the equation of a plane, then it is always possible to find points in the plane which also lie in the level set. In this case the hyperboloid is called a *hyperboloid of one sheet.*

The zero-level set of a non-singular indefinite quadratic function, that is, one with equation $\xi_1^2 + \xi_2^2 - \xi_3^2 = 0$, is called a *cone*. Fig. 14.3 shows some level sets of the functions $\xi_1^2 + \xi_2^2 + \xi_3^2$ and $\xi_1^2 + \xi_2^2 - \xi_3^2$.

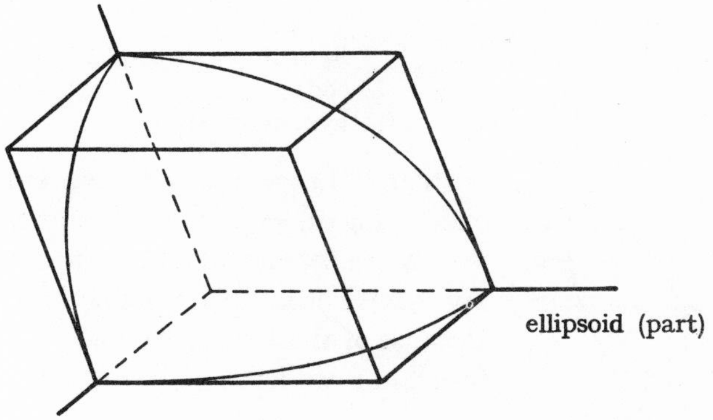


Fig. 14.3a

In fig. 14.4 the midpoints of some parallel chords of an ellipse are indicated by dots, and it appears that these points lie on a line. We will prove this in a generalized version:

Theorem [14.4]: *Let* x *be a vector in an n-dimensional vector space* V *over* **F**, *and* $\varphi$ *be a bilinear symmetric function such that* $\varphi(\mathrm{x}, \mathrm{x}) =$

$= \varphi^{\cdot}(x) \neq 0$. *Then the midpoints of all chords of* $\varphi^{\cdot}(u) = \alpha$ *which are parallel to* x *lie in an* $(n - 1)$*-dimensional subspace of* V.

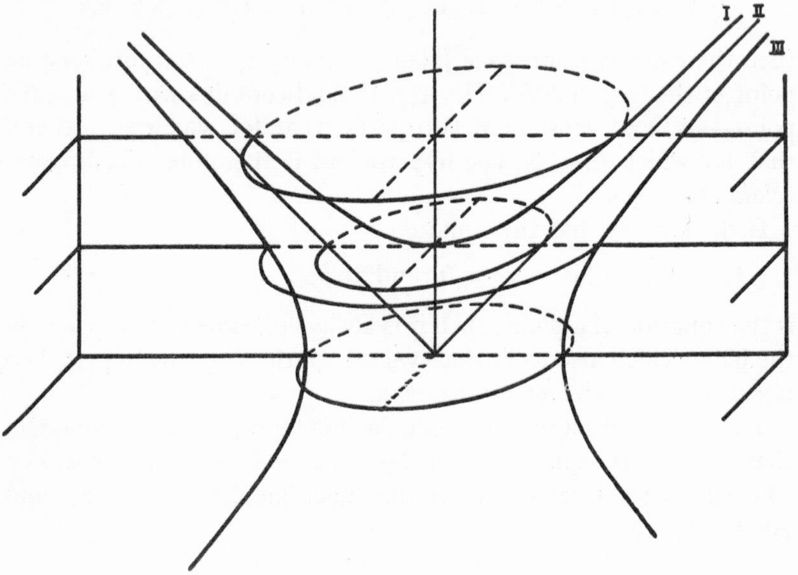


Fig. 14.3b

I hyp. of two sheets } (only the upper half is
II cone } suggested in the figure)
III hyp. of one sheet

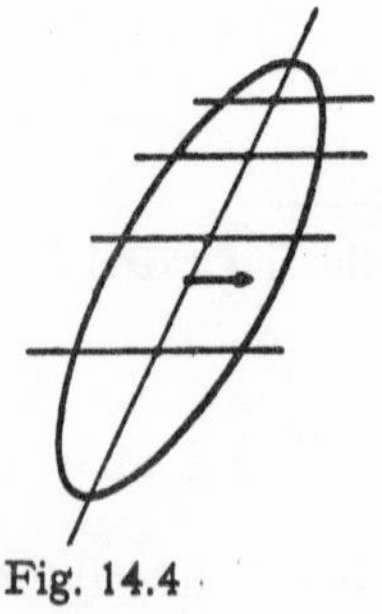

Fig. 14.4

Proof: Let v and w be the end-points of a chord of $\varphi^{\cdot}(u) = \alpha$ with direction x. Then x and $v - w$ are dependent and $\lambda$ exists such that $x = \lambda(v - w)$. The midpoint of the chord is $\frac{1}{2}(v + w)$. Because of the bilinearity and symmetry of the function $\varphi$ we have

$$\varphi(v - w, v + w) =$$
$$= \varphi(v, v) + \varphi(v, w) - \varphi(w, v) - \varphi(w, w) =$$
$$= \varphi(v, v) - \varphi(w, w) = 0$$

since v and w lie in the same level set.

It follows that

$$\varphi\{x, \tfrac{1}{2}(v + w)\} = \varphi\{\lambda(v - w), \tfrac{1}{2}(v + w)\} = \tfrac{1}{2}\lambda\varphi(v - w, v + w) = 0$$

and the midpoint thus lies in the $(n-1)$-dimensional space of all $u \in V$ that satisfy the equation $\varphi(x, u) = 0$.

Two *vectors* u and v satisfying $\varphi(u, v) = 0$ are called *conjugate* or *polar* with respect to the quadratic function $\varphi^{\cdot}$ and also with respect to any level set of this function. Two subspaces B and C of the vector space V are called *polar* with respect to $\varphi^{\cdot}$ and its level sets, if any vector in B is polar to any vector in C. The relation "being polar" is a *symmetric relation* since the function $\varphi$ is symmetric.

PROBLEM (14.2). If the two different vectors $u_1$ and $u_2$ are polar with respect to the quadratic function $\varphi^{\cdot}$ and if the line through the points $u_1$ and $u_2$ intersects the level set $\varphi^{\cdot} = 0$ in the points $v_1$ and $v_2$ both different from $u_1$ and $u_2$, then the pair $u_1, u_2$ separates the pair $v_1, v_2$ harmonically. Prove this and draw a picture for the two-dimensional real case. Formulate and also prove the converse of this theorem.

Fig. 14.5 shows a two-dimensional vector space with an ellipse as level set of a quadratic function. Furthermore two polar vectors $a_1$ and $a_2$ with endpoints on the ellipse, the parallelogram with sides $a_1$ and $a_2$ and the parallelogram with sides parallel to $a_1$ and $a_2$ and passing through $a_2$, $-a_2$, $a_1$ and $-a_1$ are drawn (each side of the latter has only one point in common with the ellipse: they are tangents). If $(\xi_1, \xi_2)$ is the cobasis of $(a_1, a_2)$ then the set of points which lie on and inside the latter parallelogram is given by $\{|\xi_1| \leqslant 1\} \cap \{|\xi_2| \leqslant 1\}$, and the ellipse is given by the equation $\xi_1^2 + \xi_2^2 = 1$. Similarly a circumscribed parallelogram has been drawn corresponding to the polar vectors $b_1$, $b_2$. We shall now prove that these two parallelograms and, therefore, all parallelograms that can be obtained in a similar way, have the same area. To do so it is sufficient to prove that the endomorphism mapping $(a_1, a_2)$ to $(b_1, b_2)$ has determinant of absolute value 1. We give the proof for the more general:

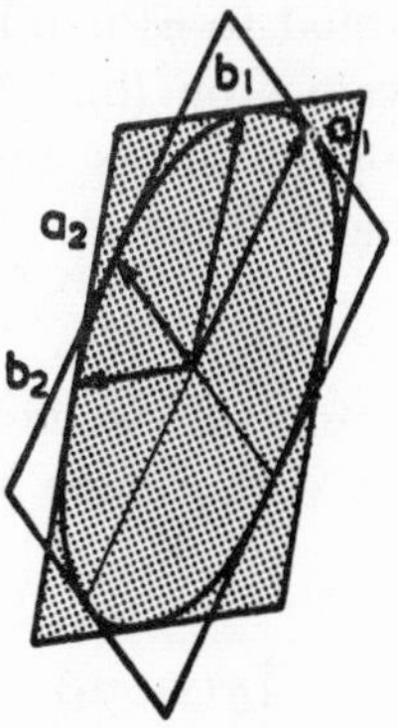


Fig. 14.5

Theorem* [14.5]: *Let* $\varphi^{\cdot}$ *be a non-singular quadratic function on the n-dimensional real vector space* V. *Let* $a_1, \cdots a_n$ *and* $b_1, \cdots b_n$ *form two bases of mutually polar vectors of* V, *and let the endpoints of these basis vectors all lie on the* $+1$ *or* $-1$ *level sets of* $\varphi$, *i.e.* $|\varphi(a_i, a_j)| = |\varphi(b_i, b_j)| = \delta_{ij}$ $i, j = 1, \cdots n$. $\xi_1, \cdots \xi_n$ *and* $\eta_1, \cdots \eta_n$ *are the cobases of* $a_1, \cdots a_n$ *and* $b_1, \cdots b_n$ *respectively. Then the volume of the parallelopiped*

$$\{|\xi_1| \leqslant 1\} \cap \{|\xi_2| \leqslant 1\} \cap \cdots \cap \{|\xi_n| \leqslant 1\}$$

*equals that of*

$$\{|\eta_1| \leqslant 1\} \cap \cdots \cap \{|\eta_n| \leqslant 1\}.$$

Proof: Following the proof of the main theorem we may put, after possible rearrangement

$$\varphi^{\cdot} = \Sigma_{i=1}^{p} \xi_i^2 - \Sigma_{i=p+1}^{n} \xi_i^2 = \Sigma_{i=1}^{p} \eta_i^2 - \Sigma_{i=p+1}^{n} \eta_i^2 \quad (14.6)$$

where $p$ is determined by $\varphi$.

Let $\sigma$ be the automorphism determined by the action $\sigma(b_i) = a_i$, $i = 1, \cdots n$. The function $\varphi_\sigma$: $(x, y) \to \varphi(\sigma x, \sigma y)$ is bilinear and symmetric, and associates to $(b_i, b_j)$ the value $\varphi(a_i, a_j)$, which is equal to $\varphi(b_i, b_j)$. Thus the functions $\varphi_\sigma$ and $\varphi$ assume the same values on $(b_i, b_j)$ for $i, j = 1, \cdots n$, and are therefore identically equal, linear functions being determined by their values on a basis. Thus

$$\varphi(\sigma x, \sigma y) = \varphi(x, y). \quad (14.7)$$

From this we now deduce $|\det \sigma| = 1$. Consider the function $H$ of $2n$ variables on V defined by

$$H(x_1, \cdots x_n, y_1, \cdots y_n) =$$

$$\begin{vmatrix} \varphi(x_1, y_1) & \varphi(x_1, y_2) & \cdots & \varphi(x_1, y_n) \\ \cdot & \cdot & \cdots & \cdot \\ \cdot & \cdot & \cdots & \cdot \\ \varphi(x_n, y_1) & \varphi(x_n, y_2) & \cdots & \varphi(x_n, y_n) \end{vmatrix} = \det \{\varphi(x_i, y_j)\}. \quad (14.8)$$

For fixed $x_1, \cdots x_n$ the function

$$H_1: (y_1, \cdots y_n) \to H(x_1, \cdots x_n, y_1, \cdots y_n)$$

is $n$-linear and antisymmetric as the reader may verify. Let $\Delta$ be the $n$-linear antisymmetric function with $\Delta(a_1, \cdots a_n) = 1$; then by chapter 12 there exists a function $F$ of $n$ variables such that

$$H(x_1, \cdots x_n, y_1, \cdots y_n) = F(x_1, \cdots x_n) \cdot \Delta(y_1, \cdots y_n).$$

Since the function $F$, like $H_1$, is $n$-linear and antisymmetric, there exists a constant $\lambda$ such that

$$F = \lambda \cdot \Delta$$

$$H(x_1, \cdots x_n, y_1, \cdots y_n) = \lambda \cdot \Delta(x_1, \cdots x_n) \cdot \Delta(y_1, \cdots y_n). \quad (14.9)$$

The substitution $x_i = y_i = a_i$, $i = 1, \cdots n$, transforms the matrix in (14.8) into one with $p$ numbers 1 and $q = n - p$ numbers $-1$ in the diagonal and zeros elsewhere.

Substitution in (14.9) then gives $(-1)^q = \lambda \cdot 1 \cdot 1$ and

$$H(x_1, \cdots x_n, y_1, \cdots y_n) = (-1)^q \Delta(x_1, \cdots x_n) \cdot \Delta(y_1, \cdots y_n). \quad (14.10)$$

Since $\varphi(\sigma x, \sigma y) = \varphi(x, y)$, we have $H(\sigma x_1, \cdots \sigma y_n) = H(x_1, \cdots y_n)$ and hence, with (14.10),

$$\Delta(x_1, \cdots x_n) \cdot \Delta(y_1, \cdots y_n) = \Delta(\sigma x_1, \cdots \sigma x_n) \cdot \Delta(\sigma y_1, \cdots \sigma y_n) =$$
$$= \det \sigma \cdot \Delta(x_1, \cdots x_n) \cdot \det \sigma \cdot \Delta(y_1, \cdots y_n)$$
$$(\det \sigma)^2 = 1, \quad |\det \sigma| = 1.$$

The assertion now follows from the relation (13.3):
Volume par. $(a_1, \cdots a_n)$ = Volume par.$(\sigma b_1, \cdots \sigma b_n)$ =
= $|\det \sigma|$ Volume par.$(b_1, \cdots b_n)$ = Volume par.$(b_1, \cdots b_n)$.

Theorem* [14.6]: *A quadratic function* $\varphi^{\cdot} = \sum_{i,j=1}^{n} \alpha_{ij}\zeta_i\zeta_j$ *on an n-dimensional vector space with cobasis* $\zeta_1, \cdots \zeta_n$ *is singular if and only if the determinant of the matrix with scalars* $\alpha_{ij} \in \mathbf{F}$ *satisfies*

$$\det\{\alpha_{ij}\} = 0.$$

Proof: If $c_1, \cdots c_n$ is the basis of V dual to $\zeta_1, \cdots \zeta_n$, then the right-hand side of (14.8) assumes for $x_i = y_i = c_i$ the value $\det\{\alpha_{ij}\}$. (14.8) and (14.9) hold for any field $\mathbf{F}$ (with characteristic $\neq 2$), any basis $a_1, \cdots a_n$ and corresponding functions $\Delta$. If $a_1, \cdots a_n$ is taken to be the basis dual to $\xi_1, \cdots \xi_n$ in theorem [14.3], then substitution of $a_1, \cdots a_n$ in (14.9) yields $\lambda = \lambda_1, \cdots \lambda_n$ with $\lambda_j = 0$ for $j > r$. Hence the theorem.

Theorem [14.7]: *Let $\varphi^{\cdot}$ be a positive-definite quadratic function on the real n-dimensional vector space* V, *let $\eta$ be a linear function, let* $a_1, \cdots a_n$ *and* $b_1, \cdots b_n$ *be as in theorem* [14.5]. *Then*

$$\textstyle\sum_{i=1}^{n} \eta^2(a_i) = \sum_{i=1}^{n} \eta^2(b_i)$$

*so that the value of this expression is apparently independent of the special choice of the basis of polar vectors of* V.

Proof: The linear functions $\xi_i$: $x \to \varphi(a_i, x)$, $i = 1, \cdots n$ form the cobasis of $a_1, \cdots a_n$. $\eta$ is a uniquely determined linear combination of them. Hence

$$\begin{aligned} \eta(x) &= \textstyle\sum_i \alpha_i \varphi(a_i, x) & \alpha_i \in \mathbf{R} \\ &= \varphi(\textstyle\sum_i \alpha_i a_i, x) = \varphi(c, x) & c = \textstyle\sum \alpha_i a_i. \end{aligned}$$

The vector c is independent of the choice of the basis $a_1, \cdots a_n$. Then from $\eta(a_i) = \varphi(c, a_i) = \varphi(\sum_i \alpha_j a_j, a_i) = \sum_i \alpha_j \delta_{ji} = \alpha_i$, we have

$$\textstyle\sum_i \eta^2(a_i) = \sum_i \varphi^2(c, a_i) = \sum_i \alpha_i^2 = \varphi(\sum_i \alpha_i a_i, \sum_j \alpha_j a_j) = \varphi(c, c)$$

and this is, therefore, independent of the special choice of $a_1, \cdots a_n$.

Problem (14.3). If $\varphi^{\cdot}$ is a positive-definite quadratic function on the real vector space V, if $a_1, \cdots a_n$, $b_1, \cdots b_n$ are as above, and if $\psi^{\cdot}$ is a quadratic function on V, then

$$\textstyle\sum_{i=1}^{n} \psi^{\cdot}(a_i) = \sum_{i=1}^{n} \psi^{\cdot}(b_i).$$

Theorem [14.8]: *In the kernel of the real quadratic function on a real n-dimensional vector space* $\varphi^{\cdot} = \xi_1 + \cdots + \xi_p^2 - \xi_{p+1}^2 - \cdots - \xi_{p+q}^2$, *with* $q \leqslant p$, *there are linear subspaces of dimension* $n - p$ *and none of higher dimension.*

Proof: An example of an $(n - p)$-dimensional subspace on $\varphi^{\cdot} = 0$ is that associated with the $p$ linear equations

$$\begin{aligned} \xi_{p+i} - \xi_i &= 0 & i &= 1, \cdots q \\ \xi_j &= 0 & j &= q + 1, \cdots p. \end{aligned}$$

The $p$-dimensional subspace with equations $\xi_i = 0$ for $i > p$ is intersected by an arbitrary $(n - p + 1)$-dimensional subspace in a subspace of dimension at least $(n - p + 1) + p - n = 1$ (cf.

theorem [5.5]). Because of the given form of $\varphi^{\cdot}$, however, we have $\varphi^{\cdot}(x) > 0$ for any non-zero vector such that $\xi_i(x) = 0$ for all $i > p$. But then this $(n - p + 1)$-dimensional subspace (and hence any other one) contains vectors which are not in the kernel of $\varphi^{\cdot}$.

As an example we mention the function $\varphi^{\cdot} = \xi_1^2 + \xi_2^2 - \xi_3^2 - \xi_4^2$. In its kernel there are two systems of two-dimensional subspaces with parameter $\lambda$:

viz. I $(\xi_1 - \xi_3) = \lambda(\xi_2 - \xi_4),\ \lambda(\xi_1 + \xi_3) = -(\xi_2 + \xi_4),$

and II $(\xi_1 - \xi_4) = \lambda(\xi_2 - \xi_3),\ \lambda(\xi_1 + \xi_4) = -(\xi_2 + \xi_3).$

### $A_H$. *Hermitian functions* [1])

The symmetric bilinear functions studied in part A of this chapter are defined for vector spaces over any field **F**. However, in case **F** = **C**, an analogous notion, the hermitian function, plays a more important role in mathematics. Some theorems concerning symmetric bilinear functions over **R**, like for example the law of inertia, have their analogues with the hermitian functions on vector spaces over **C**.

Let V be a vector space over **C**. A function of two variables $\varphi$: V × V → **C** is called *sesquilinear* in case:
(a) For any $x \in V$, the function $y \to \varphi(x, y)$ is linear

$$\varphi(x, y_1 + y_2) = \varphi(x, y_1) + \varphi(x, y_2)$$
$$\varphi(x, \lambda y) = \lambda\varphi(x, y)$$

for any $y_1\ y_2 \in V$, $\lambda \in \mathbf{C}$; *and*
(b). For any $y \in V$, the function $x \to \varphi(x, y)$ is *anti-linear*, that is

$$\varphi(x_1 + x_2, y) = \varphi(x_1, y) + \varphi(x_2, y)$$
$$\varphi(\lambda x, y) = \bar{\lambda}\varphi(x, y)$$

for any $x_1 \in V$, $x_2 \in V$, $\lambda \in \mathbf{C}$;
$\bar{\lambda}$ is the complex conjugate of $\lambda$.

A function $\varphi$: V × V → **C** is called ***hermitian*** in case $\varphi$ is *ses-*

[1]) Also called Hermitian forms.

*quilinear and moreover*

$$\varphi(x, y) = \overline{\varphi(y, x)} \text{ for any } x \in V,\ y \in V.$$

This last condition concerning sesquilinear functions is *the analogue of symmetry* for bilinear functions.

It is immediate from the definition that the *diagonal* of a hermitian function assumes real values only: $\varphi^{\cdot}(x) = \varphi(x, x) = \overline{\varphi(x, x)}$ [1]).

Some theorems concerning hermitian functions are proved in the same way as the analogous theorems concerning symmetric bilinear functions. For example:

Theorem [14.1 H]: *If the hermitian functions* $\varphi$ *and* $\psi$: $V \times V \to C$ *have the same diagonal then they are identical.*

Proof: Consider $\chi = \varphi - \psi$. Let $\chi(x, x)$ be zero for all $x \in V$. Then $0 = \chi(x + y, x + y) - \chi(x, x) - \chi(y, y) = \chi(x, y) + \chi(y, x)$ $= \chi(x, y) + \bar{\chi}(x, y) =$ twice the real part of $\chi(x, y)$. The real part of the linear function $y \to \chi(x, y)$ is zero, hence this linear function is zero and $\chi(x, y) = 0$ for any $x \in V$, $y \in V$. q.e.d.

The analogue of a part of theorem [14.2] is

Theorem [14.2 H]: *If* $(\xi_1, \cdots \xi_n)$ *is a cobasis of a vectorspace* $V^n$ *over* $C$, $\varphi$: $V \times V \to C$ *is sesquilinear, and* $\bar{\xi}_i$ *is the complex conjugate of* $\xi_i$, *then there exist constants* $\alpha_{ij} \in C$ *for* $i, j = 1, \cdots n$, *such that*

$$\varphi(x, y) = \textstyle\sum_{i,j=1}^{n} \alpha_{ij}\bar{\xi}_i(x)\xi_j(y) \text{ for } x \in V,\ y \in V.$$

*The diagonal of* $\varphi$ *is* $\varphi^{\cdot} = \sum_{i,j=1}^{n} \alpha_{ij}\bar{\xi}_i\xi_j$.

$\varphi$ *is hermitian if and only if* $\alpha_{ij} = \bar{\alpha}_{ji}$ *for* $i, j = 1, \cdots n$.

Proof: For the first part we refer to the proof of theorem [14.2]. $\varphi$ is hermitian if and only if for all $x \in V$, $y \in V$,

$$0 = \varphi(x, y) - \overline{\varphi(y, x)} = \sum \alpha_{ij}\bar{\xi}_i(x)\xi_j(y) - \overline{\sum \alpha_{ij}\bar{\xi}_i(y)\xi_j(x)} =$$
$$= \sum (\alpha_{ij} - \bar{\alpha}_{ji})\bar{\xi}_i(x)\xi_j(y).$$

In particular with the vectors $x = a_i$, $y = a_j$, of the cobasis of

---

[1]) Some authors also call hermitian the diagonal $\varphi^{\cdot}$ of a hermitian function $\varphi$.

$\xi_1, \cdots \xi_n$, we obtain the necessity of $\alpha_{ij} = \bar{\alpha}_{ji}$. The sufficiency of this condition for all $i, j = 1, \cdots n$, is clear.

Main theorem on hermitian functions [14.3 H]: *If $\varphi$ is a hermitian function $\varphi$: $V \times V \to \mathbf{C}$, then there exists a cobasis $\xi_1, \cdots \xi_n$ of* V, *such that*

$$\varphi(x, y) = \Sigma_{i=1}^{p} \bar{\xi}_i(x)\xi_i(y) - \Sigma_{i=p+1}^{p+q} \bar{\xi}_i(x)\xi_i(y) \text{ for all } x \in V,\ y \in V.$$

*The diagonal of $\varphi$ is*

$$\varphi^{\cdot} = \Sigma_{i=1}^{p} \bar{\xi}_i\xi_i - \Sigma_{i=p+1}^{p+q} \bar{\xi}_i\xi_i.$$

*The numbers $p$, $q$ and $p + q = r$ are independent of the choice of the coordinates. $q$ is called the index of inertia of $\varphi$. The last statement is the law of inertia for hermitian functions.*

Proof: This we leave to the reader as it is almost literally the same as the proof of [14.3] and [14.3′]. While rewriting this proof for hermitian functions we only have to observe that in (14.7) $\lambda_j \in \mathbf{R} \subset \mathbf{C}$.

The hermitian function $\varphi$ is called *positive* in case $\varphi(x, x) = \varphi^{\cdot}(x) \leqslant 0$ implies $x = O$. Applying the main theorem we then obtain $p = r = n$, $q = 0$,

$$\varphi(x, y) = \Sigma_{i=1}^{n} \bar{\xi}_i(x)\xi_i(y)$$

and

$$\varphi^{\cdot}(x) = \Sigma_{i=1}^{n} \bar{\xi}_i\xi_i.$$

B. *Functions on a real affine space*

A second-degree or quadratic function on an affine $n$-dimensional space has the form

$$(\varphi^{\cdot} + \eta + \alpha) \circ \kappa.$$

Here $\kappa$: $A \to V$ is an $\mathscr{A}$-map of $A$ onto the $n$-dimensional vector space V. $\varphi^{\cdot}$, $\eta$ and $\alpha$ are (homogeneous) functions on V of degree 2, 1 and 0 respectively, so that $\alpha$ is a constant. $\circ$ is meant as symbol for the composition of the two mappings $\kappa$ and $\varphi^{\cdot} + \eta + \alpha$.

$\varphi^{\cdot} + \eta + \alpha$ is a function on V, the expression for the function on $A$ under the $\mathscr{A}$-map $\kappa$. We restrict ourselves to the *real number field* **R**. By the main theorem, there then exist linear functions

$$\xi_1, \cdots \xi_r,\ r = p + q, \text{ on V such that}$$

$$\varphi^{\cdot} = \xi_1{}^2 + \cdots + \xi_p{}^2 - \xi_{p+1}{}^2 - \cdots - \xi_r{}^2.$$

*The most important case* is that where $\eta$ is *linearly dependent* on $\xi_1, \cdots \xi_r$, which is always so if $\varphi^{\cdot}$ is non-singular:

$$\eta = 2\alpha_1\xi_1 + \cdots + 2\alpha_r\xi_r.$$

In this case

$$\varphi^{\cdot} + \eta + \alpha = \Sigma_{i=1}^{p} (\xi_i + \alpha_i)^2 - \Sigma_{j=p+1}^{r} (\xi_j - \alpha_j)^2 + \alpha'$$

$$\alpha' = \alpha - \Sigma_{i=1}^{p} \alpha_i^2 + \Sigma_{j=p+1}^{r} \alpha_j^2.$$

Now let d be a vector such that $\xi_i(\mathrm{d}) + \alpha_i = 0$, $i = 1, \cdots r$. Replace the $\mathscr{A}$-map $\kappa$ by another, $\kappa'$, which maps the point to which d is associated by $\kappa$, into $0 \in \mathrm{V}$:

$$\kappa'\kappa^{-1}(\mathrm{x}) = \mathrm{x} - \mathrm{d} \quad \text{for } \mathrm{x} \in \mathrm{V}. \tag{14.11}$$

In other words, we choose the linear functions $(\xi_i + \alpha_i)\circ\kappa$ as new coordinates on $A$:

$$\xi_i\circ\kappa' = (\xi_i + \alpha_i)\circ\kappa.$$

With the new $\mathscr{A}$-map $\kappa'$ the quadratic function gets the following simple form on V (*normal form*):

$$\xi_1{}^2 + \cdots + \xi_p{}^2 - \xi_{p+1}{}^2 - \cdots - \xi_r{}^2 + \alpha'. \tag{14.12}$$

A point of the affine space, represented by the vector m, is called *a centre* with respect to the quadratic function $f$ if for every vector v the relation

$$f(\mathrm{m} + \mathrm{v}) - f(\mathrm{m} - \mathrm{v}) = 0 \tag{14.13}$$

is satisfied.

If $\mu_1, \cdots \mu_n$ and $\nu_1, \cdots \nu_n$ are the coordinates of m and v, then substitution in (14.2) shows that the set of all centres is given by

$$\xi_i = 0 \quad i = 1, \cdots r.$$

It follows that the constant $\alpha'$ is the constant value of the given function on this set of centres, and $\alpha'$ is therefore uniquely determined by the function on $A$. If $r = n$ there is exactly one centre.

In applications the centre(s) can be *determined* as follows. Let $f$ be a second-degree function whose expression in the coordinates $\xi_1, \cdots \xi_n$ of the vector space V is:

$$f = \sum_{i,j=1}^{n} \beta_{ij}\xi_i\xi_j + \sum_{i=1}^{n} \beta_i\xi_i + \beta \qquad \beta_{ij} = \beta_{ji}.$$

If m and v are vectors, then

$$f(\mathrm{m}+\mathrm{v}) = \sum_{i,j} \beta_{ij}\xi_i(\mathrm{m})\xi_j(\mathrm{m}) + 2\sum_{i,j} \beta_{ij}\xi_i(\mathrm{m})\xi_j(\mathrm{v}) + \sum_{i,j}\beta_{ij}\xi_i(\mathrm{v})\xi_j(\mathrm{v})$$
$$+ \sum_i \beta_i\xi_i(\mathrm{m}) + \sum_j \beta_j\xi_j(\mathrm{v}) + \beta.$$

Since $\xi_i(-\mathrm{v}) = -\xi_i(\mathrm{v})$, it follows that

$$f(\mathrm{m}+\mathrm{v}) - f(\mathrm{m}-\mathrm{v}) = 2\sum_{j=1}^{n} \xi_j(\mathrm{v})\{\sum_{i=1}^{n} 2\beta_{ij}\xi_i(\mathrm{m}) + \beta_j\} =$$
$$= 2\sum_{j=1}^{n} \xi_j(\mathrm{v})\cdot\left(\frac{\partial f}{\partial \xi_j}\right)_{\mathrm{m}}. \qquad (14.14)$$

Here $\dfrac{\partial f}{\partial \xi_j}$ is defined by the usual formulae for the derivative of a polynomial, and subsequently the value is calculated for $\xi_i = \xi_i(\mathrm{m})$, $i = 1, \cdots n$. From (14.14) we see that m is a centre if and only if

$$\left(\frac{\partial f}{\partial \xi_j}\right)_{\mathrm{m}} = 0 \text{ for } j = 1, \cdots n, \qquad (14.15)$$

since the left-hand member must be zero for *all* v.

The centre is then found from the equations (14.15).

*We now consider the case that $\eta$ is linearly independent of $\xi_1, \cdots \xi_r$.* Let d be a vector such that $\xi_i(\mathrm{d}) = 0$, $i = 1, \cdots r$, and $\eta(\mathrm{d})+\alpha=0$.

Using the new $\mathscr{A}$-map $\kappa'$ defined by (14.11) we find the simple form (*normal form*)

$$\xi_1^2 + \cdots + \xi_p^2 - \xi_{p+1}^2 - \cdots - \xi_r^2 + \xi_{r+1} \qquad (14.16)$$

for the function on V, where $\xi_{r+1}$ is written instead of $\eta$. This yields

Theorem [14.9]: *For any quadratic function on a real affine n-space there exists a set of linear functions $\xi_1, \cdots \xi_n$ such that the given quadratic function is expressed by one of the normal forms given in* (14.12) *and* (14.16).

The level sets of (14.12) have already been discussed in the first part of this chapter. The varieties in $A$ which are mapped onto these level sets by an $\mathscr{A}$-map $\kappa'$ have the same names, such as ellipsoid, hyperboloid etc. The point mapped to the vector O is called the *centre* of the variety, for this point is the midpoint of any chord passing through it. A chord through a centre is called *diameter*.

The varieties in $A$ which are mapped onto a level set of (14.16) by an $\mathscr{A}$-map $\kappa'$ are called *parabolic*.

Example (cf. fig. 14.6)

| | | |
|---|---|---|
| $n = 2$ | $\xi_1^2 + \xi_2 = 0$ | *parabola* |
| $n = 3$ | $\xi_1^2 + \xi_2^2 + \xi_3 = 0$ | *elliptic paraboloid* |
| | $\xi_1^2 - \xi_2^2 + \xi_3 = 0$ | *hyperbolic paraboloid* |
| | $\xi_1^2 - \xi_2 = 0$ | *parabolic cylinder.* |

If $f$ is a quadratic function then the set of all points satisfying the equation $f = 0$ is called a *quadratic variety*. Let $Q$ be a real quadratic variety, belonging to a quadratic function $f$. We want to know all other quadratic functions that determine the same quadratic variety $Q$. In the first place the functions $\lambda f$ with $\lambda \neq 0$ have this property. A special, exceptional case which we mention first, is a variety having the equation

$$f = \xi_1^2 + \cdots + \xi_r^2 = 0 \qquad r \geqslant 2.$$

This is the linear $(n - r)$-variety with equations $\xi_1 = \xi_2 = \cdots \xi_r = 0$, which is also represented by any equation

$$\alpha_1^2\xi_1^2 + \cdots + \alpha_r^2\xi_r^2 = 0 \quad \alpha_i > 0 \quad i = 1, \cdots r.$$

We now prove the following theorem:

Theorem [14.10]: *If in a real affine n-space $Q$ is a quadratic variety, (not a linear $(n - r)$-variety with $r \geqslant 2$, nor the empty set), and $f$ and $g$ are quadratic functions having $Q$ as kernel, $f^{-1}(0) = g^{-1}(0) = Q$, then there exists a real number $\lambda$ such that $g = \lambda f$.*

Proof: Choose coordinates such that $f$ has the normal form (14.12) or (14.16). Let $g$ be equal to

$$\textstyle\sum_{i,j=1}^{n} \beta_{ij}\xi_i\xi_j + \sum_{i=1}^{n} \beta_i\xi_i + \beta, \qquad \beta_{ij} = \beta_{ji}.$$

We only deal with the case (14.12) and:

$$f = \xi_1^2 + \cdots + \xi_p^2 - \xi_{p+1}^2 - \cdots - \xi_r^2 + \alpha, \quad \alpha = -\gamma^2 < 0, p > 0.$$

Then we see from the expression for $f$ that the point with coordinates $(\xi_1, \cdots \xi_n) = (0, \cdots 0)$ is not on $Q$, hence $\beta \neq 0$. The real number $\lambda$ can now be defined by $\beta = \lambda\alpha = -\lambda\gamma^2$.

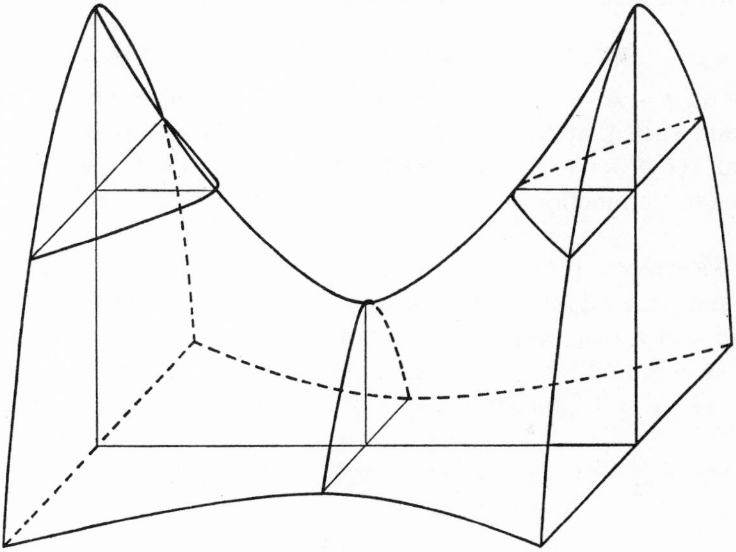

hyperbolic paraboloid

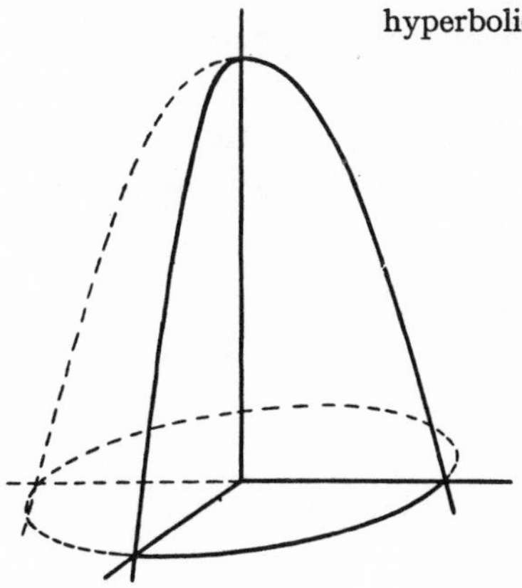

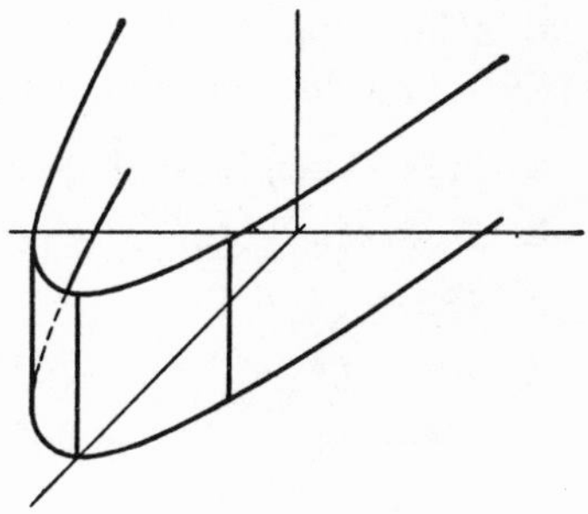

elliptic paraboloid Fig. 14.6 parabolic cylinder

If the point $(\xi_1, \cdots \xi_n) \neq (0, \cdots 0)$ lies on $f = 0$, then so does the point $(-\xi_1, \cdots - \xi_n)$. Both points, and the point $(0, \cdots 0)$ too, also lie on $g - \lambda f = 0$. The line with parameter $\mu$, $(\mu\xi_1, \cdots \mu\xi_n)$ will then intersect $g - \lambda f = 0$ in three distinct points which may be obtained from solutions of a quadratic equation in $\mu$. This equation is then identically satisfied.

Hence, if $(\xi_1, \cdots \xi_n)$ lies on $f = 0$, then all points $(\mu\xi_1, \cdots \mu\xi_n)$, with variable $\mu$, lie on $g - \lambda f = 0$. It follows that all points for which

$$\xi_1^2 + \cdots + \xi_p^2 - \xi_{p+1}^2 - \cdots - \xi_r^2 > 0 \qquad (14.17)$$

lie on $g - \lambda f = 0$, since there corresponds a number $\nu$ to any such point such that $(\nu\xi_1, \cdots \nu\xi_n)$ lies on $f = 0$. All points of the solid ball $(\xi_1 - 3)^2 + \sum_{i=2}^{n} \xi_i^2 \leqslant 1$ belong to the set (14.17), whence the quadratic function $g - \lambda f$ is identically zero and $g = \lambda f$.

PROBLEMS. (14.4). If $\alpha$ is an $n \times n$-matrix of elements of **F**, x and y are columns of $n$ elements of **F**, ${}^t$x and ${}^t$y are the transposed of x and y, then ${}^t$x$\alpha$y is a bilinear function on $\mathbf{F}^n$ which is symmetric if ${}^t\alpha = \alpha$, and ${}^t$x$\alpha$x is a quadratic function on $\mathbf{F}^n$.

(14.5). If in problem (14.4) x is a column of three real numbers, and

$$\alpha = \begin{bmatrix} 2 & 10 & -2 \\ 10 & 11 & -14 \\ -2 & -14 & -1 \end{bmatrix},$$

determine the normal form of the quadratic function ${}^t$x$\alpha$x as in main theorem [14.3′].

(14.6). Find for each of the following quadratic functions on real affine spaces the corresponding normal form (cf. theorem [14.9]), and discuss the level sets.

a. $11\xi^2 - 6\xi\eta + 19\eta^2 + 6\xi - 38\eta + 15$

b. $\xi^2 + 4\xi\eta + 4\eta^2 - 6\xi - 12\eta + 10$

c. $4\xi\eta + \zeta^2 - 1$

d. $4\xi\eta - \zeta^2 - 1$

e. $2\xi^2 + 8\xi\eta + 8\xi\zeta + 8\eta^2 + 8\eta\zeta - 8\xi + 17\eta - 17\zeta + 4$.

(14.7). The intersection of a plane and a cone in the real three-dimensional space is a conic. Any kind of conic can be so obtained, except a pair of parallel lines.

(14.8)*. There exist two systems of lines on the hyperboloid of one sheet. (Cf. theorem [14.8]).

(14.9)*. There are two systems of lines on the hyperbolic paraboloid.

# 15. EUCLIDEAN SPACE

A *real* vector space with a fixed positive definite quadratic function $\varphi^{\cdot}$ is called a *euclidean vector space* E. As coordinates for a euclidean vector space we always choose linear functions $\xi_1, \cdots \xi_n$ (*euclidean coordinates*) such that

$$\varphi^{\cdot} = \xi_1^2 + \cdots + \xi_n^2.$$

By main theorem [14.3] this is possible and the construction given there can be done in many different ways. The bilinear symmetric function $\varphi$ of which $\varphi^{\cdot}$ is the diagonal, is called the *inner product* in the euclidean vector space. The inner product of the vectors x and y is usually written as

$$\mathrm{xy} \text{ or } (\mathrm{x}, \mathrm{y}) \tag{15.1}$$

and then $\varphi^{\cdot}(\mathrm{x}) = \mathrm{xx} = \mathrm{x}^2$.

The most important properties of the inner product are *symmetry* and *bilinearity*. These properties entail a number of the usual algebraic rules for the inner product. By the *length* or *norm* $\|\mathrm{x}\|$ of x we mean $\sqrt{\mathrm{xx}} = \sqrt{\mathrm{x}^2}$, that is, the non-negative number whose square is $\mathrm{x}^2$ (thus $\sqrt{\mathrm{x}^2}$ is quite distinct from x). In euclidean coordinates

$$\mathrm{x}^2 = \xi_1^2(\mathrm{x}) + \cdots + \xi_n^2(\mathrm{x})$$

$$\mathrm{xy} = \xi_1(\mathrm{x})\xi_1(\mathrm{y}) + \cdots + \xi_n(\mathrm{x})\xi_n(\mathrm{y}). \tag{15.2}$$

The inner product in the euclidean vector space is the inner product in the sense of chapter 9, with respect to any basis which is cobasis of a set of euclidean coordinates $\xi_1, \cdots \xi_n$. For, in such a case, for any two vectors x and y

$$\mathrm{x} = \textstyle\sum_{i=1}^n \xi_i(\mathrm{x})\mathrm{a}_i; \quad \mathrm{y} = \sum_{i=1}^n \xi_i(\mathrm{y})\mathrm{a}_i,$$

we have

$$^t\mathrm{x} = \textstyle\sum_{i=1}^{n} \xi_i(\mathrm{x})\xi_i,$$

and this linear function assumes the value

$$^t\mathrm{xy} = \textstyle\sum_{i=1}^{n} \xi_i(\mathrm{x})\xi_i(\mathrm{y})$$

on y. This is just the inner product according to (15.2). If the coordinates of x and y are $\xi_i(\mathrm{x}) = \alpha_i$ and $\xi_i(\mathrm{y}) = \beta_i$, then

$$\mathrm{xy} = \textstyle\sum_{i=1}^{n} \alpha_i\beta_i.$$

In the ordinary plane $\xi_1$ for example is a linear function whose absolute value is the ordinary distance from a vertical line and similarly $\xi_2$ is the distance from a horizontal line. Then $\|\mathrm{x}\|^2 = \xi_1^2(\mathrm{x}) + \xi_2^2(\mathrm{x})$, which is known from plane geometry.

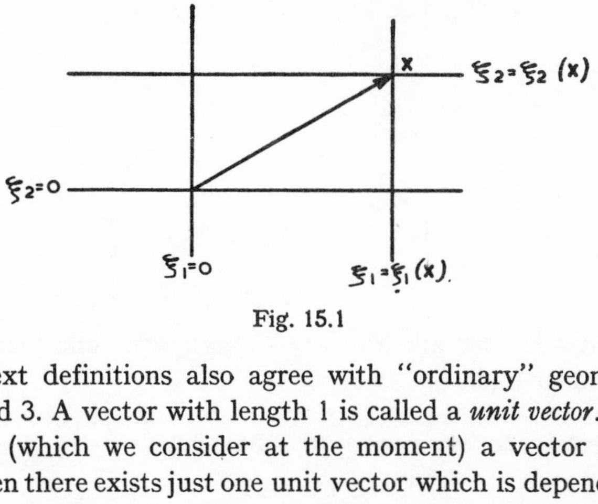


Fig. 15.1

Our next definitions also agree with "ordinary" geometry for $n = 2$ and 3. A vector with length 1 is called a *unit vector*. If in the real case (which we consider at the moment) a vector $\mathrm{x} \neq \mathrm{O}$ is given, then there exists just one unit vector which is dependent on x and has a positive ratio with x. It is $\lambda\mathrm{x}$, with $\lambda > 0$, for which

$$(\lambda\mathrm{x})(\lambda\mathrm{x}) = \lambda^2\mathrm{xx} = \lambda^2\mathrm{x}^2 = 1,\ \lambda = \|\mathrm{x}\|^{-1}.$$

Hence the desired unit vector is $\dfrac{\mathrm{x}}{\|\mathrm{x}\|}$.

Two vectors x and y are said to be *perpendicular* if they are polar with respect to the inner product: $\mathrm{xy} = 0$. Similarly two subspaces B and C are called (totally) perpendicular if they are polar with respect to the inner product.

Theorem [15.1]: *If each of the vectors of a basis of* B *is perpendicular to the vectors of a basis of* C, *then* B *is perpendicular to* C, *i.e. any vector of* B *is perpendicular to any vector of* C.

In the case that B and C are of dimension 1 and 2, this is a well-known theorem in solid geometry.

Proof: Let $b_1, \cdots b_p$ be a basis of B ,let $c_1, \cdots c_q$ be a basis of C and let $b_i c_j = 0$ for $i = 1, \cdots p$, $j = 1, \cdots q$. Then for arbitrary vectors

$$b = \sum_{i=1}^{p} \beta_i b_i \text{ and } c = \sum_{j=1}^{q} \gamma_j c_j ,$$

$$bc = \sum_{i=1,j=1}^{p\ \ q} \beta_i \gamma_j b_i c_j = 0.$$

As an application we mention Pythagoras's theorem in the following form: *The relation* $(x - y)^2 = x^2 + y^2$ *holds if and only if the vectors* x *and* y *are perpendicular, i.e.* $xy = 0$. For,

$$(x - y)^2 - x^2 - y^2 = - 2xy = 0.$$

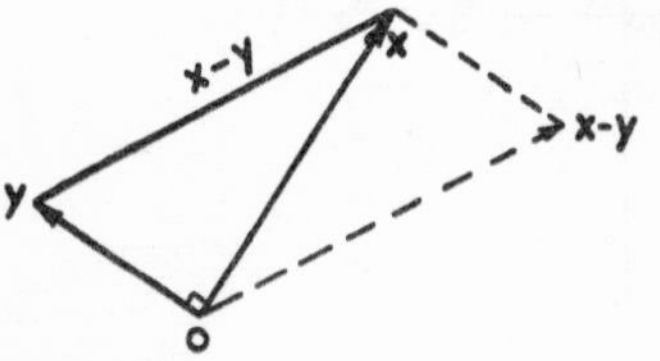


Fig. 15.2

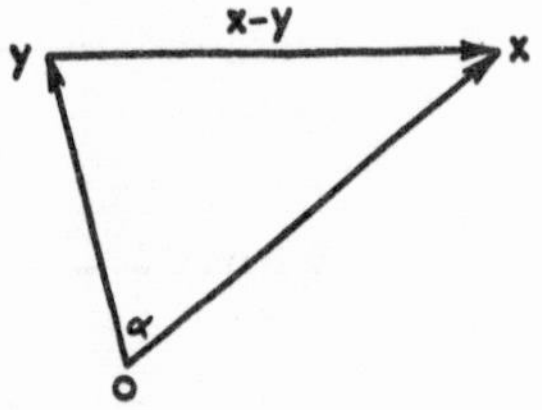


Fig. 15.3

More generally, for an arbitrary triangle with one vertex at O we have similarly (cf. fig. 15.3):

$$(x-y)^2 = x^2 + y^2 - 2xy = x^2 + y^2 - 2\,\|x\|\,\|y\| \cdot \left(\frac{x}{\|x\|}\right)\left(\frac{y}{\|y\|}\right). \quad (15.3)$$

The vectors $\dfrac{x}{\|x\|}$ and $\dfrac{y}{\|y\|}$ are unit vectors. In view of the cosine rule in trigonometry we can now give a suitable *definition* of the "cosine of the angle $\alpha$ between the vectors x and y, both $\neq$ O":

$$\cos \alpha = \frac{x}{\|x\|} \frac{y}{\|y\|} = \frac{xy}{\|x\| \cdot \|y\|}.$$

As we shall show in a lemma, the right-hand side is a number of absolute value $\leqslant 1$.

With this definition, the *cosine rule* takes the form:

$$(\mathrm{x} - \mathrm{y})^2 = \mathrm{x}^2 + \mathrm{y}^2 - 2\,\|\mathrm{x}\|\cdot\|\mathrm{y}\| \cos \alpha. \tag{15.3}$$

A *metric* in a point set $W$ is a non-negative function $d$, called *distance*, on the set $W \times W$ of pairs of points, with the following properties:

(a) $d(P, P) = 0$ for $P \in W$

(b) $d(P, Q) = d(Q, P) > 0$ for $P \neq Q$ both in $W$

(c) $d(P, R) \leqslant d(P, Q) + d(Q, R)$ for $P, Q, R \in W$.

The last property is called the *triangle inequality*.

*We now introduce a euclidean metric in a real affine n-space.* Let $\kappa\colon A \to \mathrm{V}$ be an $\mathscr{A}$-map of $A$. Let $\mathrm{V} = \mathrm{E}$ be a euclidean vector space. To the pair $(P, Q) \in (A \times A)$ we associate the non-negative number

$$\|\kappa(Q) - \kappa(P)\|.$$

The affine $n$-space with this metric is called the *euclidean n-space E*. If $\mathrm{x} = \kappa(P)$ and $\mathrm{y} = \kappa(Q)$ represent $P$ and $Q$ under $\kappa$, then their distance is

$$d(\mathrm{x}, \mathrm{y}) = \|\mathrm{y} - \mathrm{x}\| = \sqrt{(\mathrm{y} - \mathrm{x})^2}. \tag{15.4}$$

First observe that properties (a) and (b) hold. It remains to prove (c). Choose the $\mathscr{A}$-map $\kappa$ such that the point $Q$ is mapped to O, $P$ to x and $R$ to y. Then the assertion reads

$$\|\mathrm{y} - \mathrm{x}\| \leqslant \|\mathrm{x}\| + \|\mathrm{y}\| \text{ i.e. } \sqrt{(\mathrm{y} - \mathrm{x})^2} \leqslant \sqrt{\mathrm{x}^2} + \sqrt{\mathrm{y}^2}$$

or, equivalently,

$$(\mathrm{y} - \mathrm{x})^2 \leqslant \mathrm{x}^2 + \mathrm{y}^2 + 2\sqrt{\mathrm{x}^2\mathrm{y}^2}$$

$$\mathrm{y}^2 - 2\mathrm{xy} + \mathrm{y}^2 \leqslant \mathrm{x}^2 + \mathrm{y}^2 + 2\sqrt{\mathrm{x}^2\mathrm{y}^2}$$

$$-\mathrm{xy} \leqslant \sqrt{\mathrm{x}^2\mathrm{y}^2}.$$

If $-\mathrm{xy} \leqslant 0$ then the relation holds, since the right-hand side is non-negative. If $-\mathrm{xy} > 0$ then the inequality is equivalent to the lemma:

Lemma: $(\mathrm{xy})^2 \leqslant \mathrm{x}^2\mathrm{y}^2$ for $\mathrm{x}, \mathrm{y} \in \mathrm{E}$.

Proof: Since $z^2 \geqslant 0$ for any $z \in E$, we have for any real $\lambda$:

$$(x + \lambda y)^2 \geqslant 0$$

so that

$$x^2 + 2\lambda xy + \lambda^2 y^2 \geqslant 0.$$

The left-hand side is a quadratic function of $\lambda$ with real numbers as coefficients. This can be $\geqslant 0$ for all real numbers $\lambda$ only if

$$\text{discriminant} = 4(xy)^2 - 4x^2y^2 \leqslant 0.$$

The assertion follows from this. In the triangle inequality there can be equality if and only if $x = y = 0$, or if for some real $\lambda$: $x + \lambda y = 0$ and $-xy > 0$. Then $-xy = \lambda y^2 > 0$, hence $\lambda > 0$, i.e. $P, Q, R$, represented by x, O, y lie on a line in the order "$Q$ lies between $P$ and $R$".

Summarizing:

Theorem [15.2]: *In a euclidean space E, the triangle inequality*

$$d(P, R) \leqslant d(P, Q) + d(Q, R) \qquad \textit{for } P, Q, R \in E$$

*holds. The equality sign holds if and only if P, Q, R are collinear and Q lies on the line segment PR.*

The linear functions $\xi_1, \cdots \xi_n$ on an affine euclidean $n$-space $E$ are called *euclidean coordinates* if the distance $d(P, Q)$ for $P, Q \in E$ is given by the expression

$$d^2(P, Q) = \sum_{i=1}^{n} \{\xi_i(Q) - \xi_i(P)\}^2.$$

If $\xi_i(P) = \xi_i(Q)$ for $i = 1, \cdots n$ then $P = Q$. The mapping

$$P \to \{\xi_1(P), \cdots \xi_n(P)\} \tag{15.5}$$

is then a one-to-one mapping of $E$ into the set of sequences of $n$ numbers. By introducing an inner product associating with $(\alpha_1, \cdots \alpha_n)$ and $(\beta_1, \cdots \beta_n)$ the number $\sum_{i=1}^{n} \alpha_i\beta_i$, we obtain a euclidean vector space E. The functions $\xi_1, \cdots \xi_n$ define an $\mathscr{A}$-map $\kappa$ as in (15.5) under which

$$d(P, Q) = \|\kappa(Q) - \kappa(P)\|.$$

This $\mathscr{A}$-map is then called a *euclidean $\mathscr{A}$-map* in the euclidean vecto space E. Without mentioning this all the time, we shall always use euclidean $\mathscr{A}$-maps when dealing with euclidean spaces.

Two intersecting linear varieties $W_1$ and $W_2$ in $E$ are called (totally) perpendicular if there exists an $\mathscr{A}$-map which maps them onto perpendicular subspaces $\kappa(W_1)$ and $\kappa(W_2)$ of E. Two linear varieties are called (totally) perpendicular if they are parallel to perpendicular intersecting linear varieties.

Problem (15.1). If $W_1$ and $W_2$ are perpendicular linear varieties then any line in $W_1$ is perpendicular to any line in $W_2$.

If $W$ is a linear variety in $E$, if x is a point not in $W$, and if $x_W \in W$ is such that the line through x and $x_W$ intersects $W$ perpendicularly, then this line is called a *perpendicular* from x to $W$, and $x_W$ is called its *pedal point* or *foot*.

Theorem [15.3]: *Through a point outside a linear variety W in a euclidean space E there exists exactly one perpendicular to W.*

Proof: Cf. fig. 15.4.

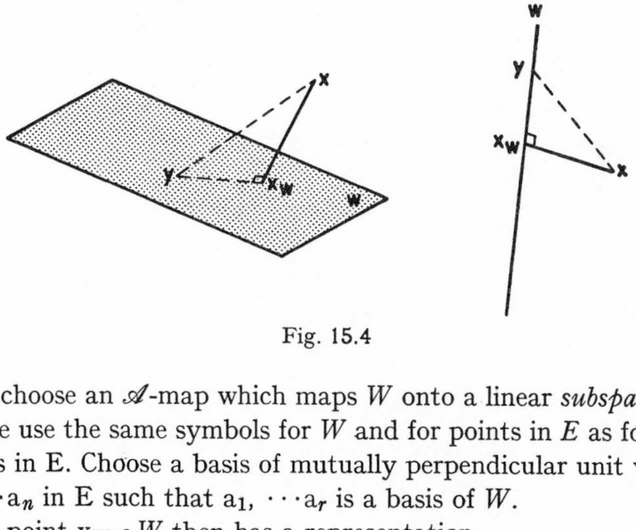


Fig. 15.4

We choose an $\mathscr{A}$-map which maps $W$ onto a linear *subspace* of E and we use the same symbols for $W$ and for points in $E$ as for their images in E. Choose a basis of mutually perpendicular unit vectors $a_1, \cdots a_n$ in E such that $a_1, \cdots a_r$ is a basis of $W$.

The point $x_W \in W$ then has a representation

$$x_W = \alpha_1 a_1 + \cdots + \alpha_r a_r.$$

The vector $x - x_W$ is perpendicular to $W$, and hence perpendicular to $a_1, \cdots a_r$. Hence a necessary and sufficient condition is

$$\{x - (\alpha_1 a_1 + \cdots + \alpha_r a_r)\} a_i = 0 \qquad i = 1, \cdots r$$

or

$$xa_i - \alpha_i(a_i a_i) = xa_i - \alpha_i = 0.$$

Hence the coefficients $\alpha_i$ are uniquely determined and

$$x_W = (xa_1)a_1 + \cdots + (xa_r)a_r. \tag{15.6}$$

If $G$ is a point set in $E$, and x is a fixed point of $E$, we can consider the distances $\|x - y\|$ for all $y \in G$. If there is a smallest among these distances, this distance is called the distance from x to $G$. However, such a smallest distance does not necessarily exist. If for example a is an arbitrary vector, and $G$ is the set of points $\lambda a$, $\lambda > 1$, and $x = 0$, then there is no smallest among the distances between x and the points of $G$. Therefore we define more generally: The *distance* $d(x, G)$ from a point x to a point set $G$ is the greatest lower bound or inf. of the set of distances $\|x - y\|$, $y \in G$, i.e. the greatest number which is not greater than any of the distances $\|x - y\|$, $y \in G$. It is a property of real numbers that this greatest lower bound exists. If the distances have a minimum, then $d(x, G)$ is that minimum. Thus we may write

$$d(x, G) = \inf. \{\|x - y\|, y \in G\}.$$

Theorem [15.4]: *The distance from a point to a linear variety $W$ is its distance from the foot of its perpendicular to $W$.*

Proof: (cf. fig. 15.4). Let x be the point in question, $x_W$ the pedal point, y an arbitrary point in $W$. Because of the perpendicularity of $x - x_W$ and $x_W - y$ we have

$$(x - y)^2 = \{(x - x_W) + (x_W - y)\}^2 =$$

$$= (x - x_W)^2 + 2(x - x_W)(x_W - y) + (y - x_W)^2 = (x - x_W)^2 + (y - x_W)^2$$

and this is $> (x - x_W)^2$ in the case that $y \neq x_W$. Hence the distance from x to $W$ is $\|x - x_W\|$.

Theorem [15.5]: *The function $x \to d^2(x, W)$, where $W$ is an $r$-dimensional linear variety in the euclidean $n$-space $E$, is a quadratic* *function, which, in suitable euclidean coordinates* $\xi_1, \cdots \xi_n$ *satisfies*

$$d^2(\mathrm{x}, W) = \xi_{r+1}{}^2 + \cdots + \xi_n{}^2. \tag{15.7}$$

The level sets are called *cylinders* if $1 \leqslant r \leqslant n-2$ and *hyperspheres* (more specifically $(n-1)$-spheres) if $r = 0$. The 1-spheres are also called circles, 2-spheres are also called spheres.

The distance from a point to an $(n-1)$-dimensional linear variety $W$ is the absolute value of each of two linear functions, each called a *function of Hesse.* (If $\eta$ is a linear function with $W$ as zero-level set $\eta = 0$, then by problem (6.4) there exists a constant $\lambda$ such that $\lambda\eta$ is a function of Hesse of $W$. Then $-\lambda\eta$ is also a function of Hesse of $W$).

Proof: Choose an $\mathscr{A}$-map such that $\kappa(W)$ is a linear subspace of E. Select a basis of perpendicular unit vectors $\mathrm{a}_1, \cdots \mathrm{a}_n$ of E with $\mathrm{a}_1, \cdots \mathrm{a}_r \in \kappa W$. For $i = 1, \cdots n$ the functions $\mathrm{x} \to \mathrm{x}\mathrm{a}_i$ form the cobasis of $\mathrm{a}_1, \cdots \mathrm{a}_n$. Denote $\mathrm{x}\mathrm{a}_i$ by $\xi_i(\mathrm{x})$. Since $\mathrm{x} = \sum_{i=1}^n (\mathrm{x}\mathrm{a}_i)\mathrm{a}_i$ we find, using (15.6),

$$\begin{aligned} d^2(\mathrm{x}, W) = (\mathrm{x} - \mathrm{x}_W)^2 &= \{\textstyle\sum_{i=1}^n (\mathrm{x}\mathrm{a}_i)\mathrm{a}_i - \sum_{i=1}^r (\mathrm{x}\mathrm{a}_i)\mathrm{a}_i\}^2 \\ &= (\textstyle\sum_{i=r+1}^n \xi_i(\mathrm{x})\mathrm{a}_i)^2 \\ &= \textstyle\sum_{i=r+1}^n \xi_i{}^2(\mathrm{x}) \qquad (\mathrm{a}_i\mathrm{a}_j = \delta_{ij}). \end{aligned}$$

This is the assertion. This holds also if $r = n - 1$, for in that case we find $d^2(\mathrm{x}, W) = \xi_n{}^2(\mathrm{x}) = |\xi_n(\mathrm{x})|^2$,

$$d(\mathrm{x}, W) = |\xi_n(\mathrm{x})|.$$

Theorem [15.6]: *The locus of the points* x *whose distance from a given linear variety* $W$ *is* $\lambda(>0)$ *times as large as that from a given variety* $U$, *is a variety of degree at most* 2.

Proof: The locus in question consists of those points x for which

$$d(\mathrm{x}, W) = \lambda d(\mathrm{x}, U)$$

or equivalently, since both members are positive,

$$d^2(\mathrm{x}, W) = \lambda^2 d^2(\mathrm{x}, U)$$
$$d^2(\mathrm{x}, W) - \lambda^2 d^2(\mathrm{x}, U) = 0.$$

It follows from theorem [15.5] that the function $\mathrm{x} \to d^2(\mathrm{x}, W) -$

$- \lambda^2 d^2(\mathrm{x}, U)$ is a quadratic function on $E$ or a function of lower degree, and this proves the assertion.

PROBLEMS. (15.2). (Cf. fig. 15.5) If in theorem [15.6] $U$ is a point in a euclidean plane, and $W$ is a line not through that point, then the locus is an ellipse if $\lambda > 1$, a parabola if $\lambda = 1$ and a hyperbola if $\lambda < 1$. $U$ is called the *focus* and $W$ the *directrix* of the ellipse, parabola or hyperbola.

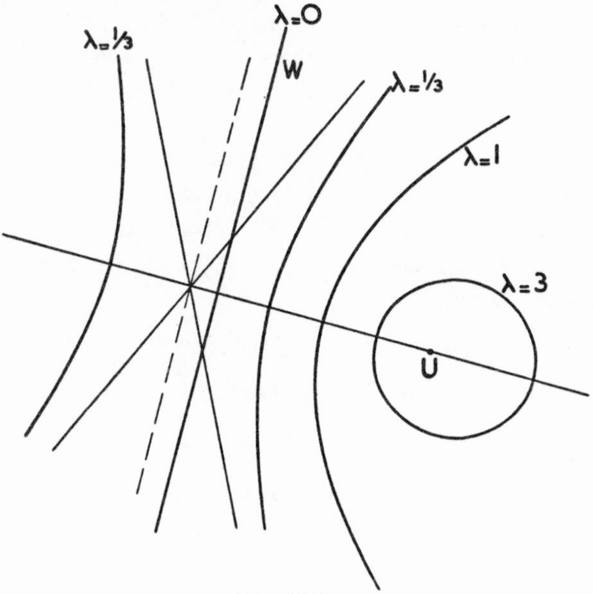


Fig. 15.5

Fig. 15.5 may also be interpreted as a collection of level sets of the rational quadratic function $\mathrm{x} \to d^2(\mathrm{x}, W)/d^2(\mathrm{x}, U) = \lambda^2$. Each curve corresponds to a value of $\lambda^2$.

(15.3). If $U$ and $W$ are points in a plane then the locus mentioned in theorem [15.6] is a circle for $\lambda \neq 1$, and is the perpendicular bisector of $UW$ if $\lambda = 1$. The circles are called *Apollonius's circles* of $U$ and $W$. Fig. 15.6 may also be interpreted as a collection of level sets of the function $\mathrm{x} \to d^2(\mathrm{x}, W)/d^2(\mathrm{x}, U)$. Consider also the case when $U$ and $W$ are points in an $n$-dimensional euclidean space.

(15.4). If $U$ and $W$ are intersecting lines in a plane, then the locus in question is a pair of lines. For $\lambda = 1$ this is the pair of bisectors of $U$ and $W$.

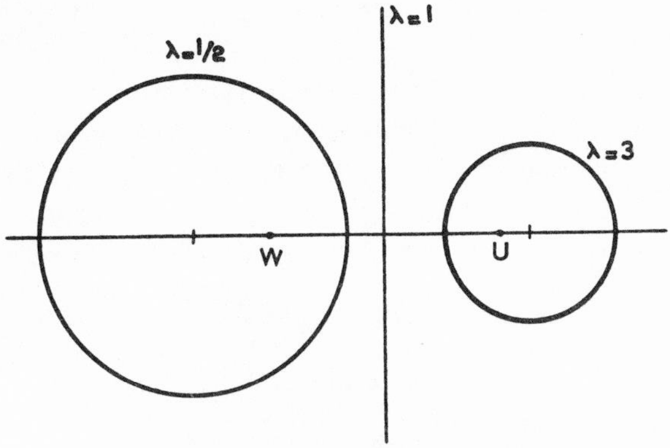


Fig. 15.6. Apollonius's circles

(15.5). If $U$ and $W$ are two disjoint linear varieties in $E$ such that no line in $U$ is parallel to any line in $W$, then there exists exactly one line which intersects $U$ and $W$ perpendicularly. It is called the common perpendicular. (Hint: consider the smallest linear variety containing $U$ and $W$).

(15.6)*. If $U^p$ and $W^q$ are two disjoint perpendicular linear varieties of dimension $p$ and $q$ in $E$, and if $\alpha$ is the distance between the points of intersection with the common perpendicular, then for $\lambda = 1$ and in suitable euclidean coordinates the locus in theorem [15.6] has the equation

$$\sum_{i=1}^{p} \xi_i^2 - \sum_{i=p+1}^{p+q} \xi_i^2 + 2\alpha\xi_{p+q+1} = 0.$$

(15.7). In a plane the locus of the points of which the distances from two given points $B_1$ and $B_2$ have a constant sum (difference), is an ellipse (hyperbola). $B_1$ and $B_2$ are called the *foci* of the ellipse (hyperbola). An ellipse with $B_1 = B_2$ is a circle.

Let $\xi_1$ and $\xi_2$ be euclidean coordinates for a two-dimensional euclidean vector space. Vectors are mapped by means of these coordinates in a one-to-one way onto the set of sequences of two numbers. $x \leftrightarrow \{\xi_1(x), \xi_2(x)\}$. Since real numbers are special complex numbers, the set of sequences of two complex numbers forms a complex vector space which contains the space of sequences of two real numbers .In this way any real vector space can be considered as a subset of a complex vector space, which is then called the *complexification* of the former. In ch. 17 we consider this in more detail. We shall also consider the quadratic function $\xi_1^2 + \xi_2^2$ for the complex space. This extension, however, implies some remarkable consequences with respect to our notions of distance and angle if we adhere to the definitions used previously.

In the first place there will be vectors with length zero:

$$\xi_1^2 + \xi_2^2 = 0$$

viz. those with coordinates $(\lambda, \lambda i)$ and $(\lambda, -\lambda i)$, $\lambda \neq 0$ complex, $i^2 = -1$.

Furthermore the same vectors turn out to be perpendicular to themselves according to the formula

$$\xi_1(x)\xi_1(y) + \xi_2(x)\xi_2(y) = 0 \text{ for } x = y.$$

If $x \neq O$ is a vector, then the set of vectors $\lambda x$ is called a *direction* and each of these vectors is said to have this direction. The direction of a vector which is perpendicular to itself is called an *isotropic direction* (in this terminology x and $-$ x have the same direction).

We shall now derive a remarkable formula for the angle $\alpha$, $0 < \alpha < \pi$, between two real vectors x and y, both different from zero, *which could even be used as a definition.* It is no essential restriction to consider the two-dimensional case only, since two vectors always lie in a two-dimensional space. Now consider the line $x + \mu(y - x)$ with (complex) parameter $\mu$, and its intersections u and v with the *isotropic cone,* that is the set of all vectors which are perpendicular to themselves. We wish to determine the cross-ratio (xyuv); by theorem [7.4] it is no restriction to assume that x and y have already been replaced by unit vectors with the same direction. Thus $x^2 = y^2 = 1$. Moreover the cross-ratio is equal to the cross-ratio of the four values of $\mu$ which determine the four points: $\mu = 0$ for x, $\mu = 1$ for y and the two other points by the roots $\mu_1$ and $\mu_2$ of the equation

$$\{(1 - \mu)x + \mu y\}^2 = 0.$$

Putting $\frac{1-\mu}{\mu} = \nu$ this equation becomes

$$(\nu x + y)^2 = \nu^2 + 2\nu xy + 1 = 0$$

with roots $\nu_{1,2} = -xy \pm i\sqrt{1-(xy)^2} = -\cos\alpha \pm i\sin\alpha$. The above cross-ratio then is

$$(xyuv) = \frac{0-\mu_1}{0-\mu_2} : \frac{1-\mu_1}{1-\mu_2} = \frac{1-\mu_2}{\mu_2} : \frac{1-\mu_1}{\mu_1} = \frac{\nu_2}{\nu_1} =$$

$$= \frac{-\cos\alpha - i\sin\alpha}{-\cos\alpha + i\sin\alpha} = e^{2i\alpha} \text{ (or } e^{-2i\alpha}\text{)}.$$

This yields *Laguerre*'s formula for the angle $\alpha$ between two vectors x and y: (ln = $\log_e$, the natural logarithm)

$$\boxed{\alpha = \frac{1}{2i}\ln(xyuv)} \quad \left(\text{or } \frac{-1}{2i}\ln(xyuv)\right) \qquad (15.8)$$

PROBLEMS. (15.8). In a euclidean $n$-space any $(n-1)$-variety has an equation in $x \in E$ of type

$$\alpha_1\xi_1(x) + \cdots + \alpha_n\xi_n(x) + \alpha = ax + \alpha = 0 \qquad \alpha \in \mathbf{R}.$$

The corresponding *functions of Hesse* are $\frac{ax+\alpha}{\|a\|}$ and $-\frac{ax+\alpha}{\|a\|}$.

(15.9). The sum of the squares of the lengths of any pair of conjugate diameters of an ellipse is the same. Cf. problem (14.3).

(15.10). The sum of the squares of the distances from the end-points of any pair of conjugate diameters of an ellipse to a fixed diameter $m$ is the same, viz. twice the square of the distances between $m$ and a tangent parallel to $m$.

(15.11). (Cf. fig. 15.7) All circumscribed rectangles of an ellipse have their vertices on the same

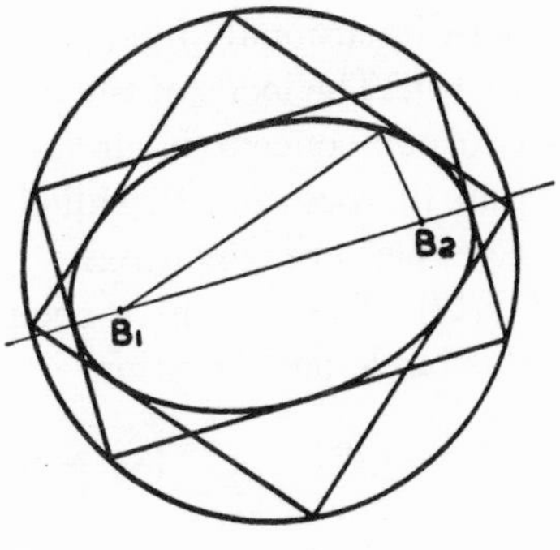


Fig. 15.7

circle, *Monge's circle.* (*Circumscribed* means that any side has exactly one point in common with the ellipse, i.e. it is tangent to the ellipse.)

(15.12). Give three-dimensional analogues of the assertions in the three foregoing problems.

(15.13). A line with isotropic direction not passing through a focus of a given ellipse, hyperbola or parabola, cuts this conic in two (complex) points. If the line does pass through a focus, it has only one point in common with the conic so that the two points of intersection coincide; in other words: the line is tangent to the conic. Cf. problem (15.2) and (15.7). We call a quadratic curve which does not degenerate into two lines, a *non-degenerate* quadratic curve. Now prove that a tangent with isotropic direction to a non-degenerate quadratic curve passes through a focus of the curve.

(15.14). Two real vectors in a plane are perpendicular if and only if their directions are harmonic with respect to the isotropic directions.

(15.15). A circle with centre m and radius $r$ has equation $(x - m)^2 = r^2$. Let y be an arbitrary point and b a unit vector so that $b^2 = 1$. The distance of a point $y + \lambda b$ from y is $|\lambda|$. Prove that the product of the distances of y from the points of intersection of the line $y + \lambda b$ with the circle is independent of the direction of b, and is equal to the absolute value of

$$(y - m)^2 - r^2.$$

This value is called the *power* of y with respect to the circle. The higher-dimensional analogue holds also.

(15.16). The locus of the points with the same power with respect to two non-concentric circles is a line through the points of intersection (if these exist), called the radical axis. The radical axes of three circles are concurrent.

(15.17). The tangent at the point $x_0$ on the circle $(x - m)^2 - r^2 = 0$ to this circle has equation

$$(x_0 - m)(x - x_0) = 0.$$

(15.18). Two circles are called *perpendicular* if the tangents at the intersections are perpendicular. The circles

$$(\mathrm{x} - \mathrm{m})^2 = r^2 \text{ and } (\mathrm{x} - \mathrm{n})^2 = s^2$$

$$[\mathrm{x}^2 + 2\mathrm{ax} + \alpha = 0 \text{ and } \mathrm{x}^2 + 2\mathrm{bx} + \beta = 0]$$

are perpendicular if and only if

$$(\mathrm{m} - \mathrm{n})^2 = r^2 + s^2 \quad [2\mathrm{ab} = \alpha + \beta].$$

(15.19)*. The mapping $\iota$ of a euclidean space with exception of one point $O$ (to be mapped to the zero-vector by the $\mathscr{A}$-map which is going to be used), given by

$$\iota \colon \mathrm{x} \to \alpha \frac{\mathrm{x}}{\mathrm{x}^2} \quad \alpha \neq 0 \quad (\mathrm{x}^2 = \mathrm{xx}, \text{ inner product})$$

is called an *inversion* with power $\alpha$ with respect to $O$.

*a.* If $\alpha > 0$ then the points invariant under $\iota$ form the hypersphere (sphere, circle) with equation $\mathrm{x}^2 = \alpha$.

*b.* $\iota$ maps any linear variety through $O$ onto itself (but not point-wise).

*c.* The composite mapping $u = \iota^2$ is the identical mapping so that $\iota = \iota^{-1}$.

*d.* The set of all points having their images on the hypersphere or hyperplane (sphere or plane, circle or line) with equation in $\mathrm{u} \in \mathrm{E}$,

$$p\mathrm{u}^2 + \mathrm{qu} + r = 0$$

is the hypersphere with equation in $\mathrm{x} \in \mathrm{E}$,

$$r\mathrm{x}^2 + \alpha\mathrm{qx} + \alpha^2 p = 0.$$

Thus the mapping $\iota$ has the action:

hypersphere not through $O$ $\leftrightarrow$ hypersphere not through $O$
hypersphere through $O$ $\leftrightarrow$ hyperplane not through $O$
hyperplane through $O$ $\leftrightarrow$ hyperplane through $O$.

Remark: Inversion leaves angles invariant: inversion is a *conformal* mapping.

(15.20). The inversion in a three-dimensional euclidean space with power 2 with respect to the point $(\xi_1, \xi_2, \xi_3) = (0, 0, 1)$ maps the plane $\xi_3 = 0$ onto the sphere (minus $(0, 0, 1)$) with equation

$$\xi_1^2 + \xi_2^2 + \xi_3^2 = 1.$$

The intersections with spheres or planes are mapped onto intersections with spheres or planes, so that circles and lines in the plane are transformed into circles on the sphere.

The restriction of the inversion to the above plane is a projection from $O$. This so-called *stereographic projection* is conformal by the remark at the end of problem (15.19).

*Unitary vector space*

A vector $n$-space over **C** with a fixed positive-definite hermitian form $\varphi$ is called a *unitary vector space*. The set of coordinates $\xi_1, \cdots \xi_n$ is called unitary when

$$\varphi(\mathrm{x}, \mathrm{y}) = \Sigma_{i=1}^n \bar{\xi}_i(\mathrm{x})\xi_i(\mathrm{y}) \text{ for } \mathrm{x}, \mathrm{y} \in V.$$

$\varphi(\mathrm{x}, \mathrm{y})$ is called the *inner product* of x and y and is also denoted by xy. The *length* or *norm* of a vector x is $\|\mathrm{x}\| = \sqrt{\mathrm{xx}}$. A *unit vector* is a vector with length 1.

Two vectors x and y are called unitary-orthogonal when $\mathrm{xy} = 0$. If $\eta_j, \zeta_j$ are defined by $\xi_j + \bar{\xi}_j = 2\eta_j$, $\xi_j - \bar{\xi}_j = 2i\zeta_j$, then

$$\xi_j = \eta_j + i\zeta_j$$

and

$$\|\mathrm{x}\|^2 = \mathrm{xx} = \Sigma_{j=1}^n \bar{\xi}_j\xi_j = \Sigma_{j=1}^n (\eta_j^2 + \zeta_j^2).$$

The given length is therefore the same as that of a euclidean vector space with the $2n$ real coordinates $\eta_j$ and $\zeta_j$, $j = 1, \cdots n$.

PROBLEM (15.21). The functions $\xi_1, \cdots \xi_n$ form a set of unitary coordinates if and only if they form the cobasis of a set of $n$ unitary orthogonal unit vectors.

(15.22). The function $\varphi\cdot$ which assigns to any real polynomial in x of degree $< n$, $\alpha_0 + \alpha_1\mathrm{x} + \cdots + \alpha_{n-1}\mathrm{x}^{n-1}$, the value

$$\varphi\cdot[(\alpha_0 + \alpha_1\mathrm{x} + \cdots)] = \int_0^1 (\alpha_0 + \alpha_1\mathrm{x} + \cdots)^2\, d\mathrm{x} \in \mathbf{R}$$

defines a euclidean vectorspace structure. (Cf. Problem (3.10) p. 12.)

# 16. SOME APPLICATIONS IN STATISTICS

In physics, biology, economics and other sciences problems are often encountered which can be very well treated with the theory developed in the previous sections. In this chapter we present some of these.

*I. Method of least squares, linear adjustment, regression*

Many problems in statistics can be formulated as follows. Under the same or different circumstances, numbers $x_1, \cdots x_n$ have been found as experimental results. The sequence $\mathrm{x} = (x_1, \cdots x_n)$ is a vector in $\mathbf{R}^n$, and it is considered as a "value" assumed by a random vector x as a result of an experiment. On repeating the experiment the result need not be the same. The aim is to estimate the expectation value $E(\mathrm{x})$ of x. $E(\mathrm{x}) = \mathrm{a}$ is a vector in $\mathbf{R}^n$ which is assumed to exist and which has the property that when many values of x are determined, that is, the experiment is repeated many times, then the probability that their average is close to a is large.

Before the experimental result x has been obtained, the investigator will conclude from theoretical and other considerations the existence of some subspace $\mathrm{A} \subset \mathbf{R}^n$, in which "a" must be contained. [1]) It would lead us too far to treat the statistical aspects in any detail; it may be sufficient to say that our problem is to estimate $\mathrm{a} \in \mathrm{A}$ from x.

A choice of $\mathrm{a} \in \mathrm{A}$ for given x is called the *adjustment* of x on the set A. The choice that we are now going to treat is that $\mathrm{a} = (a_1, \cdots a_n) \in \mathrm{A}$ for which the sum of the squares of the deviations

$$\Sigma_{i=1}^{n} (x_i - a_i)^2$$

---

[1]) In this chapter we no longer follow our convention to denote numbers by Greek characters.

is minimal. This choice is called the choice by *the method of least squares.*

The space $\mathbf{R}^n$ of sequences of numbers $(\xi_1, \cdots \xi_n)$ with the quadratic function

$$\varphi = \sum_{i=1}^{n} \xi_i^2$$

is a euclidean vector space. Using the corresponding inner product, the problem can be formulated as follows: For given x and $A \subset \mathbf{R}^n$ to determine the vector $a \in A$ such that $\|x - a\|$ is minimal. By the preceding chapter the solution is the pedal point $a = x_A$ of the perpendicular from x to A. From the perpendicularity of $x_A$ and $x - x_A$ it follows that

$$x = x_A + (x - x_A)$$
$$x^2 = x_A^2 + (x - x_A)^2 \qquad (16.1)$$

and $(x - x_A)^2$ then is the (minimal) sum of the squares of the deviations.

*Examples*

(*a*) *The mean as a "least squares solution"*

Let $x = (x_1, \cdots x_n)$ be a set of measurements of one unknown quantity, for example a distance which has to be estimated. Then A consists of the vectors of type

$$(t, \cdots t) = t(1, \cdots 1) = t \cdot r$$

where r is the vector with all coordinates equal to 1.

Our estimate of $x_A$ is determined by the value of $t$ for which $tr = x_A$. Since $x - x_A$ and A are perpendicular, we have

$$(x - tr)r = xr - trr = x_1 + \cdots + x_n - tn = 0.$$

The solution for $t$ is the mean $t = \dfrac{1}{n}(x_1 + \cdots + x_n)$.

This mean will be denoted by $\bar{x}$, and $x_A$ in this case by $\bar{\mathrm{x}} = (\bar{x}, \cdots \bar{x})$. Then (16.1) becomes:

$$x = \bar{\mathrm{x}} + (x - \bar{\mathrm{x}}); \qquad x^2 = \bar{\mathrm{x}}^2 + (x - \bar{\mathrm{x}})^2. \qquad (16.2)$$

The vectors perpendicular to those with equal coordinates are called *contrasts*. They are the sequences of $n$ numbers with zero sum, and they form an $(n-1)$-dimensional subspace $(\mathbf{R}^n)^0$ of $\mathbf{R}^n$.

(*b*) *Linear regression on two variables*

An investigator assumes that a relation $\zeta = p + sx + ty$ with unknown $p$, $s$ and $t$ exists between the variables $x$, $y$ and $\zeta$. In a number of situations $i = 1, \cdots n$ measurements $x_i$ and $y_i$ of $x$ and $y$ have been made, and in those cases $z_i$ will denote the observation of $\zeta_i = p + sx_i + ty_i$, which is not necessarily equal to $\zeta_i$. In order to estimate $p$, $s$ and $t$ we use the least squares method: we determine $p$, $s$ and $t$ such that

$$\Sigma_{i=1}^{n} \{z_i - (p + sx_i + ty_i)\}^2$$

is minimal.

In this case A is the space generated by the vectors r, $\mathrm{x} = (x_1, \cdots x_n)$ and $\mathrm{y} = (y_1, \cdots y_n)$. From the condition that $\mathrm{z} - \mathrm{z}_\mathrm{A}$ is perpendicular to A, and thus perpendicular to r, x and y, we obtain the following equations

$$\left.\begin{array}{l} (\mathrm{z}-\mathrm{z_A})\mathrm{r} = \{\mathrm{z} - (p\mathrm{r} + s\mathrm{x} + t\mathrm{y})\}\,\mathrm{r} = 0 \\ (\mathrm{z}-\mathrm{z_A})\mathrm{x} = \{\mathrm{z} - (p\mathrm{r} + s\mathrm{x} + t\mathrm{y})\}\,\mathrm{x} = 0 \\ (\mathrm{z}-\mathrm{z_A})\mathrm{y} = \{\mathrm{z} - (p\mathrm{r} + s\mathrm{x} + t\mathrm{y})\}\,\mathrm{y} = 0 \end{array}\right\} \qquad (16.4)$$

which are called the *normal equations*. They may also be written as

$$\left\{\begin{array}{l} p\mathrm{rr} + s\mathrm{rx} + t\mathrm{ry} = \mathrm{rz} \\ p\mathrm{xr} + s\mathrm{xx} + t\mathrm{xy} = \mathrm{xz} \\ p\mathrm{yr} + s\mathrm{yx} + t\mathrm{yy} = \mathrm{yz}, \end{array}\right.$$

three equations with three unknowns $p$, $s$ and $t$, with in general one solution (cf. chapter 11 and 13).

(*c*) *Regression with respect to a one-way classification* [1])

Suppose that the circumstances under which part of the experimental results have been obtained, were not essentially different, namely those corresponding to a row (any row) of the following

---

[1]) CORSTEN, L. C. A.: Vectors, a tool in statistical regression theory; Thesis Wageningen 1958; Mededelingen Landbouwhogeschool, 58(1).

scheme (= *vector*(!) = x) of results

$$\begin{array}{l} x_{11}, \cdots x_{1k_1} \\ x_{21}, \cdots\cdots x_{2k_2} \\ \cdots\cdots\cdots\cdots\cdots \\ x_{m1}, \cdots\cdots\cdots x_{mk_m} \end{array}$$

In that case the relevant space A consists of all vectors with mutually equal coordinates in each row of this scheme. A is called the characteristic space of the classification $A$. A basis of A consists of the characteristic vectors of the rows, i.e. the vectors with coordinates 1 in one row of the scheme and zeros elsewhere.

PROBLEMS. (16.1). Find an expression for $\mathrm{x_A}$ in the above case.

(16.2). Prove the perpendicularity of the three vectors (cf. (*a*) for the meaning of $\bar{\mathrm{x}}$) $\bar{\mathrm{x}}$, $(\mathrm{x_A} - \bar{\mathrm{x}})$ and $(\mathrm{x} - \mathrm{x_A})$, and prove:

$$\mathrm{x}^2 = \bar{\mathrm{x}}^2 + (\mathrm{x_A} - \bar{\mathrm{x}})^2 + (\mathrm{x} - \mathrm{x_A})^2.$$

The expressions $(\mathrm{x_A} - \bar{\mathrm{x}}) = \mathrm{x_A}^{\circ}$ and $(\mathrm{x_A} - \bar{\mathrm{x}})^2$ are indications of the influence of the various circumstances. The expression $(\mathrm{x} - \mathrm{x_A})^2$ suggests what influence chance can have.

### (*d*) *Calculation in the general case, also in matrix notation*

In this part we write *columns* of $n$ numbers instead of rows. Let x be the column of $n$ experimental results. Suppose that the $m$-dimensional subspace A has a basis $\mathrm{a}_1, \cdots \mathrm{a}_m$. The problem is then to determine numbers $s_1, \cdots s_m$ such that the vector

$$\mathrm{a}_1 s_1 + \cdots + \mathrm{a}_m s_m - \mathrm{x} \tag{16.5}$$

is as short as possible, and this is true if it is perpendicular to A, that is, to $\mathrm{a}_1, \cdots \mathrm{a}_m$. Thus we obtain the *normal equations*

$$\mathrm{a}_i(\mathrm{a}_1 s_1 + \cdots + \mathrm{a}_m s_m - \mathrm{x}) = 0 \qquad i = 1, \cdots m. \tag{16.6}$$

These equations become particularly simple if the vectors $\mathrm{a}_1, \cdots \mathrm{a}_m$ form an orthogonal basis of A, namely

$$\mathrm{a}_i^2\, s_i - \mathrm{a}_i \mathrm{x} = 0 \qquad s_i = (\mathrm{a}_i \mathrm{x})/(\mathrm{a}_i^2).$$

Therefore in applications the basis is often chosen to be orthogonal.

(16.6) may also be written as one matrix equation. In order to show this, we introduce the following matrices:

$$\mathrm{a}_i = \begin{bmatrix} a_{1i} \\ a_{2i} \\ \cdot \\ \cdot \\ \cdot \\ a_{ni} \end{bmatrix}; \; A = \begin{bmatrix} a_{11} & \cdots & a_{1m} \\ \cdots & \cdots & \cdots \\ & & \\ a_{n1} & \cdots & a_{nm} \end{bmatrix}; \; \mathrm{x} = \begin{bmatrix} x_1 \\ \cdot \\ \cdot \\ \cdot \\ \cdot \\ x_n \end{bmatrix}; \; \mathrm{s} = \begin{bmatrix} s_1 \\ \cdot \\ \cdot \\ \cdot \\ s_m \end{bmatrix}$$

Then (16.6) reads:

$$^t\mathrm{a}_i(A\mathrm{s} - \mathrm{x}) = 0 \qquad i = 1, \cdots m$$

yielding the *normal equations*:

$$^tA(A\mathrm{s} - \mathrm{x}) = 0 \tag{16.6}$$

which, observing that the $m \times m$-matrix $^tAA$ is non-singular, we can solve by

$$^tAA\mathrm{s} - {}^tA\mathrm{x} = 0, \; \mathrm{s} = ({}^tAA)^{-1}{}^tA\mathrm{x}.$$

The orthogonal projection in question is, in matrix notation:

$$\mathrm{x}_{\mathrm{A}} = A\mathrm{s} = A({}^tAA)^{-1}\, {}^tA\mathrm{x}.$$

The *sum of the squares of the deviations* is the inner product $(\mathrm{x} - \mathrm{x}_{\mathrm{A}})^2 = \mathrm{x}(\mathrm{x} - \mathrm{x}_{\mathrm{A}})$, i.e. in matrix notation:

$$^t\mathrm{x}(\mathrm{x} - \mathrm{x}_{\mathrm{A}}) = {}^t\mathrm{x}\mathrm{x} - {}^t\mathrm{x}A({}^tAA)^{-1}\, {}^tA\mathrm{x}.$$

(*e*) In surveying, the subspace A or the linear variety $M \subset \mathbf{R}^n$ (not necessarily a subspace) is sometimes given by equations instead of by a basis. For example, the angles of a triangle are measured, and it is known that the true angles add up to $\pi$ (or 180 degrees).

Suppose that $M$ consists of those sequences of numbers $(u_1, \cdots u_n)$ for which

$$\textstyle\sum_{j=1}^{n} b_{ij}u_j = b_i \qquad i = 1, \cdots p; \; p < n, \tag{16.7}$$

and let A be the subspace of the sequences satisfying

$$\textstyle\sum_{j=1}^{n} b_{ij}u_j = 0.$$

A is parallel to $M$. Assuming that the rank of the matrix of the numbers $b_{ij}$ is $p$, A is an $(n - p)$-dimensional subspace. The vectors $\mathrm{b}_i$ with components $b_{ij}$, $j = 1, \cdots n$ span a space B of dimension $p$ perpendicular to A (cf. fig. 16.1).

Further, let the vector x be given. A vector $\mathrm{x}_M \in M$ is required such that the sum of the squares of the deviations $(\mathrm{x} - \mathrm{x}_M)^2$ is as small as possible. The solution is the orthogonal projection $\mathrm{x}_M$ of x onto $M$. This point $\mathrm{x}_M$ can be obtained by adding to x a suitable vector of B, say

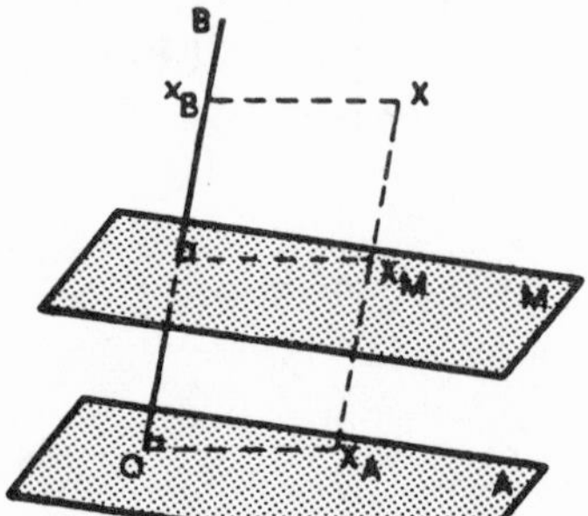


Fig. 16.1

$$\mathrm{x}_M = \mathrm{x} + \lambda_1 \mathrm{b}_1 + \cdots + \lambda_p \mathrm{b}_p.$$

The components $u_1, \cdots u_n$ of $\mathrm{x}_M$ and the extra unknowns $\lambda_1, \cdots \lambda_p$ which we just introduced, are solutions of the following set of $n + p$ linear equations

$$\begin{array}{llll}
u_1 & & -b_{11}\lambda_1 - \cdots - b_{p1}\lambda_p & = x_1 \\
& u_2 & -b_{12}\lambda_1 - \cdots - b_{p2}\lambda_p & = x_2 \\
& & \cdot \quad \cdots \quad \cdot & \cdot \\
& \quad u_n & -b_{1n}\lambda_1 - \cdots - b_{pn}\lambda_p & = x_n \\
b_{11}u_1 + \cdots + b_{1n}u_n & & & = b_1 \\
\cdot \quad \cdots \quad \cdot & & & \cdot \\
b_{p1}u_1 + \cdots + b_{pn}u_n & & & = b_p.
\end{array}$$

PROBLEMS. (16.3). Let $x_1, \cdots x_n$ be mutually different numbers and consider the vectors

$$\mathrm{x}^{[0]} = (1, \cdots 1), \ \mathrm{x}^{[r]} = (x_1{}^r, \cdots x_n{}^r) \quad r = 1, 2, \cdots.$$

Prove that the vectors $\mathrm{x}^{[r]}$, $r = 0, \cdots p$ are linearly independent when $p < n$, and linearly dependent when $p \geqslant n$. Hint: The number of roots of an equation of degree $n$ in one unknown which is not satisfied identically, is at most $n$.

(16.4)*. *Orthogonal polynomials: Adjustment on a cubic function.* In the previous problem take $n = 6$, $\mathrm{x} = (-5, -3, -1, 1, 3, 5)$ and let A be the subspace generated by $\mathrm{x}^{[r]}$, $r = 0, 1, 2, 3$. Choose an orthogonal basis of A consisting of vectors $a_r$ with integral components such that $a_r$ lies in the space generated by $x^{[s]}$, $s \leqslant r$. Solve the least squares problem for A with this orthogonal basis and for the experimental results $z = (2, 37, 24, 14, 2, 53)$. Each vector of the basis so obtained has components which are polynomials in the components of x. These polynomials are called *orthogonal polynomials.* [1])

(16.5)*. Consider the intersections $A^0$ and $B^0$ of the characteristic spaces A and B of two classifications $A$ and $B$ of $n$ elements, each with its contrast space.

Let $n_i(m_j)$ be the non-zero number of elements in the $i$-th ($j$-th) class of the classification $A(B)$. $\sum n_i = \sum m_j = n$. Then $A^0$ and $B^0$ are perpendicular if and only if the number of elements which are in the $i$-th class of $A$ as well as in the $j$-th class of $B$ is $n_i m_j n^{-1}$ for any choice of $i$ and $j$. If $A^0$ and $B^0$ are orthogonal then the classification also is called orthogonal (cf. p. 55).

(16.6). Let $A$ be a matrix with $m$ columns of $n \geqslant m$ elements each. Let $D$ be a non-singular $m \times m$-matrix. If ${}^tA$ is the transposed of $A$ prove that: rank $AD =$ rank $A$; rank ${}^tD{}^tAAD =$ rank ${}^t(AD) \cdot AD =$ rank ${}^tAA$; and using this if $A$ is real, prove that

$$\text{rank } {}^tAA = \text{rank } A.$$

Hint: Choose $D$ such that the columns of $AD$ are orthogonal (orthogonalization).

## *II. The correlation coefficient*

If $x = (x_1, \cdots x_n) \in \mathbf{R}^n$, and $\bar{x}$ the column consisting of $n$ times the number $\frac{1}{n} \sum_{i=1}^{n} x_i$, $x - \bar{x} \neq O$, then $x - \bar{x}$ is called the *contrast vector* of x and

$$X = \frac{x - \bar{x}}{\|x - \bar{x}\|}$$

---

[1]) Literature: Fisher-Yates: Statistical tables for Biological Agricultural and Medical Research p. 27–29 and p. 80–90, 1953.

is called the normalized contrast vector of x. In this section we use capitals for normalized contrast vectors, and restrict ourselves to vectors x with $x - \bar{x} \neq O$.

Definition: The *correlation coefficient* of two vectors x and $y \in \mathbf{R}^n$ is the cosine of the angle between the contrast vectors of x and y:

$$r(x, y) = \cos\{x - \bar{x}; y - \bar{y}\} = \frac{(x - \bar{x})(y - \bar{y})}{\|x - \bar{x}\| \cdot \|y - \bar{y}\|} = XY. \qquad (16.8)$$

We have immediately from the definition that always $-1 \leqslant \leqslant r(x, y) \leqslant 1$.

Furthermore $r(x, y) = 1$ (or $-1$ respectively) if and only if there exists a $\lambda > 0$ ($< 0$) such that

$$y - \bar{y} = \lambda(x - \bar{x})$$

or

$$y = \lambda x + (\bar{y} - \lambda\bar{x}).$$

In that case the vector y is linearly dependent on the vectors

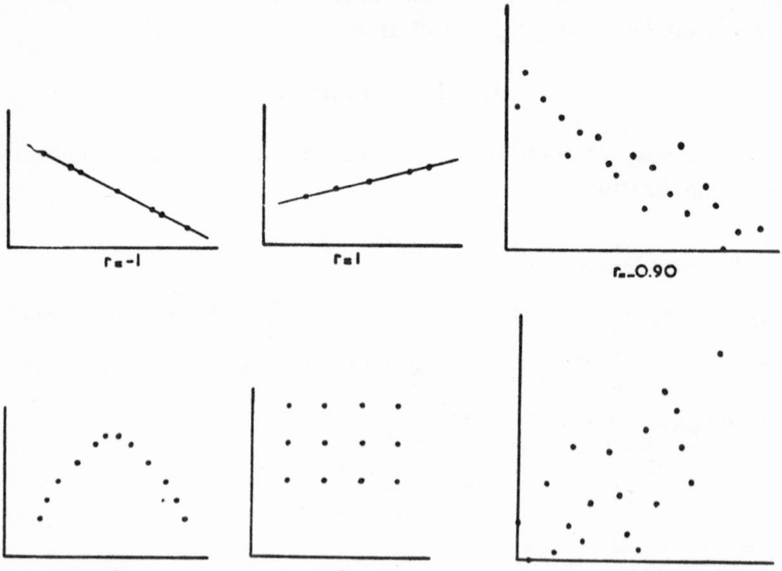


Fig. 16.2

x and r, the vector defined on page 144. If we plot $y_i$ against $x_i$ ($i = 1, \cdots n$) we obtain $n$ points on a line. Therefore the correlation coefficient is used to discover a tendency to linear dependence. In fig. 16.2 some scatter-diagrams are shown.

We now give a theorem concerning the correlation coefficient: *Let $\Pi$ be the set of the $n!$ permutations $\pi$ of $n$ elements. Let $\pi(\mathrm{x})$ denote the image of $\mathrm{x} = (x_1, \cdots x_n)$ under $\pi$. Then for arbitrary* x *and* $\mathrm{y} \in \mathbf{R}^n$:

$$\frac{1}{n!} \Sigma_{\pi \in \Pi} [\pi(\mathrm{x} - \bar{\mathrm{x}})]\, \mathrm{y} = 0 \tag{16.9}$$

$$\frac{1}{n!} \Sigma_{\pi \in \Pi} \{[\pi(\mathrm{x} - \bar{\mathrm{x}})]\, \mathrm{y}\}^2 = \frac{(\mathrm{x} - \bar{\mathrm{x}})^2(\mathrm{y} - \bar{\mathrm{y}})^2}{\mathrm{n} - 1}. \tag{16.10}$$

*In particular for the correlation coefficients* ($\mathrm{x} \neq \bar{\mathrm{x}}, \mathrm{y} \neq \bar{\mathrm{y}}$) *we have*

$$\frac{1}{n!} \Sigma_{\pi \in \Pi}\, r(\pi \mathrm{x}, \mathrm{y}) = 0 \tag{16.9'}$$

$$\frac{1}{n!} \Sigma_{\pi \in \Pi} \{r(\pi \mathrm{x}, \mathrm{y})\}^2 = \frac{1}{n - 1}\ ^{1)}. \tag{16.10'}$$

Proof: The left-hand side of (16.9) is equal to

$$\frac{1}{n!} [\Sigma_{\pi \in \Pi}\, \pi(\mathrm{x} - \bar{\mathrm{x}})]\, \mathrm{y}$$

and this equals zero since each component of the vector $\Sigma_{\pi \in \Pi}\, \pi(\mathrm{x} - \bar{\mathrm{x}})$ is zero.

The left-hand side of (16.10) is a quadratic function of the vector y if x is constant. If $y_1, \cdots y_n$ are the components of y, then for fixed x it is equal to

$$\Sigma_{i,j=1}^{n}\, \alpha_{ij} y_i y_j. \tag{16.11}$$

---

1) In the related statistical theories x and y are experimental values of the random vectors x and y. If, for any y, any permutation of x has the same probability as x, then from (16.9′ and 10′) it follows that the *expectation* (= what may be expected on the average) of the correlation coefficient is zero and the expectation of its square is $1/(\mathrm{n} - 1)$. The latter quantity is also called the *variance* of the correlation coefficient.

If in (16.10), x is subjected to the permutation $\pi'$, then the left-hand side remains unaltered. If x and y are both replaced by their images $\pi''$x and $\pi''$y under the permutation $\pi''$, then indeed each term of the sum remains unchanged. Application of both operations consecutively when $\pi'$ is the inverse of $\pi''$ shows that the value of the left-hand side of (16.10) does not change either if the row y is subjected to an arbitrary permutation.

Now the vector $y = (1, 0, \cdots 0)$ in (16.11) gives the value $\alpha_{11}$. Interchanging the first and the $j$-th number in the sequence y gives a vector yielding $\alpha_{jj}$ in (16.11), which should therefore be equal to $\alpha_{11}$:

$$\alpha_{jj} = \alpha_{11} \qquad j = 1, \cdots n.$$

The vector $y = (1, 1, 0, \cdots 0)$ in (16.11) gives the value

$$\alpha_{11} + 2\alpha_{12} + \alpha_{22} = 2\alpha_{11} + 2\alpha_{12}$$

which for similar reasons is equal to

$$2\alpha_{11} + 2\alpha_{ij} \quad i \neq j \quad i, j = 1, \cdots n.$$

Therefore (16.11) is equal to

$$\frac{n-1}{n} \alpha \sum_i y_i^2 + \beta \sum_{i \neq j} y_i y_j; \; \alpha_{11} = \frac{n-1}{n} \alpha, \; \alpha_{12} = \beta \text{ constants.}$$

Substitution of the vector $y = (1, 1, \cdots 1)$ gives zero in any term of the left-hand member of (16.10), hence

$$\frac{n-1}{n} \alpha \cdot n + \beta n(n-1) = 0, \quad \beta = -\frac{\alpha}{n}.$$

The expression in (16.10) is then equal to

$$\alpha \frac{n-1}{n} \sum_i y_i^2 - \alpha \frac{1}{n} \sum_{i \neq j} y_i y_j = \alpha \sum_i y_i^2 - \alpha \frac{1}{n} \sum_{i,j} y_i y_j =$$

$$= \alpha \left\{\sum_i y_i^2 - \frac{1}{n} (\sum_i y_i)^2\right\}$$

$$= \alpha(y - \bar{y})^2. \qquad (16.12)$$

Now $\alpha$ remains to be calculated. In order to do so we choose in the $(n-1)$-dimensional contrast space (orthogonal to $(1, 1, \cdots 1)$) a basis of mutually perpendicular unit vectors $e_1, \cdots e_{n-1}$.

The component of the vector $\pi(x-\bar{x})$ in the direction of $e_i$ is $\{[\pi(x-\bar{x})]e_i\}e_i$. The square of the length of this component is $\{[\pi(x-\bar{x})]e_i\}^2$ and, using Pythagoras's theorem, we get

$$\{\pi(x-\bar{x})\}^2 = \Sigma_{i=1}^{n-1} \{[\pi(x-\bar{x})]e_i\}^2 = (x-\bar{x})^2 \text{ for any } \pi \in \Pi.$$

$$(x-\bar{x})^2 = \frac{1}{n!} \Sigma_{\pi\epsilon\Pi} \{\pi(x-\bar{x})\}^2 = \frac{1}{n!} \Sigma_{\pi\epsilon\Pi} \Sigma_{i=1}^{n-1} \{[\pi(x-\bar{x})]\, e_i\}^2 =$$

$$= \Sigma_{i=1}^{n-1} \frac{1}{n!} \Sigma_{\pi\epsilon\Pi} \{[\pi(x-\bar{x})]\, e_i\}^2.$$

By substitution of (16.10) = (16.12) with $e_i = y$ it follows that

$$(x-\bar{x})^2 = \Sigma_{i=1}^{n-1} \alpha = (n-1)\alpha.$$

If we solve $\alpha$ from this relation and substitute it in (16.12) we obtain (16.10).

Some related quantities used in statistics are the coefficients of partial and multiple correlation, for which (16.9′) and (16.10′) are not true.

If x is a vector of $\mathbf{R}^n$ and B is a subspace of $\mathbf{R}^n$ containing $(1, \cdots 1)$ then the *coefficient of multiple correlation* $r(x, B)$ is the ordinary correlation coefficient $r(x, x_B)$. Observe that $0 \leqslant r(x, B) \leqslant 1$.

If $B^0$ is the intersection of B and the contrast space then this quantity is equal to the cosine of the angle between $x-\bar{x}$ and its perpendicular projection onto $B^0$:

$$\frac{(x-\bar{x})x_{B^0}}{\|x-\bar{x}\|\cdot\|x_{B^0}\|} = \frac{\|x_{B^0}\|}{\|x-\bar{x}\|}.$$

If A is a subspace of $\mathbf{R}^n$ containing $(1, \cdots 1)$ then the *coefficient of partial correlation relative to* A of the vectors x and y is the ordinary correlation coefficient of $x_A$ and $y_A$

$$r_A(x, y) = r(x_A, y_A).$$

If both x and y are strongly correlated with a vector z perpendicular to A, i.e. $r(x, z)$ and $r(y, z)$ are large, then $r(x, y)$ is large.

The coefficient of partial correlation relative to A is "purified" from such common correlations with a vector z.

Some special kinds of vectors are the following:

A *Spearman vector* is a permutation of $(1, 2, \cdots n)$. It is useful if $n$ observed situations have only to be ordered according to some property without actually measuring this property. One may think for example of a particular ability of $n$ students in a class.

A Spearman vector may also be obtained if only the order of magnitude of some measured property is retained for the various situations and more detailed information is disregarded.

A *two-class-vector:* $\mathrm{x} = (x_1, \cdots x_n)$ consists of the numbers 0 or 1 and is an expression for a classification of the situations $i = 1, \cdots n$ into two classes.

A *Van der Waerden vector:* $\mathrm{x} = (x_1, \cdots x_n)$ is a permutation of the numbers $(\alpha_1, \cdots \alpha_n)$ with the $\alpha_i$ given by

$$\int_{-\infty}^{\alpha_i} \frac{e^{-\frac{1}{2}u^2}}{\sqrt{2\pi}}\, du = \frac{i}{n+1} \qquad i = 1, \cdots n.$$

The integrand is the probability of the standardized normal (Gaussian) density random variable.

The *correlation coefficient* of two vectors x and y is called after *Spearman* if x and y are Spearman vectors, after *Wilcoxon* if x is a Spearman vector and y a two-class-vector, after *Van der Waerden* if x is a Van der Waerden vector and y a two-class-vector. Of course it is possible to form coefficients of multiple and partial correlation from Spearman-vectors. All these "*rank-correlation coefficients*" are measures for the concordance.

PROBLEMS. (16.7). If $\mathrm{x} = (x_1, \cdots x_n)$ and $\mathrm{y} = (y_1, \cdots y_n)$ are Spearman vectors then the correlation coefficient is equal to

$$r = 1 - \frac{6(\mathrm{x} - \mathrm{y})^2}{n^3 - n}.$$

Here $(x - y)^2$ is the sum of the square of the differences of the ranks.

(16.8)*. If x is a Spearman vector and y a two-class-vector with class sizes $p$ and $q$, and if $W$ is the sum of the $q$ ranks in x belonging to situations in the second class, then the correlation coefficient of Wilcoxon (of which only the absolute value is uniquely determined) is

$$(\pm)\, r(\mathrm{x}, \mathrm{y}) = \frac{\left[W - q\,\frac{(n+1)}{2}\right]}{\sqrt{\frac{pq(n^2-1)}{12}}}.$$

(16.9)*. For $m$ Spearman vectors $\mathbf{x}_1, \cdots \mathbf{x}_m$ with normalized contrast vectors $\mathbf{X}_1, \cdots \mathbf{X}_m$ the *coefficient of concordance* is defined by

$$M = (\Sigma_{i=1}^{m} \mathbf{X}_i)^2.$$

Then: a) $0 \leq M \leq m^2$.

b) $M = m^2$ if and only if $\mathbf{X}_1 = \mathbf{X}_i$ for $i = 1, \cdots m$.

c) for $m = 2$, $M = 2 + 2r(\mathbf{x}_1, \mathbf{x}_2)$.

d) $M = m + 2 \Sigma_{i<j}^{m} r(\mathbf{x}_i, \mathbf{x}_j)$.

e) The mean of the numbers $M$ for all permutations of $\mathbf{x}_1, \cdots \mathbf{x}_m$ is $m$. In practice the number $W = Mm^{-2}$, $0 \leq W \leq 1$ is also used.

f) The mean of the numbers $(M - m)^2$ for all permutations of $\mathbf{x}_1, \cdots \mathbf{x}_m$ is equal to $\dfrac{2m(m-1)}{n-1}$.

(16.10). Compute the correlation coefficient of $y = (0, 9, 8, 7)$ and $\mathbf{z} = (4, 3, -3, -4)$.

Find a vector $\mathbf{x}$ with length 10 with the following properties: The angle between $\mathbf{x}$ and the vector $(1, 1, 1, 1)$ equals $\pi/4$; the coefficient of multiple correlation of $\mathbf{x}$ with respect to $\mathbf{y}$ and $\mathbf{z}$ is 1; the correlation coefficient of $\mathbf{x}$ and $\mathbf{y}$ is $\frac{1}{2}$; the Spearman correlation coefficient of $\mathbf{x}$ and $\mathbf{y}$ is maximal, that is, as great as the other conditions permit.

## 17. CLASSIFICATION OF ENDOMORPHISMS

If $\sigma$ is an endomorphism of an $n$-dimensional vector space V over $\mathbf{F}$ with basis $a_1, \cdots a_n$ and cobasis $\xi_1, \cdots \xi_n$, then by theorem [9.1] $\sigma$ is already determined by the action (cf. (5.8))

$$a_j \to \sigma a_j = \sum_{i=1}^{n} \xi_i(\sigma a_j)\cdot a_i \quad j = 1, \cdots n \tag{17.1}$$

and hence by the matrix of elements $\sigma_{ij} = \xi_i(\sigma a_j)$:

$$\sigma a_j = \sum_{i=1}^{n} \sigma_{ij} a_i. \tag{17.1}$$

The image of a vector $a = \sum_{i=1}^{n} \alpha_i a_i$ under $\sigma$ is then

$$\sum_{i=1}^{n} \alpha_i' a_i = \sigma(\sum_{j=1}^{n} \alpha_j a_j) = \sum_{j=1}^{n} \alpha_j(\sigma a_j) = \sum_{i,j=1}^{n} \alpha_j \sigma_{ij} a_i$$

$$\alpha_i' = \sum_{j=1}^{n} \sigma_{ij}\alpha_j. \tag{17.2}$$

The coordinates $\xi_1, \cdots \xi_n$ determine an isomorphic mapping $\iota$: $V \to \mathbf{F}^n$ given by

$$a \to \{\xi_1(a), \cdots \xi_n(a)\} \text{ for } a \in V.$$

By use of these coordinates, $\sigma$ is represented by the endomorphism $\iota\sigma\iota^{-1}$ of $\mathbf{F}^n$, under which the column of the scalars $\alpha_1, \cdots \alpha_n$ is mapped into $\alpha_1', \cdots \alpha_n'$ by (17.2), and so by the matrix with elements $\sigma_{ij}$. Cf. (10.8).

In particular this can be applied when $V = \mathbf{F}^n$, where $\sigma$ and $\iota$ themselves may be considered as matrices, and where $\iota\sigma\iota^{-1}$ is the matrix whose elements have just been denoted by $\sigma_{ij}$, a notation which in this case might be replaced by the more complicated notation $(\iota\sigma\iota^{-1})_{ij}$.

Definition: Two endomorphisms $\sigma$ of V and $\sigma'$ of V′ are called *equivalent* if there exists an isomorphic mapping $\rho$: $V \to V'$ with inverse $\rho^{-1}$: $V' \to V$ such that

$$\sigma' = \rho\sigma\rho^{-1}.$$

If in this case $\iota$: $V \to \mathbf{F}^n$ is a coordinate system for V and $\iota\rho^{-1}$: $V' \to \mathbf{F}^n$ is a corresponding coordinate system for V', then the matrix representations of the endomorphisms $\sigma$ and $\sigma'$ are identical:

$$\iota\sigma\iota^{-1} = (\iota\rho^{-1})(\rho\sigma\rho^{-1})(\iota\rho^{-1})^{-1} = (\iota\rho^{-1})\sigma'(\iota\rho^{-1})^{-1}.$$

Conversely, two endomorphisms which have identical representations in $\mathbf{F}^n$ are equivalent. Equivalent endomorphisms cannot be distinguished by "internal" properties. The ranks of equivalent endomorphisms are equal (= rank of the matrix) and so are the determinants.

PROBLEM (17.1). Prove this latter assertion.

When $\sigma$ and $\sigma'$ are equivalent endomorphisms of $\mathbf{F}^n$, the matrices $\sigma$ and $\sigma'$ are called *similar matrices*.

In this chapter we discuss the equivalence classes of endomorphisms of complex and real vector spaces. If a function on the set of endomorphisms has the property that it associates the same value to any two equivalent endomorphisms (as indeed do the determinant "function" and the rank "function"), then this function is called an *invariant* of the endomorphisms. The word invariant is occasionally also used for the value of such a function for a particular endomorphism under consideration. According to the definition, an invariant may also be interpreted as a function on the set of equivalence classes of endomorphisms, but then the "invariance" is less conspicuous.

First of all we shall define a particular set of invariants of endomorphisms of complex vector spaces, and subsequently prove that any endomorphism admits a representation by means of coordinates which is entirely determined by these invariants. Hence these invariants provide a complete survey of all equivalence classes of endomorphisms.

By theorem [9.6] endomorphisms of a vector space form a ring. Let $\sigma$ be an endomorphism. We consider polynomials in $\sigma$ with coefficients in $\mathbf{F}$:

$$\lambda_0 + \lambda_1\sigma + \lambda_2\sigma^2 + \cdots + \lambda_p\sigma^p = \textstyle\sum_{i=0}^{p} \lambda_i\sigma^i.$$

In this formula $\lambda_0 = \lambda_0\sigma^0$ denotes the endomorphism with action

$$\lambda_0\colon \mathrm{a} \to \lambda_0\mathrm{a} \text{ for } \mathrm{a} \in V.$$

The sum and product of polynomials in $\sigma$ are again polynomials in $\sigma$ and the product is commutative:

$$(\Sigma_{i=0}^{p} \lambda_i\sigma^i)(\Sigma_{j=0}^{q} \mu_j\sigma^j) = (\Sigma_{j=0}^{q} \mu_j\sigma^j)(\Sigma_{i=0}^{p} \lambda_i\sigma^i).$$

*The polynomials in $\sigma$ therefore form a commutative (sub)ring of the ring of endomorphisms* (cf. theorem [9.6]). We shall often use the computational rules allowed by this property.

Definition: A vector $v \neq O$ is called an *eigenvector* (also called *proper* vector) of the endomorphism $\sigma$ if there exists a $\lambda \in \mathbf{F}$ such that

$$\sigma v = \lambda v, \text{ i.e. } (\sigma - \lambda)v = O. \tag{17.3}$$

The value $\lambda$ is called the corresponding *eigenvalue* (also called proper value, latent root or characteristic root). The set of eigenvalues is called the *spectrum* of $\sigma$. If v is eigenvector then also $\mu v$, $\mu \in \mathbf{F}$ ($\mu \neq 0$) is an eigenvector with the same eigenvalue:

$$\sigma\mu v = \mu\sigma v = \mu\lambda v = \lambda\mu v.$$

Consequently an eigenvector of $\sigma$ is a vector whose direction, (i.e. the 1-dimensional subspace generated) is invariant under $\sigma$.

The equation in v: $(\sigma - \lambda)v = O$ has a solution $v \neq O$ if and only if the endomorphism $\sigma - \lambda$ is singular. A necessary and sufficient condition is therefore

$$\det(\sigma - \lambda) = O.$$

Note that two endomorphisms which admit the same matrix representation under suitable coordinates have equal determinants. If, on the other hand, two representations of the same endomorphisms are given, then the determinants of these matrices are equal. Thus the determinant is an invariant of an endomorphism. If, by use of some coordinate system, $\sigma_{ij}$ and $\lambda\delta_{ij}$ for $i, j = 1, \cdots n$ are the elements of the matrices representing the endomorphisms $\sigma$ and $\lambda$ respectively, then

$$\det(\sigma - \lambda) = \det\{(\sigma_{ij} - \lambda\delta_{ij})\} = \begin{vmatrix} \sigma_{11}-\lambda & \sigma_{12} & \cdots & \sigma_{1n} \\ \sigma_{21} & \sigma_{22}-\lambda & \cdots & \sigma_{2n} \\ \cdots & \cdots & \cdots & \cdots \\ \cdots & \cdots & \cdots & \cdots \\ \sigma_{n1} & \sigma_{n2} & \cdots & \sigma_{nn}-\lambda \end{vmatrix} \tag{17.4}$$

This polynomial in $\lambda$ of degree $n$ which will be written briefly as $\sum_{i=0}^{n} s_i\lambda^i$ is called the *characteristic polynomial*. The eigenvalues of $\sigma$ are the roots of $\det(\sigma - \lambda) = 0$.

The characteristic polynomial as well as all its coefficients and eigenvalues depend on $\sigma$ only, and they are independent of the particular matrix representation of $\sigma$. They are invariants. In particular if $\rho$ is an arbitrary isomorphism of V onto another vector space then

$$\det(\sigma - \lambda) = \det(\rho\sigma\rho^{-1} - \lambda).$$

If the spaces V and $\rho$V both happen to be $\mathbf{F}^n$, then this is an assertion concerning matrices which can easily be verified by calculation:

$$\det(\sigma - \lambda) = (\det \rho) \det(\sigma - \lambda)(\det \rho)^{-1} = \det\{\rho(\sigma - \lambda)\rho^{-1}\} =$$

$$= \det\{(\rho\sigma - \rho\lambda)\rho^{-1}\} = \det(\rho\sigma\rho^{-1} - \lambda\rho\rho^{-1}) = \det(\rho\sigma\rho^{-1} - \lambda).$$

The coefficient of $\lambda^{n-1}$ in the characteristic polynomial, $s_{n-1} = \sigma_{11} + \sigma_{22} + \cdots + \sigma_{nn}$ is called the *trace* (or *spur*) of $\sigma$. $s_0$ is the determinant of $\sigma$. Also $s_n = 1$.

For the time being we restrict ourselves to the *complex numbers*: $\mathbf{F} = \mathbf{C}$. It is known from algebra that in this case any $n$-th degree polynomial is the product of $n$ linear factors, and this applies in particular to $\det(\sigma - \lambda)$. Since the coefficient of $\lambda^n$ is $(-1)^n$ there exist complex numbers $\lambda_i$, $i = 1, \cdots r$ such that

$$\det(\sigma - \lambda) = (-1)^n \prod_{i=1}^{r} (\lambda - \lambda_i)^{m_i}$$

$$\sum_{i=1}^{r} m_i = n, \quad \lambda_i \neq \lambda_j \text{ for } i \neq j. \tag{17.5}$$

$\lambda_i$ is an eigenvalue of $\sigma$; $m_i$ is called its *multiplicity*. The numbers $r$, $\lambda_i$ and $m_i$ (*invariants*) are uniquely determined by the polynomial $\det(\sigma - \lambda)$.

A subspace $B \subset V$ is called an *invariant subspace* of $\sigma$ if $\sigma(B) \subset B$. If the invariant subspaces $B_1, \cdots B_r$ of $\sigma$ together generate V then $\sigma$ is completely determined by its action on these invariant subspaces. For $\sigma$ is determined by its action on a basis of V, which can now be composed of the vectors of bases of $B_1, \cdots B_r$.

For the following theorem we need the notion of *partition*. A *partition* of a natural number $m$ is a set of natural numbers with sum $m$.

*Classification of endomorphisms (complex numbers)*

Let $\lambda_i$, $i = 1, \cdots r$ be the eigenvalues of the endomorphism $\sigma$ of an $n$-dimensional vector space $V^n$ over the complex numbers. If $m_i$ is the multiplicity of $\lambda_i$ then $\sum_{i=1}^{r} m_i = n$.

For the eigenvalue $\lambda$ with multiplicity $m$ and any integer $j \geqslant 0$ let $V_\lambda^{q_j}$ be the $q_j$-dimensional subspace of V which consists of all vectors $w \in V$ for which

$$(\sigma - \lambda)^j w = 0. \qquad (17.6)$$

Consequently $V_\lambda^{q_1}$ consists of the eigenvectors belonging to the eigenvalue $\lambda$. It is clear that

$$V_\lambda^{q_j} \subset V_\lambda^{q_{j+1}}. \qquad (17.7)$$

Let $p_{j+1} = q_{j+1} - q_j$. We shall prove the existence of an integer $t$ such that $q_{t'} = m$ *for* $t' > t$, *and*

$$p_1 \geqslant p_2 \geqslant \cdots \geqslant p_t > 0.$$

Hence $p_1 + p_2 + \cdots + p_t = m$. The numbers $p_j$, $j = 1, \cdots t$ form a partition $p(m)$ of $m$, belonging to the eigenvalue $\lambda$.

The space $V_\lambda^m$ containing all spaces $V_\lambda^q$ is called the *eigenspace* belonging to $\lambda$.

We now formulate the

Main Theorem [17.1]: *Two endomorphisms of* $V^n$ (*over* **C**) *are equivalent if and only if they have in common the eigenvalues* $\lambda_i$ *with their multiplicities* $m_i$ *and the characteristic partitions* $p(m_i)$ $i = 1, \cdots r$.

The nature of this theorem and its proof are not too easy. We may therefore treat a simple special case first.

Special case: If the endomorphism $\sigma$ of an $n$-dimensional vector space V has $n$ distinct eigenvalues $\lambda_1, \cdots \lambda_n$, thus each of multiplicity one, then the equivalence class of $\sigma$ is completely determined by these eigenvalues.

Proof of this special case: If $a_i$ is an eigenvector belonging to the eigenvalue $\lambda_i$, $i = 1, \cdots n$, so that $\sigma a_i = \lambda_i a_i$, then the vectors

$a_1, \cdots a_n$ are linearly independent. In order to prove this we consider $a = \alpha_1 a_1 + \cdots + \alpha_n a_n$ and apply $(\sigma - \lambda_1)$ to it:

$$(\sigma - \lambda_1)a = \sum_{i=1}^{n} \alpha_i(\sigma a_i - \lambda_1 a_i) = \sum_{i=2}^{n} \alpha_i(\lambda_i - \lambda_1)a_i.$$

This result has no component in the direction of $a_1$. Moreover we have

$$\{\prod_{i\neq j} (\sigma - \lambda_i)\}\, a =$$
$$(\sigma - \lambda_n)(\sigma - \lambda_{n-1})\cdots(\sigma - \lambda_{j+1})(\sigma - \lambda_{j-1})\cdots(\sigma - \lambda_1)a =$$
$$= \alpha_j(\lambda_j - \lambda_1)\cdots(\lambda_j - \lambda_{j-1})(\lambda_j - \lambda_{j+1})\cdots(\lambda_j - \lambda_n)a_j =$$
$$= \alpha_j[\prod_{i\neq j} (\lambda_j - \lambda_i)]a_j.$$

Now assume $a = O$. Then the above expression is zero, and hence $\alpha_j$ is zero. Since this holds for $j = 1, \cdots n$, the vectors $a_1, \cdots a_n$ are independent and form a basis of V.

If we choose as coordinates the cobasis of linear functions $\xi_1, \cdots \xi_n$, then $\sigma$ is expressed by the equations

$$\xi_i(\sigma a) = \lambda_i \xi_i(a) \quad i = 1, \cdots n,$$

which proves the assertion. The coordinates $\xi_1', \cdots \xi_n'$ of the image under $\sigma$ of a vector with coordinates $\xi_1, \cdots \xi_n$ can be found from

$$\begin{bmatrix} \xi_1' \\ \xi_2' \\ \cdot \\ \cdot \\ \cdot \\ \xi_n' \end{bmatrix} = \begin{bmatrix} \lambda_1 & 0 & \cdots & \cdots & 0 \\ 0 & \lambda_2 & \cdots & \cdots & 0 \\ & & & & \\ \cdots & \cdots & \cdots & \cdots & 0 \\ & & & & \\ 0 & 0 & \cdots & \cdots & \lambda_n \end{bmatrix} \begin{bmatrix} \xi_1 \\ \xi_2 \\ \cdot \\ \cdot \\ \cdot \\ \xi_n \end{bmatrix}.$$

Another important special case, namely that of an endomorphism which is symmetric with respect to a euclidean metric, *will be proved later in this chapter independently of the main theorem* (p. 171, after theorem [17.4]). We now give the

Proof* of the Main Theorem: We already know that the eigenvalues and multiplicities of $\sigma$ are uniquely determined by $\sigma$.

*The invariant subspaces.* The kernel of an endomorphism is a subspace. Now consider the subspace of those $w \in V$ satisfying

$$(\sigma - \lambda)^i w = O.$$

Any vector w that satisfies this relation also satisfies $(\sigma - \lambda)^{i+1}w=0$. It follows that $V_\lambda^{q_i} \subset V_\lambda^{q_{i+1}}$ (cf. definition (17.6)). In addition, if $w \in V_\lambda^{q_{i+1}}$ then $(\sigma - \lambda)w \in V_\lambda^{q_i} \subset V_\lambda^{q_{i+1}}$ and $\lambda w \in V_\lambda^{q_{i+1}}$ so that $\sigma w \in V_\lambda^{q_{i+1}}$. Consequently $V_\lambda^{q_{i+1}}$ is invariant under $\sigma$. The dimension $q_i$ is the rank of $(\sigma - \lambda)^i$ and is therefore also an invariant of $\sigma$.

*The partitions of the multiplicities.* For increasing $i$ in (17.7) the dimensions $q_i$ of $V_\lambda^{q_i}$ are increased by non-negative integral numbers. This increment can differ from zero only finitely often, since all $q_i \leqslant n$. Let $t$ be the greatest value of $i$ for which $q_i - q_{i-1} > 0$:

$$q_t - q_{t-1} > 0, \qquad q_s - q_{s-1} = 0 \text{ for } s > t. \tag{17.8}$$

Recall that $q_i$, $q_t$ and $t$ may assume different values for different eigenvalues. We concentrate on one eigenvalue.

Let $a_1, \cdots a_{q_t}$ be a basis of $V_\lambda^{q_t}$ with $a_1, \cdots a_{q_i} \in V_\lambda^{q_i}$, $i=1, \cdots t$. None of the vectors $w = \sum_{j=q_i+1}^{q_{i+1}} \alpha_j a_j \neq 0$ is contained in $V_\lambda^{q_i}$, and hence the image under $(\sigma - \lambda)$ of none of these vectors is contained in $V_\lambda^{q_{i-1}}$. This implies that these vectors are certainly $\neq 0$, and so the vectors $(\sigma - \lambda)a_j$, $j = q_i + 1, \cdots q_{i+1}$ are linearly independent. They span a subspace of $V_\lambda^{q_i}$ which is linearly independent of $V_\lambda^{q_{i-1}}$. The dimensions satisfy the relation

$$q_{i+1} - q_i \leqslant q_i - q_{i-1}.$$

Hence the differences $q_i - q_{i-1} = p_i$, $i = 1, \cdots t$, $q_0 = 0$, form a non-increasing sequence of natural numbers.

*Proof that $q_t = m$.* First of all we prove that $q_t \geqslant m$. Choose a basis $a_1, \cdots a_n$ for V with $a_1, \cdots a_{q_t} \in V_\lambda^{q_t}$ and take its cobasis as coordinate system for V.

$\sigma$ maps any vector with last $n - q_t$ coordinates zero into a vector having the same property. Hence, for variable $\mu \in \mathbf{C}$, the matrix representing $\sigma - \mu$ has the form

$$(\sigma - \mu) = \begin{pmatrix} \sigma' - \mu & \cdot\cdot \\ \mathbf{0} & \sigma'' - \mu \end{pmatrix}$$

where $\sigma'$ is a square matrix with $q_t$ rows and columns, $\sigma''$ a square matrix with $n - q_t$ rows and columns, and $\mathbf{0}$ is an $(n - q_t) \times q_t$-matrix consisting of zeros only. Then

$$\det(\sigma - \mu) = \det(\sigma' - \mu) \cdot \det(\sigma'' - \mu).$$

$\mathrm{Det}(\sigma' - \mu)$ is a polynomial of degree $q_t$ in $\mu$, and has, therefore, at most $q_t$ factors $(\mu - \lambda)$. If now $q_t < m$, then $\det(\sigma'' - \mu)$ must also contain at least one factor $\mu - \lambda$ in order to obtain the $m$ factors that $\det(\sigma - \mu)$ is known to have. Hence

$$\det(\sigma'' - \lambda) = 0.$$

But then there exists a linear combination

$$\mathrm{w} = \textstyle\sum_{j=q_t+1}^{n} \alpha_j \mathrm{a}_j \neq \mathrm{O}$$

such that the last $n - q_t$ components of $(\sigma - \lambda)\mathrm{w}$ are zero; hence

$$(\sigma - \lambda)\mathrm{w} \in \mathrm{V}_\lambda^{q_t}$$

whereas

$$\mathrm{w} \notin \mathrm{V}_\lambda^{q_t}.$$

But then this vector $\mathrm{w} \neq \mathrm{O}$ satisfies

$$(\sigma - \lambda)^{t+1}\mathrm{w} = \mathrm{O}, \qquad (\sigma - \lambda)^t\, \mathrm{w} \neq \mathrm{O},$$

contrary to our assumption (17.8). It follows that $q_t$ cannot be less than $m$, so that $q_t \geqslant m$ for any eigenvalue.

Next we prove that the eigenspaces $\mathrm{V}_\lambda^{q_t}$ are linearly independent for $\lambda = \lambda_i$, $i = 1, \cdots r$. This will then imply by theorem [5.6] that the sum of their dimensions is $\leqslant n$; on the other hand the sum is $\geqslant \sum_{i=1}^{r} m_i = n$. Hence the dimensions are equal to $m_i$: $q_t = m$ for each eigenvalue.

If $\mathrm{w} \in \mathrm{V}_{\lambda_i}^{q_j+1}$ and $\mathrm{w} \notin \mathrm{V}_{\lambda_i}^{q_j}$, then $(\sigma - \lambda_i)\mathrm{w} \in \mathrm{V}_{\lambda_i}^{q_j}$, and for $k \neq i$ we have that $(\sigma - \lambda_k)\mathrm{w} = (\sigma - \lambda_i)\mathrm{w} + (\lambda_i - \lambda_k)\mathrm{w}$ is contained in $\mathrm{V}_{\lambda_i}^{q_j+1}$ and not in $\mathrm{V}_{\lambda_i}^{q_j}$. By repeated application it follows that if $\mathrm{O} \neq \mathrm{b}_i \in \mathrm{V}_{\lambda_i}^{q_t}$ and $k \neq i$, then

$$(\sigma - \lambda_i)^n \mathrm{b}_i = \mathrm{O} \text{ and } \mathrm{O} \neq (\sigma - \lambda_k)^n \mathrm{b}_i \in \mathrm{V}_{\lambda_i}^{q_t}.$$

Now suppose that $\mathrm{O} \neq \mathrm{b}_i \in \mathrm{V}_{\lambda_i}^{q_t}$, $i = 1, \cdots r$ and

$$\textstyle\sum_{j=1}^{r} \beta_j \mathrm{b}_j = \mathrm{O}. \tag{17.9}$$

Then

$$0 = \prod_{i \neq k} (\sigma - \lambda_i)^n \sum_{j=1}^{r} \beta_j b_j = \prod_{i \neq k} (\sigma - \lambda_i)^n \beta_k b_k = \beta_k b_k'$$

where $b_k'$ is a non-zero vector. Then $\beta_k = 0$. This holds for $k = 1, \cdots r$: all coefficients in (17.9) are zero and the vectors $b_i$ are linearly independent. Since this holds for any choice of $b_i \in V_{\lambda_i}^{q_i}$, $i = 1, \cdots r$, the spaces $V_{\lambda_i}^{q_i}$, $i = 1, \cdots r$ are linearly independent.

Since $q_i = m$ for each eigenvalue, all invariants $r$, $\lambda_i$, $m_i$ and $p(m_i)$ mentioned in the main theorem are uniquely defined.

*The canonical representation.* We still have to prove that the equivalence class of an endomorphism $\sigma$ is completely determined by the above invariants. To do so, we shall choose a coordinate system so that we get a particular representation $\sigma$, such that any two equivalent endomorphisms are represented by the same matrix. This representation which we shall sketch in the sequel is called the *canonical normal form of Jordan. We choose the coordinate system by taking a suitable basis of the vector space* V *and by taking coordinates from the cobasis*. The construction of the basis runs as follows. First we order the $r$ different eigenvalues according to increasing real part. If there are two or more eigenvalues with equal real parts then we order them according to increasing real parts of the quantities $- i\lambda$. Let $\lambda_1, \cdots \lambda_r$ be the sequence of eigenvalues in this order.

The required basis will consist of the vectors of the bases of consecutively $V_{\lambda_1}^{m_1}, V_{\lambda_2}^{m_2}, \cdots V_{\lambda_r}^{m_r}$.

In the corresponding coordinates (a dual basis) the matrix representing $\sigma$ has the form:

$$\begin{bmatrix} \sigma_1 & & & \\ & \sigma_2 & & \\ & & \ddots & \\ & & & \sigma_r \end{bmatrix}$$

In this array $\sigma_i$ is an $m_i \times m_i$-matrix, and the empty places outside the "diagonal" contain zero elements only.

The basis of $V_\lambda{}^m\{(m, \lambda) = (m_i, \lambda_i); i = 1, \cdots r\}$ is constructed step by step. In order to follow this construction, it is convenient to consider the result for an example as given in the matrices below. In that example we observe that $e_1, e_2, e_3; e_4, e_5, e_6; e_7, e_8; e_9; e_{10}$ generate respectively five subspaces each of which is invariant. $e_j$ is the $j$-th standard basis vector in $\mathbf{R}^{10}$ (cf. p. 71).

The restriction of $\sigma$ to each of these subspaces is completely determined, apart from the eigenvalue $\lambda$, by its dimension. In the construction we obtain in each step such an invariant subspace of the highest possible dimension. In the example subspaces of dimension 3, 3, 2, 1 and 1 respectively are obtained in the successive steps.

We now give the construction. In each step, including the first one, a number of vectors of the basis is constructed. In any step first consider for the greatest possible $j$ a vector w which lies in $V_\lambda^{q_j}$ but not in the space generated by the basis vectors obtained so far and $V_\lambda^{q_j-1}$. For the next step basis vectors

$$(\sigma - \lambda)^k w, \; k = j - 1, j - 2, \cdots 2, 1, 0 \text{ respectively, are taken.}$$

In the example below we may take for w in the successive steps the standard basis vectors of $\mathbf{R}^{10}$: $e_3, e_6, e_8, e_9, e_{10}$. But in the first step one could also have started with $\alpha_3 e_3 + \alpha_6 e_6$, where $\alpha_3$ and $\alpha_6$ are real numbers which do not both vanish.

By use of the dual basis as coordinates, the matrices representing the restrictions of $\sigma - \lambda$ and $\sigma$ to $V_\lambda^m$ assume the *canonical form*, also called *Jordan's normal form*.

If

$$m = 10, p(m) = p_1 + p_2 + p_3 = 5 + 3 + 2, q_1 = 5, q_2 = 8, q_3 = 10,$$

then Jordan's normal form is

$$\sigma - \lambda = \begin{bmatrix} 0 & 1 &&&&&&&& \\ & 0 & 1 &&&&&&& \\ && 0 &&&&&&& \\ &&& 0 & 1 &&&&& \\ &&&& 0 & 1 &&&& \\ &&&&& 0 &&&& \\ &&&&&& 0 & 1 && \\ &&&&&&& 0 && \\ &&&&&&&& 0 & \\ &&&&&&&&& 0 \end{bmatrix}, \quad \sigma = \begin{bmatrix} \lambda & 1 &&&&&&&& \\ & \lambda & 1 &&&&&&& \\ && \lambda &&&&&&& \\ &&& \lambda & 1 &&&&& \\ &&&& \lambda & 1 &&&& \\ &&&&& \lambda &&&& \\ &&&&&& \lambda & 1 && \\ &&&&&&& \lambda && \\ &&&&&&&& \lambda & \\ &&&&&&&&& \lambda \end{bmatrix}$$

Let V itself be the space $\mathbf{C}^n$ of columns of $n$ complex numbers and let $\sigma$ be an endomorphism of it, i.e. a matrix; let $b_1, \cdots b_n$ be a basis constructed from $\sigma$ as above; let $e_1, \cdots e_n$ be the basis of standard basis vectors in $\mathbf{C}^n$; and let finally $\tau$ be the endomorphism (= matrix) with the action

$$\tau e_i = b_i;$$

then $\tau^{-1}\sigma\tau$ is a matrix having Jordan's normal form. Hence: *To any square matrix $\sigma$ there exists a non-singular matrix $\tau$ such that $\tau^{-1}\sigma\tau$ has Jordan's normal form.*

PROBLEMS. (17.2). Find the canonical matrix for an endomorphism with invariants $\lambda_1$, $m_1 = 8$, $p(m_1) = 6 + 1 + 1$; $\lambda_2$, $m_2 = 4$, $p(m_2) = 4$; and $\lambda_3$, $m_3 = 4$, $p(m_3) = 1 + 1 + 1 + 1$. $\lambda_1$, $\lambda_2$ and $\lambda_3$ are different.

(17.3). Give a survey of all equivalence classes of the endomorphisms of a 2-dimensional complex vector space.

(17.4). Do the same for a three-dimensional vector space.

(17.5). Do the same for a four-dimensional vector space.

*Endomorphisms of real vector spaces* *

Let V be an $n$-dimensional real vector space with an isomorphism, giving a coordinate system, $\vartheta$: V $\to \mathbf{R}^n$.

Since real numbers can be considered as special complex numbers, sequences of $n$ real numbers may be considered as sequences of special complex numbers. This yields a natural mapping of the real number space $\mathbf{R}^n$ into the complex number space $\mathbf{C}^n$.

We now introduce a set $\hat{V}$, containing V, whose elements admit a one-to-one representation by the elements of $\mathbf{C}^n$ such that restriction to V just yields the given $\vartheta$: V $\to \mathbf{R}^n \subset \mathbf{C}^n$. We shall denote this mapping of $\hat{V}$ into $\mathbf{C}^n$ by $\hat{\vartheta}$.

If $\vartheta'$: V $\to \mathbf{R}^n$ is another coordinate system, then $\vartheta'\vartheta^{-1}$: $\mathbf{R}^n \to \mathbf{R}^n$ is a non-singular endomorphism, i.e. a matrix of real numbers. For this second coordinate system we can also define a representation in $\mathbf{C}^n$ of elements of $\hat{V}$ which are not in V as follows: the element previously mapped to $c \in \mathbf{C}^n$ by $\hat{\vartheta}$ will now be mapped to

$$\vartheta'\vartheta^{-1}c = c', \tag{17.10}$$

a formula which makes sense since the real matrix $\vartheta'\vartheta^{-1}$ can also be considered as a special complex matrix. The new mapping will be denoted by $\hat{\vartheta}'$, and

$$\hat{\vartheta}'\hat{\vartheta}^{-1} = \vartheta'\vartheta^{-1}.$$

In $\hat{\mathrm{V}}$ addition and multiplication by complex numbers can be defined by the conventions

$$\hat{\vartheta}(\hat{\mathrm{a}} + \hat{\mathrm{b}}) = \hat{\vartheta}\hat{\mathrm{a}} + \hat{\vartheta}\hat{\mathrm{b}},\ \hat{\vartheta}(\lambda\hat{\mathrm{a}}) = \lambda\hat{\vartheta}\hat{\mathrm{a}};\ \hat{\mathrm{a}}, \hat{\mathrm{b}} \in \hat{\mathrm{V}},\ \lambda \in \mathbf{C}, \qquad (17.11)$$

i.e. by carrying over the vector space structure of $\mathbf{C}^n$ to $\hat{\mathrm{V}}$ by means of one particular mapping $\hat{\vartheta}$. From (17.11) by pre-multiplication with the endomorphism $\hat{\vartheta}'\hat{\vartheta}^{-1}$ we get:

$$\hat{\vartheta}'(\hat{\mathrm{a}} + \hat{\mathrm{b}}) = \hat{\vartheta}'\hat{\mathrm{a}} + \hat{\vartheta}'\hat{\mathrm{b}},\ \hat{\vartheta}'(\lambda\hat{\mathrm{a}}) = \lambda\hat{\vartheta}'\hat{\mathrm{a}}.$$

This means that the vector space structure as defined above is independent of the special choice of $\vartheta$ (or $\hat{\vartheta}$).

Definition: The complex vector space $\hat{\mathrm{V}}$ so constructed is called the *complexification* of V; $\hat{\vartheta}$ is an isomorphism of $\hat{\mathrm{V}}$ onto $\mathbf{C}^n$.

The vectors $\mathrm{V} \subset \hat{\mathrm{V}}$ are called *real vectors*. They are the vectors having real coordinates under the given coordinate systems of $\hat{\mathrm{V}}$.

Two vectors v and w $\in \hat{\mathrm{V}}$ are called *complex conjugates* of each other if v + w and $i$(v − w) are real, i.e. v + w and $i$(v−w) $\in$ V. The relation of being complex conjugates is symmetric (cf. chapter 2). It follows if both w and w + u are complex conjugates of v, that u and $i$u are real, hence are in V, which is possible only if u = O. Thus v has exactly one complex conjugate, which is denoted by $\bar{\mathrm{v}}$. Furthermore $\bar{\bar{\mathrm{v}}} = \mathrm{v}$, $\overline{\mathrm{v} + \mathrm{w}} = \bar{\mathrm{v}} + \bar{\mathrm{w}}$, $\overline{\lambda\mathrm{v}} = \bar{\lambda}\bar{\mathrm{v}}$. Under one of the coordinate systems for $\hat{\mathrm{V}}$ mentioned above, v and w can be complex conjugates only if the same holds for all the other coordinate systems mentioned above.

Under a coordinate system $\vartheta$ an endomorphism $\sigma$: V → V is expressed by

$$\vartheta\sigma\vartheta^{-1}: \mathbf{R}^n \to \mathbf{R}^n,$$

the matrix of which determines also an endomorphism $\rho$: $\mathbf{C}^n \to \mathbf{C}^n$. Under a coordinate system $\hat{\vartheta}$: $\hat{\mathrm{V}} \to \mathbf{C}^n$ this induces an endomorphism

$$\hat{\sigma} = \hat{\vartheta}^{-1}\rho\hat{\vartheta}: \hat{\mathrm{V}} \to \hat{\mathrm{V}}.$$

The matrices $\rho = \hat{\vartheta}\hat{\sigma}\hat{\vartheta}^{-1}$ and $\vartheta\sigma\vartheta^{-1}$ are identical.

$\hat{\sigma}$, the complexification of $\sigma$, is completely determined by $\sigma$. From the representation in $\mathbf{R}^n$ or $\mathbf{C}^n$ respectively, we see immediately that two real-equivalent endomorphisms $\sigma$ and $\sigma'$ of real vector spaces have real-equivalent (and therefore complex-equivalent) complexifications $\hat{\sigma}$ and $\hat{\sigma}'$. Hence all invariants (cf. main theorem [17.1]) of $\hat{\sigma}$ are also invariants of $\sigma$. This is the "necessary part" of the following theorem.

Theorem [17.2]: *A necessary and sufficient condition that two endomorphisms $\sigma\colon \mathrm{V} \to \mathrm{V}$ and $\sigma'\colon \mathrm{V}' \to \mathrm{V}'$ of real vector spaces are equivalent is that their complexifications $\hat{\sigma}\colon \hat{\mathrm{V}} \to \hat{\mathrm{V}}$ and $\hat{\sigma}'\colon \hat{\mathrm{V}}' \to \hat{\mathrm{V}}'$ are (complex-)equivalent.*

Furthermore we shall see that an endomorphism of a complex vector space can be considered as complexification of an endomorphism of a real vector space if and only if, for any non-real eigenvalue $\lambda$, $\bar{\lambda}$ is also an eigenvalue with the same multiplicity and partition as $\lambda$.

By the main theorem [17.1] the complete classification of the endomorphisms of real vector spaces then follows.

In the following we shall use the symbol $\sigma$ for a real endomorphism as well as for its complexification (instead of $\hat{\sigma}$).

Proof of theorem [17.2]: If $\lambda$ is a real eigenvalue of the real endomorphism $\sigma\colon \mathrm{V} \to \mathrm{V}$ with multiplicity $m$ and partition $p(m)$ then a real basis $\mathrm{a}_1, \cdots \mathrm{a}_m$ of $\mathrm{V}_\lambda^m$ is constructed in the same way as in the case of an endomorphism of a complex space, as the reader will be able to verify.

Now let $\lambda$ be a non-real eigenvalue of $\sigma$ and let $\mathrm{a}_1, \cdots \mathrm{a}_m$ be a basis of the invariant subspace $\hat{\mathrm{V}}_\lambda^m \subset \hat{\mathrm{V}}$, constructed as in the proof of the main theorem [17.1]. Then there are relations of type

$$(\sigma - \lambda)\mathrm{a}_j = \mathrm{a}_{j-1} \text{ or } (\sigma - \lambda)\mathrm{a}_j = \mathrm{O} \text{ for } j = 1, \cdots m. \quad (17.12)$$

$\sigma$ maps real vectors into real vectors, hence

$$\sigma(\mathrm{v} + \bar{\mathrm{v}}) = \sigma(\mathrm{v}) + \sigma(\bar{\mathrm{v}}) \text{ is real}$$

$$\sigma\{i(\mathrm{v} - \bar{\mathrm{v}})\} = i\{\sigma(\mathrm{v}) - \sigma(\bar{\mathrm{v}})\} \text{ is real.}$$

This means that $\sigma(\bar{v})$ is the complex conjugate of $\sigma(v)$:

$$\overline{\sigma(v)} = \sigma(\bar{v}). \qquad (17.12')$$

By taking complex conjugates we obtain from (17.12 and 12′) $(\sigma - \bar{\lambda})\,\bar{a}_j = \bar{a}_{j-1}$ and $(\sigma - \bar{\lambda})\bar{a}_j = O$ respectively, for $j = 1, \cdots m$. The vectors $\bar{a}_1, \cdots \bar{a}_m$ are *linearly* independent since $\sum \alpha_i \bar{a}_i = O$ implies $\overline{\sum \alpha_i \bar{a}_i} = \sum \bar{\alpha}_i a_i = O$; since, $a_1, \cdots a_m$ are independent we have $\bar{\alpha}_i = 0$ and $\alpha_i = 0$. $\bar{a}_1, \cdots \bar{a}_m$ lie in the invariant space of eigenvalue $\bar{\lambda}$ because

$$\overline{(\sigma - \lambda)^m a_j} = (\sigma - \bar{\lambda})^m \bar{a}_j = O \text{ for } j = 1, \cdots m.$$

Hence this space has dimension $\geqslant m$, but, since the roles of $\lambda$ and $\bar{\lambda}$ can be interchanged, it also has dimension $\leqslant m$; its dimension then is $m$.

In the $m$-dimensional space $\hat{V}_{\bar{\lambda}}{}^m$ the vectors $\bar{a}_1, \cdots \bar{a}_m$ form a basis. With respect to this basis the restriction of $\sigma$ to $\hat{V}_{\bar{\lambda}}{}^m$ has the same representation in cobasis coordinates when $\lambda$ is replaced by $\bar{\lambda}$, as has the restriction of $\sigma$ to $V_\lambda{}^m$ relative to the cobasis coordinates belonging to $a_1, \cdots a_m$.

We remark that since $\hat{V}_\lambda{}^m$ and $\hat{V}_{\bar{\lambda}}{}^m$ are linearly independent, $a_1, \cdots a_m, \bar{a}_1, \cdots \bar{a}_m$ are linearly independent so that certainly $\bar{a}_j \neq a_j$; hence none of the vectors $a_j$, $j = 1, \cdots m$ is real.

Put $a_j = b_j + ic_j$, $\bar{a}_j = b_j - ic_j$, $\lambda = \rho(\cos\varphi + i\sin\varphi)$. Now $b_j$, $c_j$, $\rho$ and $\varphi$ are real. $\sigma(b_j + ic_j) = \rho(\cos\varphi + i\sin\varphi)(b_j + ic_j) + \nu_j(b_{j-1} + ic_{j-1})$; $\nu_j = 0$ or $1$, $\nu_1 = 0$. Hence, separating real and imaginary parts:

$$\left.\begin{aligned} \sigma(b_j) &= \rho(\cos\varphi\cdot b_j - \sin\varphi\cdot c_j) + \nu_j b_{j-1} \\ \sigma(c_j) &= \rho(\sin\varphi\cdot b_j + \cos\varphi\cdot c_j) \qquad\qquad + \nu_j c_{j-1} \end{aligned}\right\}. \qquad (17.13)$$

The real $b_j$, $c_j$ can now be chosen as a basis for the space generated by $\hat{V}_\lambda{}^m$ and $\hat{V}_{\bar{\lambda}}{}^m$. Then (17.13) also gives a real endomorphism in the real vector space with basis $b_j$, $c_j$, $j = 1, \cdots m$. It also yields a canonical representation in real cobasis coordinates for the restriction of $\sigma$ to the real part of the join of $V_\lambda{}^m$ and $V_{\bar{\lambda}}{}^m$.

Any complex endomorphism with the properties mentioned after theorem [17.2] is the complexification of a real endomorphism; this may be seen as follows. Choose a canonical basis for the given complex endomorphism $\hat{\sigma}$: B → B. We retain the basis vectors corresponding to real eigenvalues, and replace the basis vectors $a_1, \cdots a_m$ and $\dot{a}_1, \cdots \dot{a}_m$ corresponding to the complex eigenvalues $\lambda_1, \cdots \lambda_m$ and $\bar{\lambda}_1, \cdots \bar{\lambda}_m$ respectively, by

$$\frac{1}{2}(a_j + \dot{a}_j) \text{ and } \frac{1}{2i}(a_j - \dot{a}_j).$$

The cobasis of this basis for B is now chosen as coordinate system $\hat{\vartheta}$: B → $\mathbf{C}^n$. In B we define a subset A consisting of the vectors with real coordinates. A is a real vector space invariant under $\hat{\sigma}$ and has the property that B is the complexification of A and $\hat{\sigma}$ is the complexification of the restriction $\sigma$ of $\hat{\sigma}$ to A.

Moreover the vector $a_i$ is the complex conjugate of $a_i$: $\dot{a}_i = \bar{a}_i$ with respect to the real vector space A.

Problems. (17.6). Find the canonical matrix representation of an endomorphism of a real 4-dimensional vector space whose complexification has the invariants

$$\lambda_1 = \rho(\cos\varphi + i\sin\varphi),\ \lambda_2 = \bar{\lambda}_1,\ m_1 = m_2 = 2,\ p(m_1) = p(m_2) = 1+1.$$

(17.7). An endomorphism of an odd-dimensional real vector space leaves at least one 1-dimensional subspace invariant.

(17.8). Give a survey of all equivalence classes of the endomorphisms of an $n$-dimensional real vector space for the case $n = 2$.

(17.9). Do the same for the case $n = 3$.

(17.10). Do the same for the case $n = 4$.

*Symmetric endomorphisms and quadratic functions on a euclidean vector space.*

An endomorphism $\sigma$ of a euclidean vector space E is called *symmetric* if for all x, y ∈ E the following inner products are equal

$$x(\sigma y) = y(\sigma x).$$

We shall now formulate and prove the special case for symmetric endomorphisms of theorem [17.1] announced on p. 161. A proof that does not depend on theorem [17.1] will be given after theorem [17.4].

Theorem [17.3]: *All eigenvalues of a real symmetric endomorphism are real and all characteristic partitions of the multiplicities are trivial*: $p(m) = m$.

Proof: If $z = x + iy$ is an eigenvector of $\sigma$ belonging to the eigenvalue $\lambda$ then $\bar{z} = x - iy$ is an eigenvector belonging to the eigenvalue $\bar{\lambda}$, and because of the symmetry of $\sigma$:

$$0 = z(\sigma\bar{z}) - \bar{z}(\sigma z) = z(\bar{\lambda}\bar{z}) - \bar{z}(\lambda z) = (\bar{\lambda} - \lambda)z\,\bar{z} =$$

$$= (\bar{\lambda} - \lambda)(x + iy)\,(x - iy) = (\bar{\lambda} - \lambda)(x^2 + y^2).$$

Since $z \neq O$, $x^2 + y^2 > 0$ and $\bar{\lambda} - \lambda = 0$, so that $\lambda$ is real. If furthermore for a real eigenvalue $\lambda$, $p(m) \neq m$ then, by the construction in the proof of the main theorem, there exist real non-zero vectors $a_1$ and $a_2$ such that

$$\sigma a_1 = \lambda a_1$$

$$\sigma a_2 = a_1 + \lambda a_2;$$

and because of the symmetry

$$0 = a_1(\sigma a_2) - a_2(\sigma a_1) = a_1(a_1 + \lambda a_2) - a_2(\lambda a_1) = a_1{}^2$$

which is a contradiction.

Theorem [17.4]: *If* a *and* b *are non-zero eigenvectors belonging to the eigenvalues* $\lambda$ *and* $\mu \neq \lambda$ *of a symmetric endomorphism of the euclidean vector space* E, *then* a *and* b *are perpendicular.*

Proof: $0 = a(\sigma b) - b(\sigma a) = a(\mu b) - b(\lambda a) = (\mu - \lambda)ab$ hence $ab = 0$.

Theorem [17.3] implies that a *symmetric endomorphism* of a euclidean vector space always has a matrix representation in euclidean coordinates in which all elements $\sigma_{ij}$ with $i \neq j$ are zero. This theorem can also be very simply proved directly, without use of the main theorem. Again we start by proving as above that all eigenvalues are real. Subsequently we remark that if $x \neq O$ is an eigenvector (eigenvalue $\lambda$) of a symmetric endomorphism $\sigma$ then the space of all vectors perpendicular to x is invariant under $\sigma$. For, if y is perpendicular to x, i.e. $xy = 0$ then $x(\sigma y) = y(\sigma x) = = y(\lambda x) = \lambda xy = 0$, hence $\sigma y$ perpendicular to x. Since there certainly exists one eigenvector of $\sigma$, there exists such an x. The same argument applies to the space perpendicular to x, and so forth. This yields a basis of mutually perpendicular eigenvectors, which may be supposed to have unit lengths. The cobasis of this basis is a set of euclidean coordinates of the euclidean vector space. Hence:

Theorem [17.5]: *Euclidean classification of symmetric endomorphisms. If $\sigma$ is a symmetric endomorphism of a euclidean (real) vector space* E *then there exists a system of euclidean coordinates* $\vartheta: \mathrm{E} \to \mathbf{R}^n$ *such that* $\vartheta\sigma\vartheta^{-1}$ *is a matrix with zeros outside the diagonal.*

$$\vartheta\sigma\vartheta^{-1} = \begin{bmatrix} \lambda_1 & & & & & \\ & \lambda_2 & & & & \\ & & \cdot & & & \\ & & & \cdot & & \\ & & & & \cdot & \\ & & & & & \lambda_m \end{bmatrix}$$

The diagonal elements are the eigenvalues of $\sigma$.

Any bilinear function $\varphi$ (not necessarily symmetric) satisfies $\varphi(\mathrm{x}, \mathrm{y}) = \mathrm{x}(\sigma\mathrm{y})$ for just one endomorphism $\sigma$. For, the function $\varphi$ is completely determined by the values $\varphi(\mathrm{a}_i, \mathrm{a}_j)$, $i, j = 1, \cdots n$, where $\mathrm{a}_1, \cdots \mathrm{a}_n$ is an orthogonal basis of unit vectors of E. The endomorphism $\sigma$ determined by $\varphi$ is the one with the action

$$\sigma\mathrm{a}_j = \textstyle\sum_{i=1}^{n} \varphi(\mathrm{a}_i, \mathrm{a}_j)\cdot\mathrm{a}_i.$$

Indeed for this endomorphism $\sigma$ and for the bilinear function $\mathrm{x}(\sigma\mathrm{y})$ we have

$$\mathrm{a}_i(\sigma\mathrm{a}_j) = \varphi(\mathrm{a}_i, \mathrm{a}_j).$$

Since any bilinear *symmetric* function on V can be written in the form $(\mathrm{x}, \mathrm{y}) \to \mathrm{x}(\sigma\mathrm{y})$ with *$\sigma$ symmetric*, the following theorem is an immediate consequence of theorem [17.5] if we choose the special coordinates mentioned there:

Theorem [17.6]: *Euclidean classification of quadratic functions on a euclidean vector space. For any quadratic function $\varphi^{\cdot}$ on an $n$-dimensional euclidean vector space there exist euclidean coordinates*

$\xi_1, \cdots \xi_n$ *such that the quadratic function is expressed by*

$$x \to x(\sigma x) = \varphi(x, x) = \varphi^{\cdot}(x) = \textstyle\sum_{i=1}^{n} \lambda_i \xi_i^2(x).$$

*The real numbers $\lambda_i$ are the eigenvalues of the symmetric endomorphism $\sigma$ determined by $\varphi^{\cdot}$ and the euclidean vector space.*

Let $\varphi$ be a bilinear symmetric function on a euclidean vector space, and let $\varphi\cdot$ be its diagonal. Then the corresponding symmetric endomorphism $\sigma$ for which

$$x(\sigma y) = \varphi(y, x)$$

can be determined geometrically.

Choose a vector y for which $\varphi\cdot(y) \neq 0$. (In fig. 17.1 we took $\varphi\cdot(y) = \varphi(y, y) = 1$.) Then $\sigma y$ is obtained as follows. Consider the conjugate hyperplane with equation in x, $\varphi(x, y) = x(\sigma y) = 0$. It is clear that $\sigma y$ is a vector orthogonal to any x in this hyperplane. Hence, $\sigma y$ is orthogonal to this hyperplane. Next, choose (the length of) $\sigma y$ so that $\varphi\cdot(y) = \varphi(y, y) = (y, \sigma y)$. In the figure where $\varphi\cdot(y) = 1$ this inner product $(y, \sigma y)$ is equal to 1. It is sufficient to do the same for the vectors of a base of such vectors y to determine $\sigma$ completely.

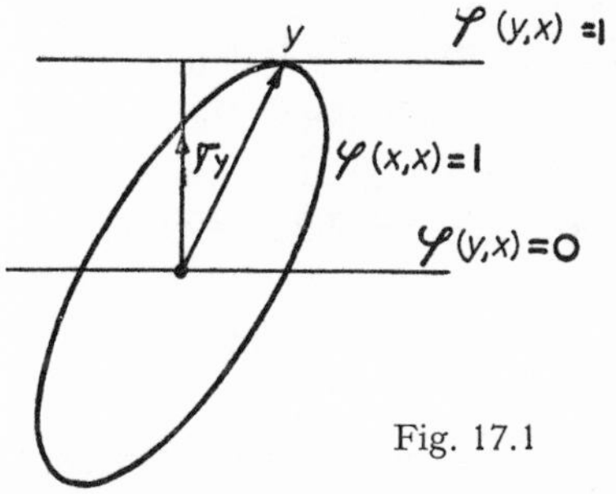


Fig. 17.1

*Orthogonal endomorphisms*

An endomorphism $\sigma$ of a euclidean vector space E is called *orthogonal* if

$$(\sigma x)(\sigma y) = xy \qquad \text{for } x, y \in E. \qquad (17.14)$$

*The length of a vector* x *is then equal to the length of its image* $\sigma$x. *The angle between two vectors* x *and* y *is equal to the angle between* $\sigma$x *and* $\sigma$y.

Using the transposed of a vector (cf. chapters 9 and 15), (17.14) can be rewritten as a product of two matrices, the first of which is a row and the other a column:

$$^t(\sigma x)(\sigma y) = {}^t xy.$$

If $\sigma$ is a matrix, i.e. an endomorphism $\sigma$: $\mathbf{R}^n \to \mathbf{R}^n$ then we obtain

$$0 = {}^t x^t \sigma \sigma y - {}^t xy = {}^t x[{}^t \sigma \sigma y - y] = {}^t x[{}^t \sigma \sigma - 1]y.$$

The bilinear function $(x, y) \to {}^t x[{}^t\sigma\sigma - 1]y$ is identically zero if and only if

$$
{}^t\sigma\sigma = 1 \text{ (the unit matrix)}, \qquad (17.15)
$$
$$
{}^t\sigma = \sigma^{-1}.
$$

A *matrix* $\sigma$ satisfying (17.15) is called *orthogonal* (cf. problem (12.12)).

Theorem [17.7]: *Classification of orthogonal endomorphisms.* If $\sigma$ is an orthogonal endomorphism of a euclidean vector space E, then E is generated by mutually perpendicular invariant subspaces of dimensions 1 or 2. $\sigma$ restricted to a 1-dimensional invariant subspace is the *identity* $x \to x$ or the *reflection*: $x \to -x$. $\sigma$ restricted to a two-dimensional invariant subspace B which does not contain invariant 1-dimensional subspaces is a *rotation*, i.e. if $a_1$ and $a_2$ are perpendicular unit vectors in B, it is an endomorphism with action

$$
\begin{cases} \sigma(a_1) = \cos\varphi \cdot a_1 + \sin\varphi \cdot a_2 \\ \sigma(a_2) = -\sin\varphi \cdot a_1 + \cos\varphi \cdot a_2 \end{cases} \qquad \varphi \not\equiv 0 \text{ mod. } \pi.
$$

*Therefore, with suitable euclidean coordinates the matrix of an orthogonal endomorphism is*

$$
\begin{bmatrix} \sigma_1 & & & & \\ & \sigma_2 & & & \\ & & \cdot & & \\ & & & \cdot & \\ & & & & \cdot \\ & & & & & \sigma_m \end{bmatrix}
$$

*with* $\sigma_i = 1, -1$ *or* $\begin{pmatrix} \cos\varphi_i & \sin\varphi_i \\ -\sin\varphi_i & \cos\varphi_i \end{pmatrix}$ *for* $i = 1, \cdots m$, *and zeros in all other places.*

Proof: If $\lambda$ is a real eigenvalue with a real eigenvector x, then

$$
xx = (\sigma x)(\sigma x) = (\lambda x)\lambda x) = \lambda^2 xx
$$

and $\lambda^2 = 1, \quad \lambda = \pm 1$.

If $\lambda$ is complex then there exist vectors $a = b + ic$ and $\bar{a} = b - ic$, which are eigenvectors of the complexification of $\sigma$

with eigenvalues $\rho(\cos\varphi + i\sin\varphi)$ and $\rho(\cos\varphi - i\sin\varphi)$, and then, by (17.13) (with $j = 1$):

$$\left.\begin{aligned}\sigma b &= \rho(\cos\varphi\cdot b - \sin\varphi\cdot c)\\ \sigma c &= \rho(\sin\varphi\cdot b + \cos\varphi\cdot c)\end{aligned}\right\}. \qquad (17.16)$$

Hence,

$$(\sigma b)(\sigma b) = \rho^2\{\cos^2\varphi\cdot b^2 - 2\sin\varphi\cos\varphi\cdot bc + \sin^2\varphi\cdot c^2\} = b^2$$

$$(\sigma b)(\sigma c) = \rho^2\{\sin\varphi\cos\varphi\cdot(b^2 - c^2) + (\cos^2\varphi - \sin^2\varphi)\cdot bc\} = bc$$

$$(\sigma c)(\sigma c) = \rho^2\{\sin^2\varphi\cdot b^2 + 2\sin\varphi\cos\varphi\cdot bc + \cos^2\varphi\cdot c^2\} = c^2.$$

The sum of the first and the last equation yields

$$\rho^2 = 1 \qquad \rho = \pm 1.$$

The case $\rho = -1$ can be disregarded, since $(\rho, \varphi) = (-1, \varphi)$ can be replaced by $(-\rho, \varphi + \pi) = (1, \varphi + \pi)$ in (17.16). Hence we assume $\rho = 1$.

Substitution of $\rho^2 = 1$ yields

$$\sin^2\varphi\cdot(c^2 - b^2) - 2\sin\varphi\cos\varphi\cdot bc = 0$$

$$-\sin\varphi\cos\varphi\cdot(c^2 - b^2) - 2\sin^2\varphi\cdot bc = 0.$$

If $\sin\varphi = 0$ then b and c themselves are eigenvectors with real eigenvalues, contrary to our assumption. If $\sin\varphi \neq 0$ then $c^2 - b^2 = bc = 0$, hence the vectors b and c have equal length and are perpendicular. b and c can be replaced by perpendicular *unit* vectors and then (17.16) becomes

$$\sigma b = \cos\varphi\cdot b - \sin\varphi\cdot c$$

$$\sigma c = \sin\varphi\cdot b + \cos\varphi\cdot c.$$

If $B \subset E$ is a one- or two-dimensional invariant subspace of $\sigma$ then the space C of all vectors perpendicular to B is also invariant, and $\sigma$ restricted to that space is also orthogonal. This follows because any vector of B can be written as $\sigma b$, $b \in B$, and for any vector $c \in C$ and any vector $\sigma b \in B$ we have: $(\sigma b)(\sigma c) = bc = 0$, so that $\sigma c \in C$.

The argument that has just been applied to E can also be applied to C. Repeating this process we finally find the reduction of E mentioned in the theorem.

PROBLEMS. (17.11). Give a survey of the euclidean equivalence classes of quadratic functions on a real $n$-dimensional vector space for the cases $n = 2, 3, 4$.

(17.12). Give a survey of the equivalence classes of the orthogonal endomorphisms of a euclidean $n$-dimensional vector space for the cases $n = 2, 3, 4$.

(17.13). The orthogonal endomorphisms of a real vectorspace form a group, the *orthogonal group* (cf. p. 96).

*Hermitian endomorphisms and hermitian functions on a unitary space*

Let xy denote the inner product of the vectors x and y in a unitary space V (complex) dimension $n$. (Cf. p. 142).

Definition: An endomorphism $\sigma$: V → V is called *hermitian* when

$$x(\sigma y) = \overline{y(\sigma x)} \text{ for all } x \in V,\ y \in V.$$

Theorem [17.3]: *The eigenvalues of a hermitian endomorphism* $\sigma$ *are all real and there exists a basis of eigenvectors.*

Proof: Let $\sigma z = \lambda z$, $z \neq O$. Then

$$0 = z(\sigma z) - \overline{z(\sigma z)} = z(\lambda z) - \overline{z(\lambda z)} = \lambda(zz) - \bar{\lambda}(zz) = (\lambda - \bar{\lambda})(zz).$$

As $zz \neq 0$ then $\lambda - \bar{\lambda} = 0$ and $\lambda$ is real.

If $z \neq O$ is an eigenvector, $\sigma z = \lambda z$ and $zw = 0$ then $z(\sigma w) = \overline{w(\sigma z)} = \overline{w(\lambda z)} = \overline{\lambda(wz)} = 0$ and $z(\sigma w) = 0$. The endomorphism $\sigma$ therefore maps the $(n - 1)$-subspace of all w for which $zw = 0$ onto itself. In that subspace we find a second eigenvector and so on.

We may assume that the $n$ unitary-orthogonal eigenvectors so obtained have norm 1. We choose the cobasis of this set of unit vectors as coordinates. Then $\sigma$ *is represented by a matrix with real numbers in the diagonal and zeros elsewhere.*

Theorem [17.8]: *There is a one-to-one correspondence between the hermitian functions and the hermitian endomorphisms on a unitary n-space* V.

The hermitian function $\varphi$ that corresponds to a given hermitian endomorphism $\sigma$ is defined by

$$\varphi(x, y) = x(\sigma y) \text{ for all } x \in V,\ y \in V.$$

Indeed the right-hand side represents a sesquilinear function which is hermitian because of the fact that $\sigma$ is hermitian.

The hermitian endomorphism $\sigma$ that corresponds to a given hermitian function $\varphi$ is defined by the same relation as above. It is determined as follows. Let $a_1, \cdots a_n$ be an unitary basis of V. Then $\sigma$ must be such that

$$a_i(\sigma a_j) = \varphi(a_i, a_j).$$

If $\sigma a_j = \sum_{i=1}^n \alpha_{ij} a_i$, then it follows easily that

$$\alpha_{ij} = \varphi(a_i, a_j).$$

Hence $\sigma$ can be defined by its action on $a_1, \cdots a_n$:

$$\sigma a_j = \sum_{i=1}^n \varphi(a_i, a_j) \cdot a_i.$$

Combining [17.3 H] and [17.8] we obtain

Theorem [17.6 H]: *For any hermitian function $\varphi$ on a unitary n-space* V *there exists unitary coördinates $\xi_1, \cdots \xi_n$ and real numbers $\lambda_1, \cdots \lambda_n$, such that*

$$\varphi(x, y) = \sum_{i=1}^n \lambda_i \bar{\xi}_i(x)\xi_i(y) \quad x \in V, y \in V.$$

*The diagonal of $\varphi$ is*

$$\varphi^{\cdot} = \sum_{i=1}^n \lambda_i \bar{\xi}_i \xi_i.$$

*$\lambda_1, \cdots \lambda_n$ are the eigenvalues of the unique hermitian endomorphism $\sigma$ for which*

$$x(\sigma y) = \varphi(x, y) \text{ for } x \in V, \ y \in V.$$

Definition: An endomorphism $\sigma$ of a unitary space V is called *unitary* in case

$$(\sigma x)(\sigma y) = xy \text{ for any } x \in V, \ y \in V.$$

Theorem [17.9]: *In terms of a set of unitary coordinates a unitary endomorphism is represented by a unitary matrix.*

Proof: Let $a_1, \cdots a_n$ be a basis of unitary-orthogonal unit vectors

$$a_i a_j = \delta_{ij}$$

and

$$a_j = \sum_{i=1}^n \sigma_{ij} a_i$$

so that $\sigma$ is represented by the matrix with elements $\sigma_{ij} \in \mathbf{C}$. Then $(\sigma \mathfrak{a}_i)(\sigma \mathfrak{a}_j) = (\sum_k \sigma_{ki}\mathfrak{a}_k)(\sum_m \sigma_{mj}\mathfrak{a}_m) = \sum_{k,m} \bar{\sigma}_{ki}\sigma_{mj}\mathfrak{a}_k\mathfrak{a}_m = \sum_k \bar{\sigma}_{ki}\sigma_{kj}$ and this equals $\mathfrak{a}_i\mathfrak{a}_j = \delta_{ij}$.

Hence, if we denote the matrix with elements $\sigma_{ij}$ temporarily by $\sigma$ we conclude that

$$^t\bar{\sigma}\sigma = 1 \text{ or } \bar{\sigma} = {}^t\sigma^{-1}$$

and the matrix $\sigma$ is unitary by the definition in problem (12.14) p. 96.

**Problems.** (17.14). The unitary endomorphisms of a unitary space form a group, the *unitary group* (cf. p. 96).

(17.15). Every eigenvalue $\lambda$ of a unitary endomorphism of a unitary space has absolute value $|\lambda| = 1$. For any unitary endomorphism there exists a basis of eigenvectors which are unitary-orthogonal and have norm one.

(17.16). If $\gamma$ is an eigenvalue of $\sigma$, then $3\sigma^2 - 2\sigma + 4$ has the eigenvalue $3\gamma^2 - 2\gamma + 4$.

# 18. QUADRATIC FUNCTIONS ON AND QUADRATIC VARIETIES IN EUCLIDEAN SPACES

A quadratic function $f$ on an affine space $A$ can be expressed in the following form by means of an $\mathscr{A}$-map $\kappa$: $A \to \mathrm{V}$ (cf. chapter 14B):

$$f = (\varphi + \eta + \alpha) \circ \kappa: \quad A \to \mathbf{F}. \tag{18.1}$$

Here $\varphi$, $\eta$ and $\alpha$ are homogeneous functions of degrees 2, 1, and 0 on the vector space V. If $A$ is a (real) euclidean space (cf. p. 131) and $\mathrm{V} = \mathrm{E}$ is a euclidean vector space of dimension $n$, then there exist by theorem [17.6] euclidean coordinates $\xi_1, \cdots \xi_n$ on E such that

$$\varphi = \sum_{i=1}^{r} \lambda_i \xi_i^2 \quad \begin{cases} \lambda_i > 0 \text{ for } 1 \leqslant i \leqslant p \\ \quad < 0 \qquad p < i \leqslant r \\ \quad = 0 \qquad r < i \leqslant n. \end{cases} \tag{18.2}$$

$\lambda_1, \cdots \lambda_n$ are the eigenvalues of the symmetric endomorphism of E determined by $\varphi$. The linear function $\eta$ on E is linearly dependent on $\xi_1, \cdots \xi_n$ and can be written as

$$\eta = \sum_{i=1}^{n} 2\alpha_i \xi_i, \qquad \alpha_i \text{ real}. \tag{18.3}$$

Substitution yields

$$\varphi + \eta + \alpha = \sum_{i=1}^{r} \lambda_i (\xi_i + \alpha_i/\lambda_i)^2 + \sum_{j=r+1}^{n} 2\alpha_j \xi_j + \alpha'.$$

*If $\eta$ is linearly dependent on $\xi_1, \cdots \xi_r$*, i.e. $\alpha_j = 0$ for $j > r$, then we choose a new $\mathscr{A}$-map $\kappa'$: $A \to \mathrm{E}$ such that

$$(\xi_i + \alpha_i/\lambda_i) \circ \kappa = \xi_i \circ \kappa' \quad 1 \leqslant i \leqslant r$$
$$\xi_i \circ \kappa = \xi_i \circ \kappa' \quad r < i \leqslant n.$$

When we use this $\mathscr{A}$-map, (18.1) becomes:

$$f = \left(\sum_{i=1}^{r} \lambda_i \xi_i^2 + \alpha'\right) \circ \kappa'. \tag{18.4}$$

Then the quadratic function is represented by the following function on E:

$$\textstyle\sum_{i=1}^{r} \lambda_i \xi_i^2 + \alpha'. \tag{18.4'}$$

If $\eta$ is *not linearly dependent* on $\xi_1, \cdots \xi_r$, we choose a new set of euclidean coordinates for E, the first $r + 1$ of which are: $\xi_1, \cdots \xi_r$ and

$$(\textstyle\sum' \alpha_j \xi_j)/\mu, \text{ where } \sum' = \sum_{j=r+1}^{n}, \mu = \sqrt{\sum' \alpha_j^2} > 0.$$

Using these coordinates, which we now denote by $\xi_1, \cdots \xi_n$, we have

$$\varphi + \eta + \alpha = \textstyle\sum_{i=1}^{r} \lambda_i(\xi_i + \alpha_i/\lambda_i)^2 + 2\mu(\xi_{r+1} + \alpha'/2\mu).$$

Hence, with a suitable new $\mathscr{A}$-map $\kappa'$: $A \to$ E, (18.1) becomes

$$f = (\textstyle\sum_{i=1}^{r} \lambda_i \xi_i^2 + 2\mu\xi_{r+1}) \circ \kappa' \tag{18.5}$$

and thus it is represented by the following function on E:

$$f\colon \textstyle\sum_{i=1}^{r} \lambda_i \xi_i^2 + 2\mu\xi_{r+1} \qquad \mu > 0. \tag{18.5'}$$

(18.4') and (18.5') allow another interpretation, namely, if $\xi_i$ has been written instead of $\xi_i \circ \kappa'$, then $\xi_i$ is a linear function on $A$ and $f$ is a function on $A$!

*In this interpretation* (18.4') *and* (18.5') *represent the given function $f$, expressed in euclidean coordinates $\xi_1, \cdots \xi_n$ on $A$.* In this interpretation the $\mathscr{A}$-map does not appear anymore.

Theorem [18.1]: *Any quadratic function on a euclidean $n$-dimensional space $A = E$ has, with suitable euclidean coordinates, exactly one of the representations* (18.4') *or* (18.5').

Proof: The only thing we have to show is that there exists at most one representation (18.4') or (18.5') for a given quadratic function $f = (\varphi + \eta + \alpha) \circ \kappa$. The numbers $\lambda_i$, being eigenvalues of $f$, are defined completely and invariantly, i.e. independently of $\mathscr{A}$-maps or coordinates. The constant $\alpha'$ in (18.4') is the constant value of $f$ on the locus of the centres of the quadratic function. In order to define $\mu$ in an invariant way we consider an arbitrary point (represented by a vector) u and all points v such that the vector v − u in E has, with respect to the homogeneous quadratic function $\varphi$ on E the entire space E as polar space: $\varphi$(x, v − u) = 0 for any

x. (N.B. $\varphi$ and v — u do not change under a change of $\mathscr{A}$-map $\kappa:A \to$ E(!)). This means that in the coordinates used in (18.5′) $\xi_1, \cdots \xi_r$ are zero on the vector v — u. The points v so determined form a linear $(n - r)$-variety $W \subset A$ on which the function

$$v \to f(v) - f(u) = 2\mu\{\xi_{r+1}(v) - \xi_{r+1}(u)\}$$

is linear, and on which $\xi_{r+1}, \cdots \xi_n$ are euclidean coordinates. Hesse's distance function of that linear function on $W$ is $|\xi_{r+1}(v) - \xi_{r+1}(u)|$ and it differs from the absolute value of the given function by the factor $2\mu > 0$ which is thus defined independently of the coordinates.

The euclidean coordinates on the euclidean space are very special. If two functions can be given identical representations in suitable affine coordinates, then it is not necessary that there are also *euclidean* coordinates which give identical representations, but the converse, of course, is true. In other words, two functions may be affinely equivalent and not euclidean equivalent. Thus the euclidean classification of quadratic (and other) functions is more detailed (more equivalence classes) then the affine classification. A similar remark holds for the quadratic varieties which we are going to discuss now.

A euclidean space has been defined as a real affine space with euclidean metric. A quadratic variety in a euclidean space thus is also a quadratic variety in an affine space. An immediate consequence is (theorem [14.10]) that if a non-linear real quadratic variety in a euclidean space is given by the equation $f = 0$ as well as by $g = 0$, then there exists a $\lambda \in \mathbf{R}$ such that $g = \lambda f$. Thus, but for a constant factor, the quadratic function $f$ is determined by the variety.

Theorem [18.2]: *In a euclidean n-space with a (non empty) real quadratic variety which is not a linear* $(n - r)$*-variety,* $2 \leqslant r \leqslant n$*, there exist euclidean coordinates such that its equation is* $f = 0$*, with* $f$ *as given by* (18.4′) *or* (18.5′). *The ratio of the coefficients in* (18.4′) *or* (18.5′) *is completely determined by the quadratic variety. Conversely, any choice of constants in* (18.4′) *or* (18.5′) *gives a quadratic variety* $f = 0$*, except possibly the empty set or one point.*

*For a given quadratic variety,* $f$ *is often chosen such that the equation has the normal form*

$$\left.\begin{aligned}\Sigma_{i=1}^{p}\left(\frac{\xi_i}{\gamma_i}\right)^2 - \Sigma_{i=p+1}^{r}\left(\frac{\xi_i}{\gamma_i}\right)^2 &= 0\\ &= 1\end{aligned}\right\}\begin{aligned}&\textit{cone } 0 < p < r \leqslant n \qquad (18.6)\\ &\textit{variety with centre(s)}\\ &0 < p \leqslant r \leqslant n \quad (18.7)^{1)}\end{aligned}$$

*or*

$$= \xi_{r+1} \textit{ parabolic variety.} \qquad (18.8)$$

The names already given to some quadratic varieties in an affine space, such as *ellipse, paraboloid* are retained for the euclidean space.

If for any of two figures in the euclidean space coordinates can be found such that their representations on these coordinates become identical, then the figures are called *congruent* [2]. In the euclidean plane two ellipses are congruent if and only if for each of them there exist euclidean coordinates such that their standard representations

$$\left(\frac{\xi_1}{\gamma_1}\right)^2 + \left(\frac{\xi_2}{\gamma_2}\right)^2 = 1 \qquad (18.9)$$

are identical.

In the real affine space no ellipse can be distinguished from any other ellipse; there always exist coordinates such that $\xi_1^2+\xi_2^2=1$.

*Theorem* [18.2] *gives the complete classification of real quadratic varieties in euclidean spaces into classes of congruent varieties.*

A class of mutually congruent varieties is characterized by one equation of one of its elements, by a normal form (18.6), (18.7) or (18.8), or, of course, by the constants (*invariants*) occurring in the equation [3]. Some special quadratic varieties in euclidean spaces have got special names. For example, the ellipses (18.9) with $\gamma_1 = \gamma_2 = \gamma$ are called *circles* with radius $\gamma$. Other names will follow.

---

1) A hyperbola ($p = 1, r = n = 2$) is called rectangular if $\gamma_1 = \gamma_2$.

2) In chapter 19 another definition of congruence will be given.

3) A function (or one of its values) associating numbers or elements of some other set to a set of euclidean figures (or other objects which have a relation to euclidean spaces) such that congruent figures obtain the same value, is called a *euclidean invariant*.

*Investigation of a given quadratic variety*

*Example I.*

On a 2-dimensional euclidean space a quadratic function $f$ is given by means of its representation on two euclidean coordinates $\xi$ and $\eta$:

$$f = 7\xi^2 - 12\xi\eta - 2\eta^2 - 16\xi + 28\eta - 8 \qquad (18.10)$$

or, what amounts to *practically* the same, the quadratic variety $f = 0$ is given. The problem is to investigate the quadratic variety or the function.

Solution: We first examine the homogeneous function

$$7\xi^2 - 12\xi\eta - 2\eta^2$$

which we consider as a quadratic function on a vector space with coordinates $(\xi, \eta)$. The corresponding bilinear symmetric function is

$$\varphi\colon (\mathrm{x}, \mathrm{y}) \to 7\xi(\mathrm{x})\xi(\mathrm{y}) - 6\xi(\mathrm{x})\eta(\mathrm{y}) - 6\xi(\mathrm{y})\eta(\mathrm{x}) - 2\eta(\mathrm{x})\eta(\mathrm{y}).$$

This function determines a symmetric endomorphism with matrix

$$\begin{pmatrix} \varphi\{(1,0), (1,0)\} & \varphi\{(0,1), (1,0)\} \\ \varphi\{(1,0), (0,1)\} & \varphi\{(0,1), (0,1)\} \end{pmatrix} = \begin{pmatrix} 7 & -6 \\ -6 & -2 \end{pmatrix}$$

and characteristic equation in $\lambda$:

$$\begin{vmatrix} 7-\lambda & -6 \\ -6 & -2-\lambda \end{vmatrix} = \lambda^2 - 5\lambda - 50 = (\lambda - 10)(\lambda + 5) = 0.$$

The eigenvalues are $\lambda = -5$ and $\lambda = 10$.

A vector with coordinates $(\xi, \eta)$ is an eigenvector belonging to $\lambda = -5$ if

$$\left.\begin{aligned} 7\xi - 6\eta &= -5\xi \\ -6\xi - 2\eta &= -5\eta \end{aligned}\right\}, \quad \eta = 2\xi, \text{ for example } (\xi, \eta) = (1, 2).$$

A unit eigenvector is for example $\left(\dfrac{1}{\sqrt{5}}, \dfrac{2}{\sqrt{5}}\right)$.

An eigenvector belonging to $\lambda = 10$ is found from

$$\left.\begin{aligned} 7\xi - 6\eta &= 10\xi \\ -6\xi - 2\eta &= 10\eta \end{aligned}\right\}.$$

For example $(\xi, \eta) = (-2, 1)$, or $\left(\dfrac{-2}{\sqrt{5}}, \dfrac{1}{\sqrt{5}}\right)$ which is a unit vector.

These two eigenvectors are perpendicular in accordance with theorem [17.4]. If the two unit vectors given above are chosen as a new basis, and if the cobasis consisting of the functions

$$\xi_1 = \frac{\xi + 2\eta}{\sqrt{5}} \quad \text{and} \quad \xi_2 = \frac{-2\xi + \eta}{\sqrt{5}} \tag{18.11}$$

is chosen as a new euclidean coordinate system, then by theorem [17.6] the homogeneous quadratic function assumes the form

$$-5\xi_1^2 + 10\xi_2^2.$$

This is also obtained by substituting (cf. (18.11))

$$\xi = \frac{\xi_1 - 2\xi_2}{\sqrt{5}}, \quad \eta = \frac{2\xi_1 + \xi_2}{\sqrt{5}}$$

in (18.10) which yields

$$f = -5\xi_1^2 + 10\xi_2^2 + 8\sqrt{5}\xi_1 + 12\sqrt{5}\xi_2 - 8 =$$
$$= -5\left(\xi_1 - \frac{4}{\sqrt{5}}\right)^2 + 10\left(\xi_2 + \frac{3}{\sqrt{5}}\right)^2 - 10.$$

The zero-level curve is a hyperbola.

Under another $\mathscr{A}$-map the type of the quadratic function is expressed by the normal form

$$-5\xi_1^2 + 10\xi_2^2 - 10. \tag{18.12}$$

Expressed in terms of the old coordinates on the euclidean space, the coordinates yielding this form are the linear functions

$$\xi_1 - \frac{4}{\sqrt{5}} = \frac{\xi + 2\eta - 4}{\sqrt{5}} \quad \text{and} \quad \xi_2 + \frac{3}{\sqrt{5}} = \frac{-2\xi + \eta + 3}{\sqrt{5}}.$$

In fig. 18.1 some level curves of these coordinates are drawn. The centre satisfies $\xi + 2\eta - 4 = -2\xi + \eta + 3 = 0$ and thus is $(\xi, \eta) = (2, 1)$ in the old coordinates. Moreover some level curves of $f$ have been drawn, viz. $f = 0, -10, -20$.

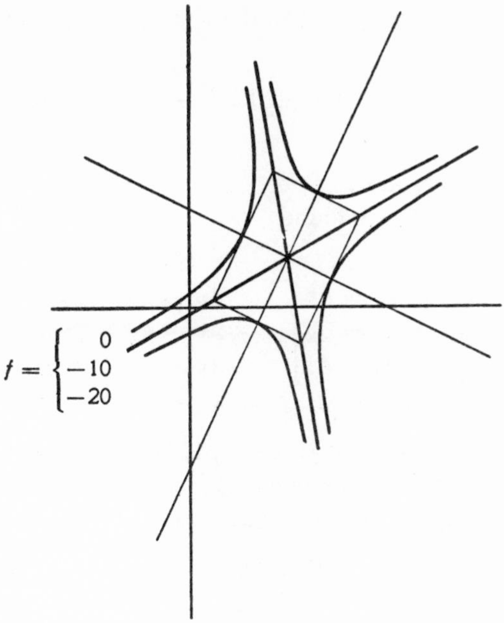


Fig. 18.1

As explained in chapter 14 the centre can also be found directly from

$$\left.\begin{aligned}\frac{\partial f}{\partial \xi} &= 14\xi - 12\eta - 16 = 0\\ \frac{\partial f}{\partial \eta} &= -12\xi - 4\eta + 28 = 0\end{aligned}\right\} (\xi, \eta) = (2,1).$$

Calculation of $f(\xi, \eta) = f(2, 1)$ yields $-10$. Together with the eigenvalues of $\varphi$ this yields at once the type of $f$, i.e. the normal form (18.12) without calculation of the relation between old and new coordinates.

*Example II*. Investigate the function $f$ on a euclidean 3-dimensional space with euclidean coordinates $x, y, z$, when

$$f = 4x^2 - 4xy - 4xz + 4y^2 - 4yz + 4z^2 - 5x + 7y + 7z + 1. \quad (18.13)$$

Solution: The endomorphism determined by the homogeneous

quadratic part of the function has the characteristic equation in $\lambda$:

$$\begin{vmatrix} 4-\lambda & -2 & -2 \\ -2 & 4-\lambda & -2 \\ -2 & -2 & 4-\lambda \end{vmatrix} = -\lambda^3 + 12\lambda^2 - 36\lambda = -\lambda(\lambda-6)^2 = 0.$$

Hence the eigenvalues are 6; 6; 0.

Eigenvectors $(x, y, z)$ are found

$$\begin{array}{lcc} & \text{for } \lambda = 6 & \text{for } \lambda = 0 \\ \text{from} & \left.\begin{array}{r} 4x - 2y - 2z = 6x \\ -2x + 4y - 2z = 6y \\ -2x - 2y + 4z = 6z \end{array}\right\} & \left.\begin{array}{r} 4x - 2y - 2z = 0 \\ -2x + 4y - 2z = 0 \\ -2x - 2y + 4z = 0 \end{array}\right\}. \\ \text{Hence} & x + y + z = 0 & x = y = z. \end{array}$$

Thus any vector perpendicular to (1, 1, 1) is an eigenvector belonging to $\lambda = 6$. In suitable euclidean coordinates $\xi_1$, $\xi_2$, $\xi_3$ the homogeneous quadratic part of $f$ then equals

$$6\xi_1^2 + 6\xi_2^2.$$

The centres of $f$ satisfy

$$\frac{\partial f}{\partial x} = 8x - 4y - 4z - 5 = 0$$

$$\frac{\partial f}{\partial y} = -4x + 8y - 4z + 7 = 0$$

$$\frac{\partial f}{\partial z} = -4x - 4y + 8z + 7 = 0.$$

The sum of the left-hand members is 9, hence the equations are contradictory: there are no centres. It follows that there exist coordinates $\xi_1$, $\xi_2$, $\xi_3$ such that {cf. (18.4′) and (18.5′)}

$$f = 6\xi_1^2 + 6\xi_2^2 + 2\mu\xi_3, \quad \mu \text{ a constant.}$$

The constant $\mu$ can be determined by following the proof of theorem [18.1]. Those vectors which have the entire three-dimensional vector space as polar space with respect to the homogeneous quadratic part of $f$ form a 1-dimensional space with basis vector (1, 1, 1).

Substituting $\mathbf{u} = (0, 0, 0)$ and $\mathbf{v} - \mathbf{u} = \mathbf{v} = (1, 1, 1)$ in (18.13) we find

$$f(0, 0, 0) = 1, \quad f(1, 1, 1) = 10.$$

Furthermore the length of $\mathbf{v} - \mathbf{u}$ is: $\sqrt{1^2 + 1^2 + 1^2} = \sqrt{3}$, and thus $\mu$ is such that $f(\mathbf{v}) - f(\mathbf{u}) = 10 - 1 = 2\mu\sqrt{3}$, $\mu = 1\frac{1}{2}\sqrt{3}$,

$$f = 6\xi_1^2 + 6\xi_2^2 + 3\sqrt{3}\xi_3.$$

The variety $f = 0$ is an *elliptic paraboloid* with (normal) equation $\xi_1^2 + \xi_2^2 + \frac{1}{2}\sqrt{3}\xi_3 = 0$.

This result can also be obtained in another way, from which moreover the relation between old and new coordinates becomes apparent.

First we choose the perpendicular eigenvectors $(1, 0, -1)$ and $(1, -2, 1)$ in the two-dimensional eigenspace belonging to $\lambda = 6$, and $(1, 1, 1)$ in the eigenspace belonging to $\lambda = 0$. Normalizing these eigenvectors to length 1, we obtain the following basis:

$$\frac{1}{\sqrt{2}}(1, 0, -1), \quad \frac{1}{\sqrt{6}}(1, -2, 1), \quad \frac{1}{\sqrt{3}}(1, 1, 1).$$

A cobasis consists of the coordinates

$$\eta_1 = \frac{x - z}{\sqrt{2}}, \quad \eta_2 = \frac{x - 2y + z}{\sqrt{6}}, \quad \eta_3 = \frac{x + y + z}{\sqrt{3}}.$$

In matrix notation

$$\begin{bmatrix} \eta_1 \\ \eta_2 \\ \eta_3 \end{bmatrix} = \begin{bmatrix} \frac{1}{\sqrt{2}} & 0 & \frac{-1}{\sqrt{2}} \\ \frac{1}{\sqrt{6}} & \frac{-2}{\sqrt{6}} & \frac{1}{\sqrt{6}} \\ \frac{1}{\sqrt{3}} & \frac{1}{\sqrt{3}} & \frac{1}{\sqrt{3}} \end{bmatrix} \begin{bmatrix} x \\ y \\ z \end{bmatrix}.$$

The square transformation matrix, which we denote by $\sigma$, is orthogonal, hence ${}^t\sigma\sigma = 1$, $\sigma^{-1} = {}^t\sigma$ and

$$\begin{bmatrix} x \\ y \\ z \end{bmatrix} = \begin{bmatrix} \frac{1}{\sqrt{2}} & \frac{1}{\sqrt{6}} & \frac{1}{\sqrt{3}} \\ 0 & \frac{-2}{\sqrt{6}} & \frac{1}{\sqrt{3}} \\ \frac{-1}{\sqrt{2}} & \frac{1}{\sqrt{6}} & \frac{1}{\sqrt{3}} \end{bmatrix} \begin{bmatrix} \eta_1 \\ \eta_2 \\ \eta_3 \end{bmatrix}$$

or

$$x = \frac{1}{\sqrt{6}}(\sqrt{3}\eta_1 + \eta_2 + \sqrt{2}\eta_3)$$

$$y = \frac{1}{\sqrt{6}}(-2\eta_2 + \sqrt{2}\eta_3)$$

$$z = \frac{1}{\sqrt{6}}(-\sqrt{3}\eta_1 + \eta_2 + \sqrt{2}\eta_3).$$

Substitution in (18.13) yields

$$\begin{aligned} f &= 6\eta_1^2 + 6\eta_2^2 - 6\sqrt{2}\eta_1 - 2\sqrt{6}\eta_2 + 3\sqrt{3}\eta_3 + 1 \\ &= 6\left(\eta_1 - \frac{1}{\sqrt{2}}\right)^2 + 6\left(\eta_2 - \frac{1}{\sqrt{6}}\right)^2 + 3\sqrt{3}\eta_3 - 3 - 1 + 1 \\ &= 6\left(\eta_1 - \frac{1}{\sqrt{2}}\right)^2 + 6\left(\eta_2 - \frac{1}{\sqrt{6}}\right)^2 + 3\sqrt{3}\left(\eta_3 - \frac{1}{\sqrt{3}}\right) \end{aligned}$$

$$f = 6\xi_1^2 + 6\xi_2^2 + 3\sqrt{3}\xi_3.$$

Euclidean coordinates yielding this standard form thus are

$$\xi_1 = \eta_1 - \frac{1}{\sqrt{2}} = \frac{x - z - 1}{\sqrt{2}}$$

$$\xi_2 = \eta_2 - \frac{1}{\sqrt{6}} = \frac{x - 2y + z - 1}{\sqrt{6}}$$

$$\xi_3 = \eta_3 - \frac{1}{\sqrt{3}} = \frac{x + y + z - 1}{\sqrt{3}}.$$

The intersection of the new coordinate planes $\xi_1 = 0$, $\xi_2 = 0$, $\xi_3 = 0$ has old coordinates $(x, y, z) = (1, 0, 0)$. The main results of the investigation can be summarized in the following identity in $x, y, z$:

$$f = 6\left[\frac{x - z - 1}{\sqrt{2}}\right]^2 + 6\left[\frac{x - 2y + z - 1}{\sqrt{6}}\right]^2 + 3\sqrt{3}\left[\frac{x + y + z - 1}{\sqrt{3}}\right].$$

The level surface $f = \text{constant} > 0$ is a paraboloid of revolution.

PROBLEMS. (18.1). Examine the following real quadratic functions (and their zero-level sets) given in terms of euclidean coordinates.

a. $x^2 + 4xy + 4y^2 - 6x - 12y + 8$ (parabola).
b. $11x^2 - 6xy + 19y^2 + 6x - 38y + 15$ (ellipse).
c. $x^2 + y^2 + 4x - 6y - 14$ (circle).
d. $4x^2 + 9y^2 + 4yz + 6z^2 + 8x + 40y + 20z + 34$ (ellipsoid).
e. $4xy + z^2 - 1$ (hyperboloid of one sheet).
f. $4xy - z^2 - 1$ (hyperboloid of two sheets).
g. $2x^2 + 8xy + 8xz + 8y^2 + 16yz + 8z^2 - 8x + 17y - 17z + 4$ (parabolic cylinder).
h. $4x^2 - 4xy + 8xz - 8xu + 4y^2 - 8yz + 8yu - 4z^2 + 4zu - 4u^2 - 4x - 4y + 4$ (hypercone).
i. $x^2 + y^2 + z^2 + u^2 - 4x + 6y - 2u - 18$ (hypersphere).

(18.2). Let the $n$ eigenvalues of the endomorphism determined by the homogeneous quadratic part of a quadratic function $f$ on a euclidean $n$-space be mutually distinct and non-zero, and let $\xi_1, \cdots \xi_n$ be euclidean coordinates which yield the normal form for $f$. Prove that the planes $\xi_1 = 0$, $\xi_2 = 0$, $\cdots \xi_n = 0$ are completely determined by $f$.

## 19. MOTIONS AND AFFINITIES

### Motions

A motion of a figure in a euclidean plane is a one-to-one mapping $\sigma$ under which the distance of any two points $P$ and $Q$ of the figure is equal to the distance between their images:

$$d(P, Q) = d(\sigma P, \sigma Q). \tag{19.1}$$

Fig. 19.1 suggests the motions $1 \to 2$ and $1 \to 3$. The motion $1 \to 2$ (and similarly $1 \to 3$) is already determined by the points $A_1, B_1, C_1, A_2, B_2, C_2$. An arbitrary point $F_1$ that is not part of the configuration also takes part in the motion if we define its image $\sigma(F_1)$ as that point $F_2$ whose distances from $A_2, B_2, C_2$ are the same

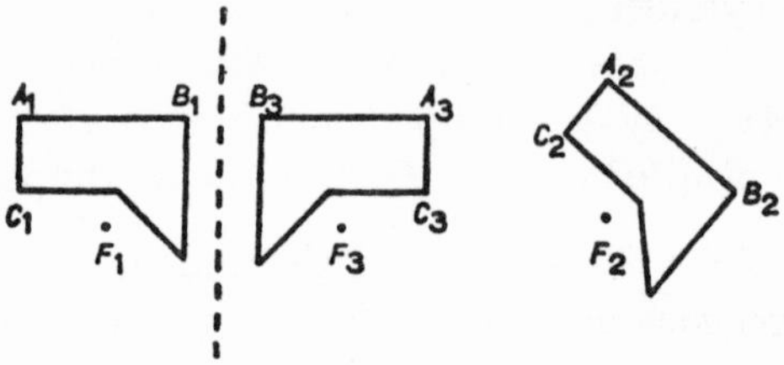


Fig. 19.1

as those of $F_1$ from $A_1, B_1, C_1$. This can be done for any point of the plane, and so we obtain a motion of the entire plane. From now on the word motion will always mean such a motion of the entire space.

Definition: A one-to-one mapping $\sigma$ of a euclidean $n$-space $E$ onto itself with the property that $d(P, Q) = d(\sigma P, \sigma Q)$ for all $P, Q \in E$ is called a *motion* of $E$.

With this notion of motion in our minds we consider a generalization: let $S$ be a set of elements and let $\sigma$ be a one-to-one mapping of $S$ onto itself:

$$\sigma : P \to \sigma P \text{ for } P \in S.$$

Then the inverse mapping of $\sigma$ is also a one-to-one mapping of $S$ onto $S$; it is the mapping associating $\sigma P$ to $P$:

$$\sigma^{-1} : \sigma P \to P.$$

If $\tau$ and $\sigma$ are one-to-one mappings of $S$ onto $S$ then their product $\tau\sigma$ with the action $P \to \tau(\sigma P)$ is also a one-to-one mapping of $S$ onto $S$ (cf. chapter 2). If $\varepsilon$ is the identity, i.e. the mapping associating to any point $P$ the point $P$ itself, then we have

$$\sigma\varepsilon = \varepsilon\sigma = \sigma \text{ and } \sigma^{-1}\sigma = \sigma\sigma^{-1} = \varepsilon.$$

Furthermore for three one-to-one mappings $\sigma$, $\tau$, $\rho$ of $S$ onto $S$ we have

$$(\rho\tau)\sigma = \rho(\tau\sigma).$$

From this and the definition of group (cf. p. 67) the following theorem will now be clear:

Theorem [19.1]: *A non-empty set $G$ of one-to-one mappings of a set $S$ onto itself with the properties:*

*I. If $\sigma \in G$ then $\sigma^{-1} \in G$*

*II. If $\sigma, \tau \in G$ then $\tau\sigma \in G$,*

*is a group with respect to the multiplication as defined above.*

PROBLEM (19.1). Instead of conditions I and II in theorem [19.1] another necessary and sufficient condition is: If $\sigma, \tau \in G$ then also $\tau^{-1}\sigma \in G$. Prove this.

Theorem [19.2]: *The motions of a euclidean n-dimensional space $E$ form a group.*

Proof: The one-to-one mapping $\sigma$ is a motion if and only if

$$d(\sigma P, \sigma Q) = d(P, Q) \text{ for } P, Q \in E$$

and then $\sigma^{-1}$ is also a motion.

If $\sigma$ and $\tau$ are motions, then for $P, Q \in E$

$$d(P, Q) = d(\sigma P, \sigma Q) = d\{\tau(\sigma P), \tau(\sigma Q)\} = d\{(\tau\sigma)P, (\tau\sigma)Q\}.$$

Then $\tau\sigma$ is also a motion and [19.1] can be applied.

In fig. 19.1 the motion $2 \to 3$ is the product of the motions $2 \to 1$ and $1 \to 3$; also $2 \to 1$ is the inverse of $1 \to 2$; the identity is the product of $1 \to 2$ and $2 \to 1$.

If $\sigma$ is a motion or some other one-to-one mapping of the euclidean space $E$ onto itself, and $f$ a real function $f: E \to \mathbf{R}$ then $f\sigma: E \to \mathbf{R}$ is another real function on $E$ which is called the *dual image* of $f$ under $\sigma$ and is denoted by $\sigma^* f$ or by $f\sigma$.

Theorem [19.3]: *The dual image $\xi\sigma$ of a linear function (or Hesse's function) $\xi$ on a euclidean space E under a motion $\sigma$ is a linear function (or Hesse's function respectively). The mapping $\sigma^*: \xi \to \xi\sigma$ is one-to-one.* In other words: The *system* of linear functions is invariant under the dual of any motion.

Proof: We use the representation of $E$ in the euclidean vector space E by some $\mathscr{A}$-map $\kappa$. Any linear function $\xi$ can be represented as follows

$$\xi : \mathrm{x} \to \mathrm{c}(\mathrm{x} - \mathrm{d})$$

where $\mathrm{c} \neq \mathrm{O}$ and d are fixed vectors. This function $\xi$ is not necessarily homogeneous. Putting

$$\mathrm{c} = 2(\mathrm{b} - \mathrm{a}), \quad \mathrm{d} = \tfrac{1}{2}(\mathrm{b} + \mathrm{a}) \quad \text{or} \quad \mathrm{a} = \mathrm{d} - \tfrac{1}{4}\mathrm{c}, \quad \mathrm{b} = \mathrm{d} + \tfrac{1}{4}\mathrm{c}$$

we get the form

$$(\mathrm{x} - \mathrm{a})^2 - (\mathrm{x} - \mathrm{b})^2 = 2(\mathrm{b} - \mathrm{a}) \left[\mathrm{x} - \frac{\mathrm{b} + \mathrm{a}}{2}\right].$$

Thus $\xi(\mathrm{x})$ is the difference of the squares of the distances of x from the points a and $\mathrm{b} \neq \mathrm{a}$.

Now $(\xi\sigma)(\mathrm{x}) = \xi(\sigma\mathrm{x})$ is the difference of the squares of the distances of $\sigma\mathrm{x}$ from the points a and $\mathrm{b} \neq \mathrm{a}$. According to the definition of motion applied to the motion $\sigma^{-1}$, this is equal to the difference of the squares of the distances of x from $\sigma^{-1}\mathrm{a}$ and $\sigma^{-1}\mathrm{b} \neq \sigma^{-1}\mathrm{a}$.

Therefore the function $\mathrm{x} \to \xi\sigma\mathrm{x}$ is also a linear function.

The function $\xi$ above is a function of Hesse if and only if

$$\{2(\mathrm{b} - \mathrm{a})\}^2 = 1, \text{ i.e. } (\mathrm{b} - \mathrm{a})^2 = \tfrac{1}{4}.$$

The distance of $\sigma^{-1}a$ from $\sigma^{-1}b$ is equal to the distance between a and b; thus the necessary and sufficient condition is equivalent to $(\sigma^{-1}b - \sigma^{-1}a)^2 = \frac{1}{4}$ and the dual function $\xi\sigma$ is a function of Hesse.

The dual mapping $\sigma^*$ of linear functions is one-to-one owing to the existence of the inverse mapping $\sigma^{-1}$. For any function $f: E \to \mathbf{R}$

$$(\sigma^{-1})^*(\sigma^* f) = (f\sigma)\sigma^{-1} = f(\sigma\sigma^{-1}) = f\varepsilon = f.$$

Theorem [19.4]: *If* $\xi_1, \cdots \xi_n$ *are a set of euclidean coordinates of a euclidean space then the linear functions* $\eta_1, \cdots \eta_n$ *are another set of euclidean coordinates if and only if there exists a motion* $\sigma$ *such that* $\eta_i = \xi_i\sigma$.

Proof: A system of linear functions $\xi_1, \cdots \xi_n$ on a euclidean $n$-space $E$ is a set of euclidean coordinates if the distance of two arbitrary points $P$ and $Q$ is given by

$$d(P, Q) = \sqrt{[\Sigma_{i=1}^n \{\xi_i(Q) - \xi_i(P)\}^2]}.$$

If $\sigma$ is a motion then

$$d(P, Q) = d(\sigma P, \sigma Q) = \sqrt{[\Sigma_{i=1}^n \{\xi_i(\sigma Q) - \xi_i(\sigma P)\}^2]} =$$

$$= \sqrt{[\Sigma_{i=1}^n \{(\xi_i\sigma)(Q) - (\xi_i\sigma)(P)\}^2]}.$$

Since this holds for any pair of points $P$ and $Q$ it follows that $\xi_1\sigma, \cdots \xi_n\sigma$ is a system of euclidean coordinates.

If, conversely, two systems of euclidean coordinates $\xi_1, \cdots \xi_n$ and $\eta_1, \cdots \eta_n$ are given, then we can consider the mapping $\sigma$ which maps the point $P$ with coordinates $\xi_1(P), \cdots \xi_n(P)$ to the point $\sigma P$ with values of the former coordinates

$$\xi_1 = \eta_1(P), \cdots \xi_n = \eta_n(P)$$

i.e.

$$\xi_i(\sigma P) = \eta_i P.$$

This mapping $\sigma$ is a motion, because

$$d^2(\sigma P, \sigma Q) = \Sigma_{i=1}^n \{\xi_i(\sigma Q) - \xi_i(\sigma P)\}^2 = \Sigma_{i=1}^n \{(\xi_i\sigma)Q - (\xi_i\sigma)P\}^2 =$$

$$= \Sigma_{i=1}^n (\eta_i Q - \eta_i P)^2 = d^2(P, Q).$$

Two functions $f$ and $f'$ on a euclidean space are called *equivalent* (chapter 18) if there exist euclidean coordinates $\xi_1, \cdots \xi_n$ and $\xi_1', \cdots \xi_n'$ such that the expression of $f$ in $\xi_1, \cdots \xi_n$ is identical to the expression of $f'$ in $\xi_1', \cdots \xi_n'$. Let $\sigma$ be a motion; let

$$f' = f\sigma (= \sigma^* f);$$

let $\xi_1, \cdots \xi_n$ be euclidean coordinates and
let

$$f = f(\xi_1, \cdots \xi_n), \quad \text{so} \quad f(P) = f\{\xi_1(P), \cdots \xi_n(P)\},$$

then

$$f'(P) = f(\sigma P) = f\{\xi_1(\sigma P), \cdots \xi_n(\sigma P)\}$$

and hence

$$f' = f(\xi_1\sigma, \cdots \xi_n\sigma).$$

This means that $f'$ is expressed in euclidean coordinates $\xi_1\sigma, \cdots \xi_n\sigma$ in the same way as $f$ is in $\xi_1, \cdots \xi_n$. Hence any motion gives a dual mapping of any function onto an equivalent function.

If, conversely, two functions are equivalent, that is, if the functions, expressed in the euclidean coordinates $\xi_1, \cdots \xi_n$ and $\xi_1', \cdots \xi_n'$ are given by

$$f(\xi_1, \cdots \xi_n) \text{ and } f(\xi_1', \cdots \xi_n')$$

then the motion $\sigma$ with action

$$\xi_i' = \xi_i\sigma$$

gives a dual mapping of the first function onto the other.

On page 182 we already gave a definition of congruent figures. According to theorem [19.4] the following definition is equivalent:

Definition: Two functions $f$ and $f'$ on, or two figures (= point sets) $W$ and $W'$ in a euclidean space are *congruent* if there exists a motion $\sigma$ such that $f' = f\sigma$ or $W' = \sigma W$ respectively.

Observe that any figure determines a unique function, the *characteristic function*, i.e. the function which assumes the value 1 on the the points of the figure and zero elsewhere.

Theorem [19.5]: *Theorems* [18.1] *and* [18.2] *provide a complete classification of quadratic functions* (*varieties*) *on a euclidean space into classes of congruent functions* (*figures*).

From [19.4] we obtain

Theorem [19.6]: *Under a motion of a euclidean n-space any linear k-variety is mapped onto a linear k-variety. In particular: lines are mapped onto lines, hyperplanes onto hyperplanes (= linear $(n-1)$-varieties).*

*Classification of motions*

Let $\xi_1, \cdots \xi_n$ be a set of euclidean coordinates for a euclidean $n$-space; let $\sigma$ be a motion. Then $\xi_i\sigma$ is a linear function, and thus of type

$\xi_i\sigma = \alpha_{i1}\xi_1 + \cdots + \alpha_{in}\xi_n + \alpha_i \quad \alpha_{ij}, \alpha_i$ constants $i = 1, \cdots n$.

Then $\xi_i\sigma - \alpha_i$, $i = 1, \cdots n$, are also euclidean coordinates and it follows that the mapping $\rho$ with dual action

$$\rho^*\xi_i = \xi_i\rho = \alpha_{i1}\xi_1 + \cdots + \alpha_{in}\xi_n$$

is a motion also. This motion maps the point $P$ with coordinates $\xi_iP$ to the point $\rho P$ with coordinates $\xi_i\rho P$, and the point $(0, 0, \cdots 0)$ *to itself*. If we now consider $\xi_1, \cdots \xi_n$ as coordinates of the euclidean vector space of sequences of $n$ numbers $(\xi_1, \cdots \xi_n)$ with inner product given by the quadratic function $\sum_{i=1}^n \xi_i^2$, then $\rho^*$ is an orthogonal endomorphism of this vector space and thus belongs to one of the types mentioned in theorem [17.7].

Next we assume that $\xi_1, \cdots \xi_n$ determine a coordinate system such that the matrix of $\rho$ assumes a normal form as given in theorem [17.7]. In these coordinates $\sigma$ is expressed by a set of equations which can be divided into sets of one or two equations of the following type:

a) set of one: translation over a distance $\beta$

$$\xi_i\sigma = \xi_i + \beta \qquad \beta \in \mathbf{R}. \tag{19.2}$$

b) set of one: reflection

$$\xi_i\sigma = -\xi_i + \beta.$$

In this case the function $\xi_i - \frac{1}{2}\beta$ is chosen as new coordinate. Then for any point $P$ one has

$$(\xi_i - \tfrac{1}{2}\beta)\sigma P = \xi_i\sigma P - \tfrac{1}{2}\beta = -\xi_iP + \beta - \tfrac{1}{2}\beta = -(\xi_i - \tfrac{1}{2}\beta)P.$$

If we denote the new coordinate by $\xi_i$ instead of by $\xi_i - \frac{1}{2}\beta$, then the representation becomes

$$\xi_i\sigma = -\xi_i. \tag{19.3}$$

c) set of two: rotation through angle $\varphi$:

$$\begin{aligned} \xi_i\sigma &= \cos\varphi\cdot\xi_i + \sin\varphi\cdot\xi_{i+1} - \beta_i \qquad \varphi \not\equiv 0 \bmod \pi \\ \xi_{i+1}\sigma &= -\sin\varphi\cdot\xi_i + \cos\varphi\cdot\xi_{i+1} - \beta_{i+1}. \end{aligned}$$

In order to obtain a further simplification we find the variables $\xi_i$ and $\xi_{i+1}$ from

$$\xi_i\sigma = \xi_i \text{ and } \xi_{i+1}\sigma = \xi_{i+1}$$

i.e. from

$$\begin{aligned} (\cos\varphi - 1)\xi_i + (\sin\varphi)\xi_{i+1} &= \beta_i \\ (-\sin\varphi)\xi_i + (\cos\varphi - 1)\xi_{i+1} &= \beta_{i+1}. \end{aligned}$$

Since

$$\begin{vmatrix} \cos\varphi - 1 & \sin\varphi \\ -\sin\varphi & \cos\varphi - 1 \end{vmatrix} = 2(1 - \cos\varphi) \neq 0$$

this system of equations has just one solution (chapter 11), $\xi_i{}^0$ and $\xi_{i+1}{}^0$ say. We now replace the functions $\xi_i$ and $\xi_{i+1}$ by $\xi_i - \xi_i{}^0$ and $\xi_{i+1} - \xi_{i+1}{}^0$ and find

$$\begin{aligned} (\xi_i - \xi_i{}^0)\sigma &= \cos\varphi\cdot(\xi_i - \xi_i{}^0) + \sin\varphi\cdot(\xi_{i+1} - \xi^0{}_{i+1}) \\ (\xi_{i+1} - \xi^0{}_{i+1})\sigma &= -\sin\varphi\cdot(\xi_i - \xi_i{}^0) + \cos\varphi\cdot(\xi_{i+1} - \xi^0{}_{i+1}). \end{aligned}$$

If the new linear functions $\xi_i - \xi_i{}^0$ and $\xi_{i+1} - \xi_{i+1}{}^0$ are again denoted by the symbols $\xi_i$ and $\xi_{i+1}$ we have

$$\left.\begin{aligned} \xi_i\sigma &= \cos\varphi\cdot\xi_i + \sin\varphi\cdot\xi_{i+1} \\ \xi_{i+1}\sigma &= -\sin\varphi\cdot\xi_i + \cos\varphi\cdot\xi_{i+1} \end{aligned}\right\}. \tag{19.4}$$

Combination of (19.2), (19.3) and (19.4) gives the normal forms for *motions in the euclidean n-dimensional space*, and thus a *classification* of them. For $n \leqslant 3$ we have

$n = 1$ a) $\xi_1\sigma = \xi_1 + \beta$ translation over distance $\beta$.
The special case $\beta = 0$ gives the identity.

b) $\xi_1\sigma = -\xi_1$ reflection.

$n = 2$ a) $\begin{cases} \xi_1\sigma = \xi_1 + \beta_1 \\ \xi_2\sigma = \xi_2 + \beta_2. \end{cases}$

If in this case

$$(\beta_1^2 + \beta_2^2)^{-\frac{1}{2}}(\beta_1\xi_1 + \beta_2\xi_2) \text{ and } (\beta_1^2 + \beta_2^2)^{-\frac{1}{2}}(\beta_2\xi_1 - \beta_1\xi_2)$$

are chosen as new coordinates and again are denoted by $\xi_1$ and $\xi_2$, then the unique normal form for the case a) is found:

a) $\begin{cases} \xi_1\sigma = \xi_1 + \beta \\ \xi_2\sigma = \xi_2 \end{cases}$ *translation over distance* $\beta$.

b) $\begin{cases} \xi_1\sigma = \xi_1 + \beta \\ \xi_2\sigma = -\xi_2 \end{cases}$ *transflection* ($\beta = 0$: *reflection* with respect to the line $\xi_2 = 0$).

c) $\begin{cases} \xi_1\sigma = \cos\varphi\xi_1 + \sin\varphi\xi_2 \\ \xi_2\sigma = -\sin\varphi\xi_1 + \cos\varphi\xi_2 \end{cases}$ *rotation over* $\varphi \not\equiv 0 \bmod 2\pi$.

$n = 3$ After a similar operation as for $n = 2$:

a) $\begin{cases} \xi_1\sigma = \xi_1 + \beta \\ \xi_2\sigma = \xi_2 \\ \xi_3\sigma = \xi_3 \end{cases}$ *translation over distance* $\beta$.

b) $\begin{cases} \xi_1\sigma = \xi_1 + \beta \\ \xi_2\sigma = \xi_2 \\ \xi_3\sigma = -\xi_3 \end{cases}$ *transflection* ($\beta = 0$: *reflection* with respect to the plane $\xi_3 = 0$).

c) $\begin{cases} \xi_1\sigma = \varepsilon\xi_1 + \beta & \varepsilon = 1 \textit{ screwmotion} \\ \xi_2\sigma = \cos\varphi\xi_2 + \sin\varphi\xi_3 & \varphi \not\equiv 0 \bmod 2\pi \\ \xi_3\sigma = -\sin\varphi\xi_2 + \cos\varphi\xi_3 & \varphi = \pi \text{ not excluded} \end{cases}$

($\beta = 0$: *rotation* through angle $\varphi$ around the line $\xi_2 = \xi_3 = 0$).

d) as c) with $\varepsilon = -1$ and $\beta = 0$.

A non-identical motion $\sigma$ of a euclidean $n$-space with the property $\sigma^2 = 1$ is called a *reflection*. From the classification of motions it then follows that there exist euclidean coordinates and a natural number $r < n$ such that

$$\begin{cases} \xi_i\sigma = \xi_i & i = 1, \cdots r \\ \xi_j\sigma = -\xi_j & j = r+1, \cdots n. \end{cases}$$

Any point with coordinates $\xi_j = 0$ for $j > r$ is mapped to itself under this reflection. None of the other points is invariant. This reflection is called a *reflection with respect to the linear r-space* $\xi_j = 0,\ j > r$.

A function $f$ on a euclidean space is called *symmetric with respect to a linear r-space* $E^r$ if $f\sigma = f$ under the reflection $\sigma$ with respect to $E^r$. A figure = pointset $W$ is called symmetric with respect to $E^r$ if $\sigma W = W$ under this reflection $\sigma$, i.e. if the characteristic function $f$ of $W$ ($f = 1$ on $W$, $f = 0$ elsewhere) is symmetric.

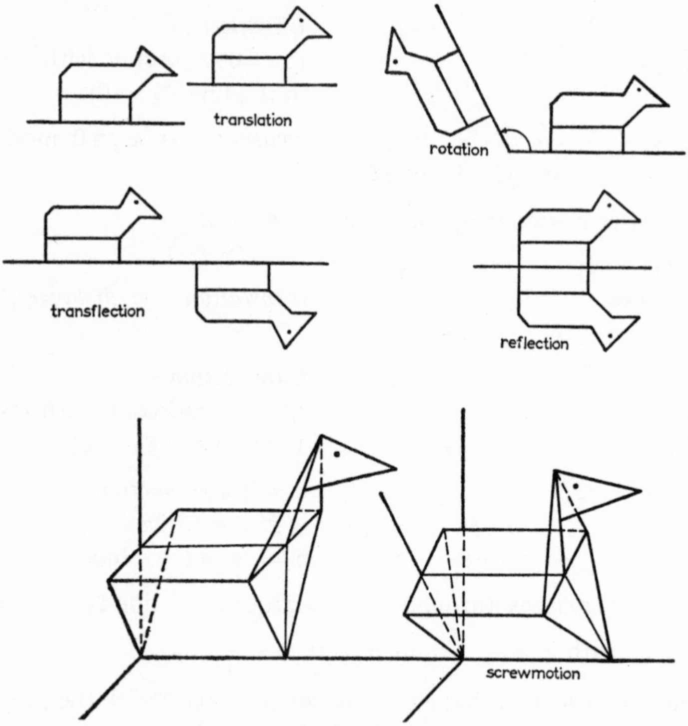


Fig. 19.2

The quadratic functions expressed in (18.4′) and (18.5′) are symmetric with respect to the linear variety (with equations)

$$\xi_{i_1} = \xi_{i_2} = \cdots = \xi_{i_k} = 0 \qquad i_j \neq r + 1 \text{ for } (18.5')$$

as is seen by substituting $-\xi_{i_1}$ for $\xi_{i_1}$ etc. in these expressions.

A function $f$ is called *rotational symmetric* with respect to $E^r$ ($r < n$) if $f\sigma = f$ for any motion $\sigma$ which leaves every point of $E^r$ invariant. If for the quadratic function (18.4′) or (18.5′) $\lambda_1 = \lambda_2$ then it is rotational symmetric with respect to the linear variety $\xi_1 = \xi_2 = 0$. This follows because any motion $\sigma$ which leaves each point of $\xi_1 = \xi_2 = 0$ invariant has the form

$$\begin{aligned} \xi_1\sigma &= \alpha_{11}\xi_1 + \alpha_{12}\xi_2 \\ \xi_2\sigma &= \alpha_{21}\xi_1 + \alpha_{22}\xi_2 \\ \xi_j\sigma &= \xi_j \end{aligned}$$

which, because of the orthogonality can even be specialized to

$$\begin{aligned} \xi_1\sigma &= \cos\varphi\,\xi_1 + \sin\varphi\,\xi_2 \\ \xi_2\sigma &= -\sin\varphi\,\xi_1 + \cos\varphi\,\xi_2 \\ \xi_j\sigma &= \xi_j, \end{aligned}$$

or

$$\begin{aligned} \xi_1\sigma &= -\cos\varphi\,\xi_1 + \sin\varphi\,\xi_2 \\ \xi_2\sigma &= \sin\varphi\,\xi_1 + \cos\varphi\,\xi_2 \\ \xi_j\sigma &= \xi_j \end{aligned}$$

$\sigma$ then leaves the function invariant.

A figure is called rotational symmetric if its characteristic function is such. A variety (surface) is called a rotational variety (surface) if it is rotational symmetric. A circle and a sphere are rotational symmetric with respect to a point. In *example II* of chapter 18 $f$ is rotational symmetric with respect to a line, and $f = 0$ is an (elliptic) *rotational paraboloid*, or a *paraboloid of revolution.*

*Motion in the euclidean plane as basic notion**

We are now going to discuss an important intellectual exercise. Suppose that we are given the point set of a euclidean $n$-dimensional space and all the mappings of this space which are called motions, and that nothing further is known about this space a priori. Can we reconstruct the euclidean space?

More exactly: Find descriptions *in terms of the notions point and motion only*, of as many important notions in the theory of euclidean spaces as possible.

We give the solution of this problem by listing a number of conveniently selected properties. We omit the (simple) proofs.

*Equal distance.* The distance of the points $A$ and $B$ is equal to the distance of $C$ and $D$, if and only if there exists a motion mapping $A$ to $C$ and $B$ to $D$. This property describes the notion "equal distance" in the way we wished.

A *hypersphere* is the locus of the points having equal distances from a fixed point, the centre.

A *hyperplane* is the locus of the points having equal distances from two fixed, different points.

The *dimension* $n$ of the space is the smallest number of hyperplanes that have only one point in common.

A *linear* $(n-k)$*-variety* is the intersection of $k$ hyperplanes which have at least one point in common, and such that by leaving out any one of these varieties a larger intersection is obtained.

A point lies *outside a hypersphere* if there exists a hyperplane through that point which has no point in common with the hypersphere.

A sequence of points $A_1, A_2, \cdots$ *converges to a limit point* $A$ if to any hypersphere with centre $A$ which does not contain $A$ (in ordinary language: with positive radius) there exists a number $N$ such that the points $A_n$ with $n > N$ are not outside that hypersphere.

If the ratio of two line segments is rational then there exists a "greatest common divisor" of which both are a multiple. The *unit of length* however is *not determined* by the group of motions, and can be chosen at will.

After this choice has been made, the *length* of any line segment with rational length is also determined. The length of an arbitrary line segment $AB$ is the limit of the lengths of rational line segments $AB_n$ where the sequence $B_1, B_2, \cdots$ converges to $B$.

As has already been pointed out the linear functions can be expressed in terms of distances. Euclidean coordinates are also determined by distances. The foregoing is summarized in

Theorem* [19.7]: *All properties and theorems in a euclidean n-dimensional space can be described in terms of its point set, the* *group of those mappings which are called motions, and a unit of length.*

*N.B.* This does not mean that a point set and the group of mappings can be chosen at will and that then always a euclidean $n$-space results. Think for example of the group of all permutations of seven elements.

## AFFINITIES IN REAL SPACES

As an introduction we consider a parallel projection of a plane $V$ in ordinary space onto another plane $V'$. Subsequently we map $V'$ onto $V$ by a motion. The product $\sigma$ of these two mappings is a one-to-one mapping of $V$ onto itself.

From the geometrical construction we derive a number of important properties of this mapping $\sigma$. (Cf. fig. 19.3 where $H$ is transformed into $H''$):

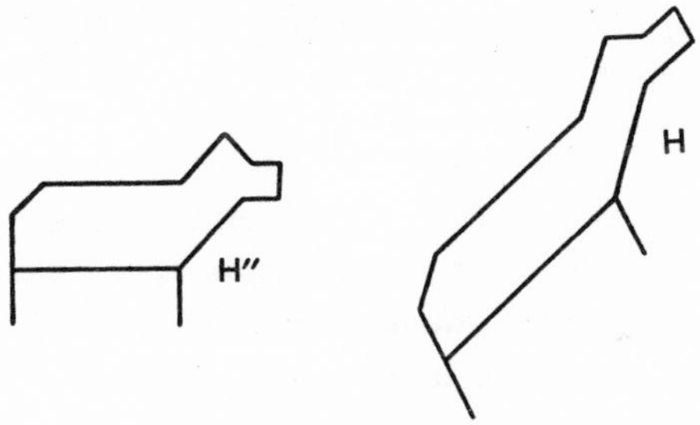


Fig. 19.3

*a*) The image of a line is a line and conversely.
*b*) The image of a pair of parallel lines is a pair of parallel lines.
*c*) If a, b, c are three (vectors representing) collinear points then

$$\frac{\sigma \mathrm{c} - \sigma \mathrm{a}}{\sigma \mathrm{b} - \sigma \mathrm{a}} = \frac{\mathrm{c} - \mathrm{a}}{\mathrm{b} - \mathrm{a}}.$$

We now consider a mapping $\sigma: A \to A$ of the affine plane $A$ which we assume to have these properties *a*), *b*), *c*). If $\xi$ is a linear function on that plane, i.e. a function with parallel lines as level curves, then $\xi\sigma$ is a function which also has parallel lines as level curves. If a is chosen on the line $\xi\sigma = 0$ and b on the line $\xi\sigma = 1$, then for arbitrary c collinear with a and b but different from them we have

$$\xi\sigma\mathrm{c} = \frac{\xi\sigma\mathrm{c} - \xi\sigma\mathrm{a}}{\xi\sigma\mathrm{b} - \xi\sigma\mathrm{a}} = \frac{\sigma\mathrm{c} - \sigma\mathrm{a}}{\sigma\mathrm{b} - \sigma\mathrm{a}} = \frac{\mathrm{c} - \mathrm{a}}{\mathrm{b} - \mathrm{a}},$$

i.e. $\xi\sigma\mathrm{c}$ is equal to the value of the linear function which is zero on $\xi\sigma = 0$ and 1 on $\xi\sigma = 1$. Hence $\xi\sigma$ *is* that linear function. In view of these considerations we give the

Definition: A one-to-one mapping $\sigma$ of an affine (or euclidean) $n$-space onto itself is called an *affinity* if the dual mapping $\sigma^*$ maps the set of non-constant linear functions onto itself:

$$\sigma^*: \{\xi\} \rightarrow \{\xi\sigma\} = \{\xi\}.$$

By theorem [19.1] we have

Theorem [19.8]: *The affinities of an affine n-space form a group.*

Definition: Two functions $f$ and $f'$ on or two figures $W$ and $W'$ in an affine $n$-space are called *affinely equivalent* if there exists an affinity $\sigma$ of $A$ such that $f' = f\sigma$ or $W' = \sigma W$ respectively.

Theorem [19.9]: *Two quadratic functions on an affine space are affinely equivalent if and only if there exist coordinate systems under which their representations become identical. Hence theorems* [14.3] *and* [14.3′] *provide the "affine classification" of quadratic functions.*

*N.B.* From this and theorem [14.9] the affine classification of quadratic varieties is obtained.

Proof: The assertion follows from the fact that if $\xi_1, \cdots \xi_n$ form a coordinate system for an affine $n$-space, the linear functions $\eta_1, \cdots \eta_n$ form another coordinate system if and only if there exists an affinity $\sigma$ such that $\eta_i = \xi_i\sigma$, $i = 1, \cdots n$.

Remark: Under coordinates $\xi_1, \cdots \xi_n$ an affinity $\sigma$ of the $n$-dimensional affine space can be represented by equations with coefficients $\alpha_{ij}$, $\alpha_i$

$$\begin{cases} (\xi_1\sigma) = \alpha_{11}\xi_1 + \cdots + \alpha_{1n}\xi_n + \alpha_1 \\ \quad\cdot \qquad\quad \cdot\quad\cdot \qquad \cdots \qquad \cdot\quad\cdot \qquad \cdot \\ (\xi_n\sigma) = \alpha_{n1}\xi_1 + \cdots + \alpha_{nn}\xi_n + \alpha_n. \end{cases}$$

$\sigma$ maps the point with $\xi_1, \cdots \xi_n \in \mathbf{F}$ as coordinates to the point with coordinates $(\xi_1\sigma), \cdots (\xi_n\sigma)$.

In the foregoing we met two large groups of one-to-one mappings of a euclidean space onto itself, viz. the motions and the affinities. Some of the properties of figures in a euclidean space are such that any affine equivalent figure possesses them also. Such a property is called an *affine property*.

Examples of affine properties are: "to be a parallelogram", "a hyperbola". An example of a property which is euclidean, but not affine, is "to be a circle".

The word property above has been used in a rather unprecise sense. It could be defined as follows: A *euclidean property* is a set $\mathscr{F}$ of figures (= subsets) in a euclidean space such that whenever $F \in \mathscr{F}$ and $\sigma$ is a motion, then also $\sigma F \in \mathscr{F}$. By definition we will say that the figure $G$ has property $\mathscr{F}$ if $G \in \mathscr{F}$.

Similarly: An *affine property* is a set $\mathscr{F}$ of figures such that whenever $F \in \mathscr{F}$ and $\sigma$ is an affinity then also $\sigma F \in \mathscr{F}$. Since any motion in a euclidean space is also an affinity, according to this definition any affine property of a figure in a euclidean space can also be considered as a (special, indeed affine) euclidean property.

Theorems in which only affine properties occur are called affine theorems. An example of an affine theorem is: A quadrangle is a parallelogram if and only if its diagonals bisect each other. In other words: The property "to be a parallelogram", i.e. the set of all parallelograms, is identical to the property "to be a quadrangle whose diagonals bisect each other", i.e. the set of all such quadrangles.

The theorem "the diagonals of a rectangle have the same length" is a euclidean but not an affine theorem.

PROBLEMS. (19.2). To any ellipse or hyperbola there exist two lines with respect to which the figure is symmetric. These lines are called the axes of symmetry. The circle, of course, has infinitely many axes of symmetry.

(19.3). A quadratic surface is a rotational surface if the endomorphism belonging to the homogeneous part of a quadratic function corresponding to the surface, has two equal non-vanishing eigenvalues.

(19.4). Give the classification of all motions in the 4-dimensional euclidean space.

(19.5). $P_0, \cdots P_n$ and $Q_0, \cdots Q_n$ respectively are $n + 1$ points in a euclidean $n$-space, not contained in any linear $(n - 1)$-variety, and such that $d(P_i, P_j) = d(Q_i, Q_j)$ for $0 \leqslant i < j \leqslant n$. Prove for the cases $n = 2$ or 3 that there exists exactly one motion $\sigma$ with the action $\sigma P_i = Q_i$.

(19.6). An affinity maps the centre of gravity of $n$ points into the centre of gravity of the image points.

(19.7). In the affine plane there exists exactly one affinity mapping three given non-collinear points into three given non-collinear points.

(19.8)*. A plane $n$-gon with vertices $P_i = P_{i+n}$, $i \geqslant 1$, is called *affine-regular* if there exists an affinity $\sigma$ with the action $\sigma P_i = P_{i+1}$. Any triangle with non-collinear vertices is affine-regular. The affine-regular quadrangles are the parallelograms.

If for an affine-regular $n$-gon $\sigma$ is the affinity in the above definition and $\chi$ is an arbitrary function on the affine plane, then the following function is invariant under $\sigma$

$$\chi + \chi\sigma + \cdots + \chi\sigma^{n-1} = \textstyle\sum_{i=0}^{n-1} \chi\sigma^i.$$

Using a positive definite quadratic function $\chi$ which is zero at the centre of gravity of the vertices of an $n$-gon, it can be shown that any affine-regular $n$-gon in the euclidean plane is affine-equivalent to an (ordinary) regular $n$-gon. (An $n$-gon with vertices $P_i$ in the euclidean plane is called *regular* if there exists a *motion* $\sigma$ with the action $\sigma P_i = P_{i+1}$).

## SOME CONSTRUCTIONS WITH PLANE AFFINITIES

With ruler, compasses and pencil a "line" can be drawn through two given points on a sheet of paper, and also a circle can be drawn with given centre and radius. In reality, however, such a line consists of a long stretched hill of carbon. And the "point of intersection", when observed through a microscope, looks much more like a mountain than like a point. Yet, the names "line" and "point" are not too badly chosen since the properties of these hills and mountains on the paper coincide more or less with the similarly formulated properties of figures in the (abstract) euclidean plane. Think for example of the property that medians of a triangle pass through one point.

The construction of figures on paper appears to be a practical activity, and as such it belongs more to physics than to mathematics. Yet, in the mathematical field also a notion of construction has been defined, which when applied to euclidean geometry on a sheet of paper becomes the ordinary construction of figures.

A (purely mathematical) "construction with ruler and compasses" is a sequence of point sets $S_1, S_2, \cdots S_n$ ,where $S_1$ is given, in which $S_n$ is a set with the desired properties (the figure to be constructed) and where the pair $S_iS_{i+1}$, $i = 1, \cdots n - 1$ is an "elementary construction". The *elementary constructions* are:

*a*) addition to the set $S_i$ of the point of intersection of a line or circle with another line or circle. The line should be given by two of its points, the circle by centre and radius.

*b*) omitting some points.

In the following examples we assume that the reader is familiar with such simple constructions as: a line parallel to another line through a given point and: a line tangent to a circle.

*Construction of the points of intersection* $S_1$ *and* $S_2$ *of an ellipse* $\mathscr{E}$ *with a line* $m$. Let the ellipse $\mathscr{E}$ be given by a pair of conjugate diameters $AC$ and $BD$ intersecting in $M$. The intersection $\mathscr{E} \cap m$ is to be constructed. First we consider an affinity $\sigma$ such that $\sigma\mathscr{E}$ is a circle. Then the intersection $\sigma\mathscr{E} \cap \sigma m$ can be constructed with

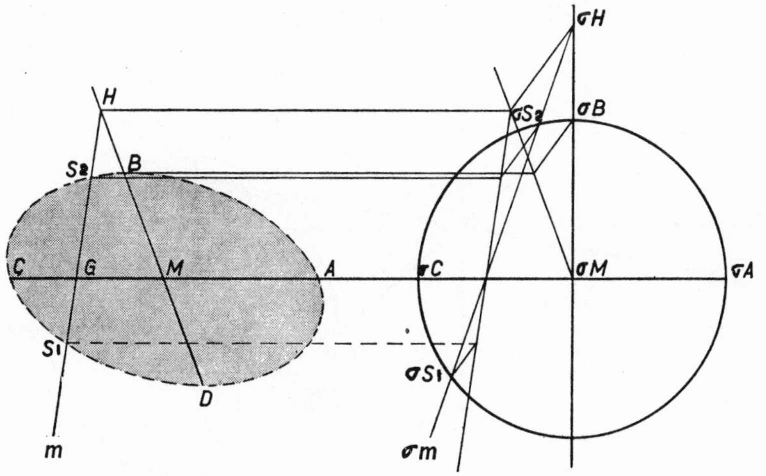


Fig. 19.4

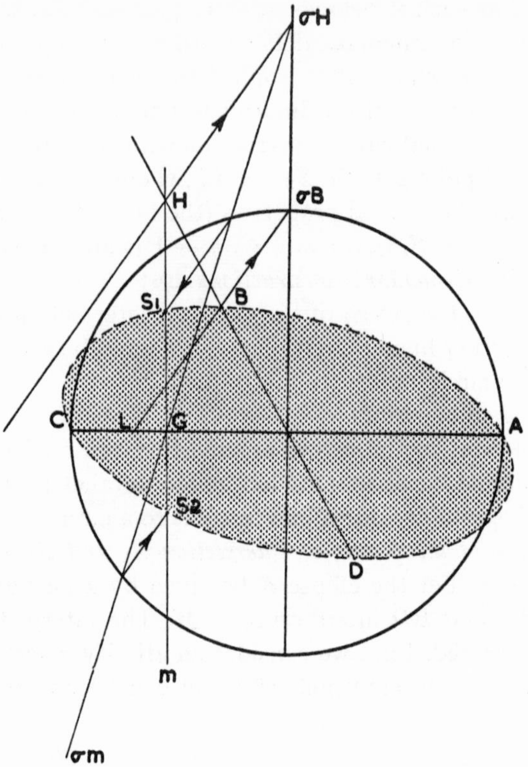


Fig. 19.5

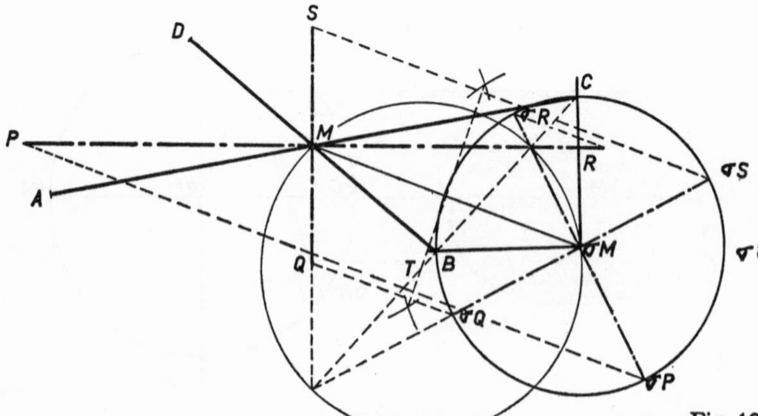


Fig. 19.6

ruler and compasses, and finally we determine $\sigma^{-1}(\sigma\mathscr{E} \cap \sigma m) = \mathscr{E} \cap m$.

In order to ensure that $\sigma\mathscr{E}$ is indeed a circle we choose $\sigma$ such that $\sigma(MA)$ and $\sigma(MB)$ have equal length and are perpendicular. The image ellipse $\sigma\mathscr{E}$ then has perpendicular equally long conjugate diameters and therefore *is* a circle. Cf. fig. 19.4 where $\sigma(MA)$ has been chosen to have the same length as $MA$ and the construction is performed using proportional line segments.

In fig. 19.5 the affinity $\sigma$ has been chosen particularly conveniently viz. such that $\sigma(M) = M$, $\sigma(A) = A$. For any point $X$ on $MA$ then we have $\sigma X = X$. For example $\sigma G = G$. In this case the affinity has a line of invariant points, called the *axis of affinity* of $\sigma$. Consider for this case the intersection $L$ of the *line* through $B$ and $\sigma B$ with $AC$. As $L$ is invariant, the line through $B$ and $L$ is mapped onto the line through $\sigma B$ and $L$, which happens to be the same line. Consequently the line through $B$ and $\sigma B$ (but not each individual point of it) remains invariant. The same invariance holds for any line parallel to the line $(B, \sigma B)$. The direction of these lines is invariant.

*Construction of the axes of an ellipse.* In fig. 19.6 two conjugate diameters $AC$ and $BD$ of an ellipse $\mathscr{E}$ are given. The axes of the ellipse are to be constructed. A construction is as follows.

Consider the affinity $\sigma$ with axis of affinity $BC$: $\sigma B = B$, $\sigma C = C$ and choose the image $\sigma M$ such that the line segments $\sigma(MB)$ and $\sigma(MC)$ are equally long and perpendicular. Then $\sigma\mathscr{E}$ is a circle. Any pair of conjugate diameters $PR$ and $QS$ of $\mathscr{E}$ has as image a pair of conjugate, i.e. perpendicular, diameters of the circle $\sigma\mathscr{E}$. If $PR$ and $QS$ are perpendicular then the quadrangle with sides along $MQ$, $MR$, $\sigma(MQ)$ and $\sigma(MR)$ has two right angles, and thus is a concyclic quadrangle with vertices at $M$ and $\sigma M$ and with a diameter on the line $BC$ (by elementary geometrical properties). The centre $T$ is then constructed on $BC$ equidistant from $M$ and $\sigma M$, and subsequently $\sigma Q$, $\sigma R$ and the endpoints $Q$ and $R$ of the axes of $\mathscr{E}$ are found.

PROBLEMS. (19.9). An ellipse is given by two conjugate nonperpendicular diameters. Construct a circumscribed rectangle with one side parallel to one of the given diameters.

(19.10). Construct two conjugate diameters of the unique ellipse which touches the sides of a given triangle at the midpoints. This ellipse is called *Steiner's ellipse*. (Hint: think of a triangle for which this problem is trivial).

(19.11)*. Construct a square circumscribed to an ellipse which is given by two non-perpendicular conjugate diameters.

## 20. PROJECTIVE GEOMETRY

### *Points at infinity of an affine plane $A^2$*

In an affine plane over an arbitrary field **F** the following properties hold:

$A_1$. Through any two points there is one line.

$A_2$. Through any point there is just one line of any complete set of mutually parallel lines. If we call such a complete set of parallel lines a *direction*, then we can also express this property by: through any point there is exactly one line of given direction, or: through any point and any direction there is just one line.

*B*. Two lines either have a point in common or they have the same direction.

It is possible to formulate these properties more concisely. For that purpose we extend the set of points by the following definition: A **point** is an element of the set of all points and directions. Instead of the word direction we also use the expression *point at infinity*. The set of all **points** is called the *projective plane*. Furthermore we define: A **line** is one of the following subsets of the projective plane: the set of all points of an ordinary line together with its direction, or the set of all directions. The **line** consisting of all directions is called the *line at infinity*.

The reader will easily verify that in the projective plane the following rules are true without exception:

*A*: Through any two **points** there is one **line**.

*B*: Any two **lines** have one **point** in common.

Observe that *A* holds also if both **points** are at infinity and *B* if one of the **lines** is at infinity.

From now on we shall write just "point" and "line" instead of **point** and **line**.

PROBLEM (20.1). What is the number of points, finite points and points at infinity all included, in the plane of chapter 8?

Not only are the properties $A$ and $B$ expressed simpler in the projective plane, but the introduction of points at infinity has other advantages.

Let us consider two intersecting planes in a 3-dimensional affine space $A^3$. From some point (which will be called the centre of projection) not on either of these planes, we *project* one of the planes onto the other. Let $\xi_1$, $\xi_2$, $\xi_3$ be coordinates in $A^3$ such that the planes are $\xi_1 = 1$ and $\xi_2 = 1$ and let the centre of projection be the point with coordinates (0, 0, 0). Then the projection is the mapping associating to the point $(1, \xi_2, \xi_3)$ in the plane $\xi_1 = 1$ the point $\left(\frac{1}{\xi_2}, \frac{\xi_2}{\xi_2}, \frac{\xi_3}{\xi_2}\right) = \left(\frac{1}{\xi_2}, 1, \frac{\xi_3}{\xi_2}\right)$ in $\xi_2 = 1$. Clearly the points with $(\xi_1, \xi_2) = (1, 0)$ and $\xi_3$ arbitrary are excluded from this projection, whereas the points with $(\xi_1, \xi_2) = (0, 1)$ are not found as images.

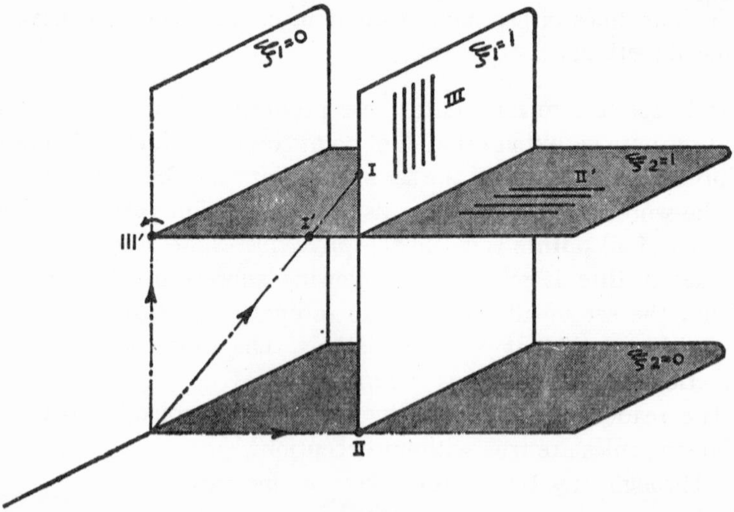


Fig. 20.1

However, if we extend both planes with their points at infinity, the projection can be extended to a one-to-one mapping!

This is done as follows: (In fig. 20.1 the points $I$, $II$, $III'$ and

(0, 0, 0) are in one plane with equation say $\xi_3 = \alpha\xi_1 + \beta\xi_2$). A point $(1, 0, \alpha)$ ($II$) is mapped to the direction ($II'$) of the line through (0, 0, 0) and $(1, 0, \alpha)$, that is the direction of the line through (0, 1, 0) and $(1, 1, \alpha)$ in the plane $\xi_2 = 1$. The direction ($III$) of the line through (1, 0, 0) and $(1, 1, \beta)$ in the plane $\xi_1 = 1$, i.e. the direction of the line through (0, 0, 0) and $(0, 1, \beta)$ is mapped to the point $(0, 1, \beta)$ ($III'$) in the plane $\xi_2 = 1$. It is now easy to verify that *this projection of the first projective plane onto the other is indeed one-to-one.*

*Coordinates also for the points at infinity.* If $\eta_1$ and $\eta_2$ are linear functions on an affine plane $A^2$, the kernels of which (lines) intersect in a point $S$, then $\eta_1/\eta_2$ is a function on $A$ which is defined on all points outside the line $\eta_2 = 0$, and which is constant on any line through $S$. Cf. fig. 20.2 and 7.6.

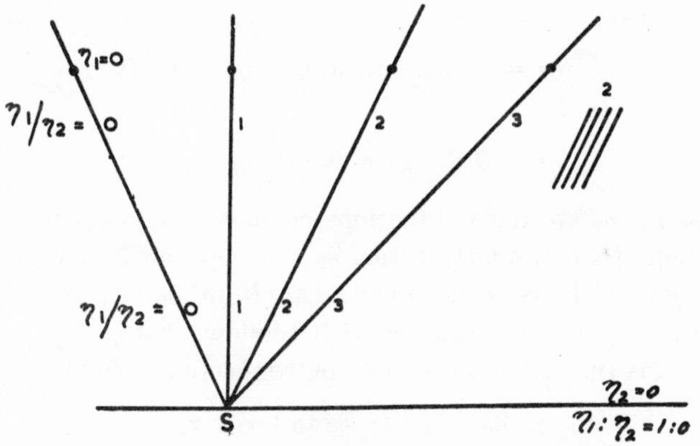


Fig. 20.2

We extend $A$ again to a projective plane $P$, by adding the directions in $A$ as points at infinity. And we extend the linear function by associating to the direction of a line through $S$ the constant value of $\eta_1/\eta_2$ on that line as function value. In this way a value is defined for any point of the projective plane not lying on the line $\eta_2 = 0$. If two points have the same function value then they are on the same line through $S$.

Two pairs of scalars $(\alpha_1, \alpha_2)$ and $(\beta_1, \beta_2)$ both different from

(0, 0), are said to have the same ratio or are called ratio-equivalent when

$$\alpha_1\beta_2 = \alpha_2\beta_1.$$

This is a proper equivalence relation (See chapter 2). An equivalence class is called *a ratio* [1]). The class of $(\alpha_1, \alpha_2)$ is denoted by $\alpha_1 : \alpha_2$. If $\lambda \neq 0$ then clearly

$$\lambda\alpha_1 : \lambda\alpha_2 = \alpha_1 : \alpha_2.$$

Above we defined a function $\eta_1/\eta_2$ for the points in the projective plane outside $\eta_2 = 0$, with values in the field **F**. We now determine a strongly related function with values in the set of ratios over **F**. For any point for which $\eta_1/\eta_2 = \alpha \in \mathbf{F}$ we now choose as "value" the ratio $\alpha$: 1. If the point is finite then this equals $\eta_1 : \eta_2$. The advantage is that the definition of this ratio function can be extended in a natural way for all points different from $S$. The value for a point on

$$\eta_2 = 0 \text{ is the ratio } \eta_1 : \eta_2 = 1 : 0$$

and on

$$\eta_1 = 0 \text{ the ratio is } \eta_1 : \eta_2 = 0 : 1.$$

If $\eta_0, \eta_1, \eta_2$ are linear functions on $A$ with non-concurrent lines as kernels, then similarly ratios $\eta_0 : \eta_1 : \eta_2$ can be considered for finite points. It is well-known that from $\eta_0 : \eta_1 = \alpha_0 : \alpha_1$ and $\eta_1 : \eta_2 = \alpha_1 : \alpha_2$ for the case $\alpha_1 \neq 0$ it follows that $\eta_0 : \eta_2 = \alpha_0 : \alpha_2$. This means that these ratios can be connected as follows

$$\eta_0 : \eta_1 : \eta_2 = \alpha_0 : \alpha_1 : \alpha_2.$$

We shall show by a different approach that this is equally true for points at infinity. *N. B.* In fig. 20.5 some ratios are given when $\eta_0, \eta_1, \eta_2$ are functions of Hesse of the sides of an equilateral triangle.

*First-degree functions on $A^2$*

We consider the 2-dimensional affine space $A^2$ as a linear variety in a three-dimensional space $A^3$, in which we choose a fixed point $O$

[1]) A simpler notion of ratio was used on page 15.

outside $A^2$, and which we identify with a 3-dimensional vector space by means of an $\mathscr{A}$-map $\kappa_0$ under which $O$ is mapped to the vector $\mathrm{O}$: $A^2 \subset \mathrm{V}^3$. Cf. fig. 20.3.

If the vector $\mathrm{a} \in A^2$, then the vectors $\mathrm{x}$ for which $\mathrm{a} + \mathrm{x} \in A^2$ form a 2-dimensional subspace $\mathrm{V}^2 \subset \mathrm{V}^3$ which is parallel to $A^2$, and $A^2 = \mathrm{a} + \mathrm{V}^2$. The mapping $\mathrm{a} + \mathrm{x} \to \mathrm{x}$ is an affine $\mathscr{A}$-map for the affine plane $A^2$. If $\psi$ is a homogeneous linear function on $\mathrm{V}^3$, then for $\mathrm{a} + \mathrm{x} \in A^2$, $\psi(\mathrm{a} + \mathrm{x}) = \psi\mathrm{a} + \psi\mathrm{x}$. This is the sum of a constant $\psi\mathrm{a}$ and a homogeneous linear function in the vector $\mathrm{x}$ of $\mathrm{V}^2$, which represents the point $\mathrm{a} + \mathrm{x} \in A^2$. Thus restriction of $\psi$ to $A^2$ gives a first-degree function on $A^2$.

Conversely, any first-degree function on $A^2$ can be written as $(\mathrm{a} + \mathrm{x} \in A^2)$

$$\mathrm{a} + \mathrm{x} \to \alpha + \varphi(\mathrm{x})$$

where $\alpha$ is a constant and $\varphi$ is a homogeneous linear function on $\mathrm{V}^2$. If $\mathrm{a}_1$, $\mathrm{a}_2$ is a basis of $\mathrm{V}^2$ then $\mathrm{a}$, $\mathrm{a}_1$, $\mathrm{a}_2$ is a basis of $\mathrm{V}^3$. The homo-

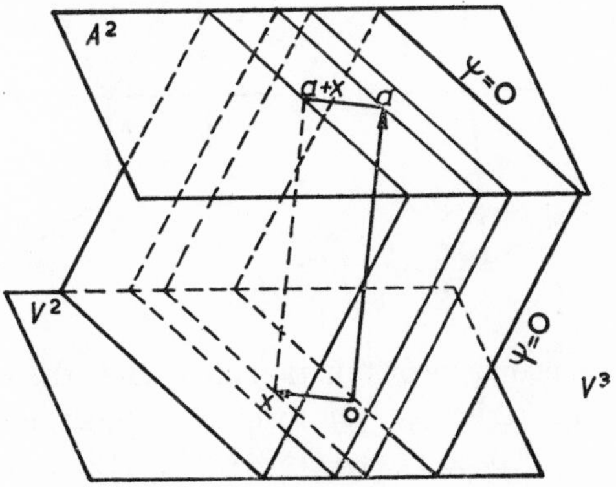


Fig. 20.3

geneous linear function $\psi$ on $\mathrm{V}^3$ which is uniquely determined by the properties $\psi\mathrm{a} = \alpha$, $\psi\mathrm{a}_1 = \varphi\mathrm{a}_1$, $\psi\mathrm{a}_2 = \varphi\mathrm{a}_2$, associates to $\mathrm{a}+\mathrm{x} \in A^2$ the value

$$\psi(\mathrm{a} + \mathrm{x}) = \psi\mathrm{a} + \psi\mathrm{x} = \alpha + \varphi\mathrm{x}$$

and is the only homogeneous linear function on $\mathrm{V}^3$ with this property. In particular the constant functions on $A^2$ are obtained in this way from the homogeneous linear functions on $V^3$ that have $A^2$ as level surface. Summarizing:

Theorem [20.1]: *The functions of degree* $\leqslant 1$ *on* $A^2 \subset V^3$, $O \notin A^2$, *are the restrictions to* $A^2$ *of the homogeneous linear functions on* $V^3$. *This correspondence between functions is one-to-one.*

To any vector $z \in A^2$ we can associate the 1-dimensional subspace $\mathbf{F}z$ of $V^3$ to which z belongs, and to any direction in $A^2$ the 1-dimensional subspace of $V^3$ with the same direction (cf. fig. 20.4). Since any 1-dimensional subspace of $V^3$ intersects $A^2$ in one point or is parallel to it, we obtain a one-to-one mapping of the finite points and points at infinity of $A^2$ onto the 1-dimensional subspaces $\mathbf{F}x$ of $V^3$.

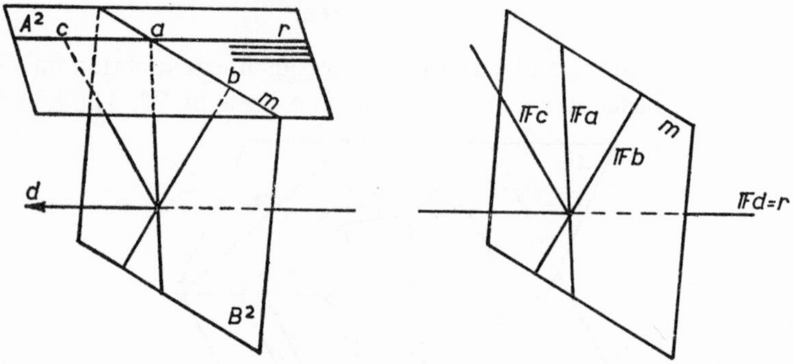


Fig. 20.4

If $\psi$ is a homogeneous linear function on $V^3$ then the 1-dimensional subspaces on the kernel $\psi^{-1}(0)$ form a 2-dimensional subspace $B^2 \subset V^3$. If this subspace intersects $A^2$, then the intersection is a line $m$, and $B^2$ consists of the 1-dimensional subspaces representing the points and directions of $m$.

Moreover under this mapping the points and direction of an arbitrary line in $A^2$ are mapped onto the 1-dimensional subspaces of a 2-dimensional subspace of $V^3$. This is also true for the set of all directions in $A^2$ and in this way any 2-dimensional subspace of $V^3$ can be interpreted in $A^2$. Summarizing:

*Under this representation any set of all 1-dimensional subspaces in a 2-dimensional subspace of* $V^3$ (*i.e. in the kernel of a homogeneous linear function on* $V^3$) *is the image of one line in the projective plane obtained from* $A^2$, *and any line in that plane has such an image.*

*The projective n-space as quotient of a vector space and a relation.* We now give a definition of a projective $n$-dimensional space. In this definition we shall *not make use of affine spaces*, nor shall we distinguish between finite and infinite points. (For $n = 2$ we get a definition of the projective plane).

Definition: Let $V^{n+1}$ be an $(n + 1)$-dimensional vector space over the field $\mathbf{F}$. The subset obtained by omitting the point O may be designated by $V^{n+1} - \{O\}$, or, more briefly, by $V^{n+1} - O$. Two vectors $\neq O$ are said to be in the *relation* $\mathbf{F}$ if they are linearly dependent. This relation is an equivalence. The equivalence classes are the 1-dimensional subspaces of $V^{n+1}$ each without the point O. The set of equivalence classes, i.e. *the quotient* $(V^{n+1} - O)/\mathbf{F}$ *is called the projective n-dimensional space over* $\mathbf{F}$: $P^n(\mathbf{F})$. If $B^{k+1}$ is a $(k + 1)$-dimensional subspace of $V^{n+1}$ then $(B^{k+1} - O)/\mathbf{F}$ is a projective $k$-dimensional space contained in the projective space mentioned before. For the cases $k = 0, 1, 2, n - 1, -1$ these spaces are called point, line, plane, hyperplane, empty set in $P^n(\mathbf{F})$. The intersection of two projective subspaces of a projective space is again a projective subspace, since the intersection of two vector subspaces is again a vector subspace. The set of all points of the lines joining a point of a projective subspace with a point of another projective subspace is again a projective subspace which is called the *join* of the two given spaces. Furthermore we have

Dimension Theorem [20.2]: *The sum of the dimensions of two projective subspaces of a projective space is equal to the sum of the dimensions of intersection and join.*

Proof: If the two subspaces are $(B - O)/\mathbf{F}$ and $(C - O)/\mathbf{F}$ then the intersection is $\{(B \cap C) - O\}/\mathbf{F}$ and the join is $\{(B + C) - O\}/\mathbf{F}$ and the theorem then follows from theorem [5.6].

*Homogeneous coordinates for the projective plane.* Suppose that $\eta_0$, $\eta_1$, $\eta_2$ form a basis of the space $V^*$ of homogeneous linear functions on the three-dimensional vector space V.

Any point of the projective plane $P = (V - O)/\mathbf{F}$ is a 1-dimensional subspace (minus O) of V. If $x \neq O$ is a vector in that subspace, then the triple of function values $\eta_0(x)$, $\eta_1(x)$, $\eta_2(x)$ is a *set of homogeneous coordinate values* for the point in question. Of course, for $\lambda \neq 0$ $\lambda x$ also is a vector in that subspace, and the triple

$$\{\eta_0(\lambda x), \eta_1(\lambda x), \eta_2(\lambda x)\} = \{\lambda\eta_0(x), \lambda\eta_1(x), \lambda\eta_2(x)\}$$

is another set of homogeneous coordinate values for the same point. Thus to any point there correspond different triples of coordinate values. If the coordinate values are given then the point $P$ is completely determined, for in $V^3$ there is just one vector with given values of the functions $\eta_0, \eta_1, \eta_2$ and the subspace with this vector as basis represents the point in $P$. Only the ratios of the function values are relevant.

Observe that the triples of coordinate values associated by $(\eta_0, \eta_1, \eta_2)$ to a point of the projective plane are the same as the triples associated to this point by $(\rho\eta_0, \rho\eta_1, \rho\eta_2)$ with constant $\rho \neq 0$.

If we wish to consider the projective plane $P$ as an extension of an affine plane then we choose an arbitrary line in $P$ with equation, say, $\xi_0 = 0$, and call its points directions or points at infinity. The other points generate an affine plane *embedded* in this projective plane. Two lines intersecting in a point at infinity are called parallel. In $V^3$ we can represent this affine plane by the set $A^2$ of vectors x with $\xi_0(x) = 1$. The directions in $A^2$ are the 1-dimensional subspaces of $V^3$ in $\xi_0^{-1}(0)$.

If $\eta_0$, $\eta_1$, $\eta_2$ are linear functions on $V^3$ whose restrictions to $A^2$ are *given* functions of degree $\leqslant 1$ on $A^2$, with kernels which are three non-concurrent lines, then the ratios $\eta_0 : \eta_1 : \eta_2$ are just the ratios of coordinates we already discussed. From the present treatment it is apparent that these ratios are also relevant for the points at infinity in $A^2$. For, in this treatment the points at infinity play no particular role.

If $\xi_0$, $\xi_1$, $\xi_2$ are independent homogeneous linear functions on $V^3$ and if $A^2$ has equation $\xi_0 = 1$, then any finite point of $A^2$ has a set of homogeneous coordinates of type $(1, \alpha_1, \alpha_2)$, which clearly can be obtained by adding a coordinate $\xi_0 = 1$ to the affine coordinates $\xi_1 = \alpha_1$, $\xi_2 = \alpha_2$. The points at infinity have sets of coordinates of type $(0, \alpha_1, \alpha_2)$. (Observe that our general arguments apply for an arbitrary field **F**.)

Fig. 20.5 shows some sets of coordinate values for finite and infinite points, when $\eta_0, \eta_1, \eta_2$ are functions of Hesse of the sides of an equilateral triangle in a euclidean plane. The line at infinity has equation $\eta_0 + \eta_1 + \eta_2 = 0$.

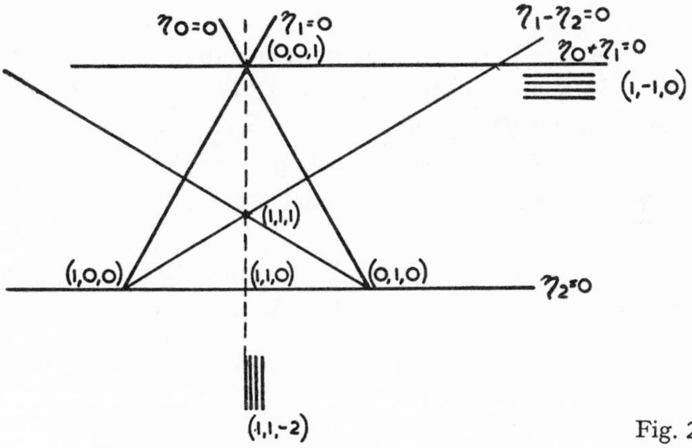


Fig. 20.5

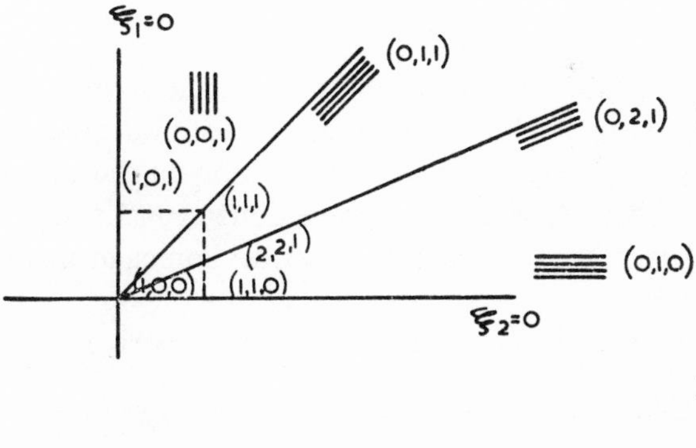


Fig. 20.6

In fig. 20.6 $\xi_1$ and $\xi_2$ are "ordinary orthogonal coordinates" and $\xi_0$ is the function which is 1 on $A^2$. In this figure homogeneous coordinates of a few points are also given. The line at infinity has equation $\xi_0 = 0$.

*N.B.* Although the triple $(\eta_0, \eta_1, \eta_2)$ is called a homogeneous coordinate system on the projective plane, the name "coordinate" makes no sense for each of the $\eta_i$ alone. But it is true that $\eta_0 = 0$ is the equation of a line, as we have seen already.

*Homogenizing a polynomial.* Similar to theorem [20.1] we have:

Theorem [20.3]: *The functions of degree $\leqslant k$ on the plane $A^2 \subset V^3$, $O \notin A^2$, are the restrictions to $A^2$ of the homogeneous k-th degree functions on $V^3$. The correspondence between the functions is one-to-one.*

Proof: Let $\xi_0, \xi_1, \xi_2$ be linearly independent linear functions on $V^3$ and let $A^2$ have equation $\xi_0 = 1$; then any homogeneous $k$-th degree function on $V^3$ can be written as a homogeneous $k$-th degree polynomial $g(\xi_0, \xi_1, \xi_2)$ and substitution of $\xi_0 = 1$ then usually yields a non-homogeneous polynomial $g(1, \xi_1, \xi_2)$ of degree $\leqslant k$ in $\xi_1, \xi_2$.

Conversely, a function of degree $\leqslant k$ on $A^2$ can be expressed in coordinates $\xi_1, \xi_2$ as polynomial $f(\xi_1, \xi_2)$ of degree $\leqslant k$. Then

$$g(\xi_0, \xi_1, \xi_2) = \xi_0{}^k f(\xi_1/\xi_0, \xi_2/\xi_0) \qquad (20.1)$$

is a polynomial in $\xi_0, \xi_1, \xi_2$, homogeneous of degree $k$ in $\xi_0, \xi_1, \xi_2$, whilst

$$g(1, \xi_1, \xi_2) = f(\xi_1, \xi_2).$$

Thus applying this method we obtain from the second-degree function $\xi_1{}^2 + 3\xi_2 + 1$ the homogeneous second-degree polynomial $\xi_1{}^2 + 3\xi_0\xi_2 + \xi_0{}^2$. If the former is a function on the affine plane $A^2$ which is the plane $\xi_0 = 1$ of the three dimensional vector space $V^3$, then the latter is an expression for a homogeneous quadratic function on $V^3$.

If a vector x satisfies the homogeneous equation

$$g(\xi_0, \xi_1, \xi_2)(\mathrm{x}) = g\{\xi_0(\mathrm{x}), \xi_1(\mathrm{x}), \xi_2(\mathrm{x})\} = 0,$$

then the vector $\lambda\mathrm{x}$, $\lambda \in \mathbf{F}$, satisfies it also.

Thus if one vector $\mathrm{x} \neq O$ representing a particular point of the projective plane $P = (V^3 - O)/\mathbf{F}$ satisfies the equation then so does any other vector $\lambda\mathrm{x} \neq O$ that represents the same point. In that case the point in $P$ is said to satisfy the equation. The set of points in $P$ which satisfy the equation is called a *k-th degree curve in the projective plane.* The equation $g(\xi_0, \xi_1, \xi_2) = 0$ is called its equation in homogeneous coordinates. $g(1, \xi_1, \xi_2) = f(\xi_1, \xi_2) = 0$ is its equation in non-homogeneous coordinates. The same equation is also the "ordinary" equation of a curve in the affine plane $A$.

Similarly from the equation $f(\xi_1, \cdots \xi_n) = 0$ of a variety of degree $\leqslant k$ in an $n$-dimensional affine space, the homogeneous equation of degree $k$

$$\xi_0{}^k f(\xi_1/\xi_0, \cdots \xi_n/\xi_0) = 0$$

of a point set in the $n$-dimensional projective space is obtained. In projective geometry the intersection of a finite number of such sets is called a *variety.* [1])

*The close connection between the 3-dimensional vector space and the projective plane, or more generally between the $(n+1)$-dimensional vector space and the $n$-dimensional projective space enables us to find many properties of projective spaces from properties of vector spaces. We give some important examples.

*Transformation of coordinates.* If $\xi_0, \xi_1, \xi_2$ is a homogeneous coordinate system for a projective plane, then $\eta_0, \eta_1, \eta_2$ is another coordinate system if and only if there exist $\alpha_{ij} \in \mathbf{F}$, $i, j = 0, 1, 2$ with $\det\{\alpha_{ij}\} \neq 0$ and $\rho \in \mathbf{F}$, $\rho \neq 0$ such that

$$\eta_i = \rho \textstyle\sum_{j=0}^{2} \alpha_{ij}\xi_j. \tag{20.2}$$

The only meaning of the scalar $\rho$ in this formula is to remind the reader that the coordinate triples associated to a point by $\eta_0, \eta_1, \eta_2$ are the same as those associated to that point by $\rho\eta_0, \rho\eta_1, \rho\eta_2$.

*Projective mappings.* An isomorphism of an $(n+1)$-dimensional vector space A onto another, B, maps 1-dimensional subspaces onto 1-dimensional subspaces, and thus determines a mapping of the projective $n$-dimensional space

$$P_a = (\mathrm{A} - \mathrm{O})/\mathbf{F} \text{ onto } P_b = (\mathrm{B} - \mathrm{O})/\mathbf{F}.$$

---

[1]) In topology, and similarly in differential geometry the word variety is used for a topological space whose local topological structure is identical to that of a euclidean space.

Such a mapping is called a projective mapping of $P_a$ onto $P_b$. A projective mapping maps lines onto lines, projective $k$-spaces onto projective $k$-spaces. A figure (= point set) $F_a \subset P_a$ is said to be *projectively equivalent* to a figure $F_b \subset P_b$ if there exists a projective mapping of $P_a$ onto $P_b$ under which $F_b$ is the image of $F_a$. This is particularly important when $P_b = P_a$, in which case the projective mapping is derived from an automorphism of A. The set of figures in $P = P_a$ can now be divided into classes of projectively equivalent figures.

In the same way as we defined euclidean and affine properties (p. 203) we define: A *projective property* is a set $\mathscr{F}$ of figures in a projective space $P$ such that whenever $F$ belongs to it, any figure projectively equivalent to $F$ also belongs to it. Collinearity of three points is a projective property; also concurrence of three lines. To be harmonic is a projective property that four points may have (cf. p. 46 and 48). In this chapter our attention will be particularly directed to projective properties, also to figures which are situated in a euclidean plane, which we then tacitly assume to be extended by the points at infinity.

The set of the euclidean, affine, projective properties of figures is called *euclidean, affine* or *projective geometry* respectively.

Since under an isomorphism of A onto B the homogeneous linear functions on B are mapped onto the homogeneous linear functions on A, and since an isomorphism is characterized by this mapping of linear functions, there exist homogeneous coordinates $\xi_0, \cdots \xi_n$ on $P_a$ and homogeneous coordinates $\eta_0, \cdots \eta_n$ on $P_b$ such that the given projective mapping of $P_a$ onto $P_b$ is represented by equating the coordinate values

$$\eta_i = \xi_i \qquad i = 0, \cdots n. \tag{20.3}$$

($\xi_i$ is the dual image of $\eta_i$ considered as a linear function on A and B respectively).

If $P_b = P_a$, B = A, then there exist $\alpha_{ij} \in \mathbf{F}$, $i, j = 0, \cdots n$, $\det\{\alpha_{ij}\} \neq 0$, such that

$$\eta_i = \textstyle\sum_{j=0}^{n} \alpha_{ij}\xi_j$$

and a point represented by the $(n + 1)$-dimensional vector x with coordinates $\xi_0(\mathrm{x}), \cdots \xi_n(\mathrm{x})$ has as image a point with coordinate values $\xi_0(\mathrm{y}), \cdots \xi_n(\mathrm{y})$, for which

$$\eta_i(\mathrm{y}) = \textstyle\sum_{j=0}^{n} \alpha_{ij}\xi_j(\mathrm{y}) = \xi_i(\mathrm{x}).$$

From (20.3) it follows that a figure $F_a \subset P_a$ is projectively equivalent to a figure $F_b \subset P_b$ if and only if there exist homogeneous coordinates for $P_a$ and homogeneous coordinates for $P_b$ such that the former coordinates give values for the points of $F_a$ which are values of the latter coordinates for points of $F_b$, and conversely. If $F_a$ consists of the points on which a homogeneous polynomial in the former coordinates assumes the value zero, then $F_b$ consists of the points on which the same homogeneous polynomial (but now written in the latter coordinates) assumes the value zero, and this property is sufficient to ensure projective equivalence.

*Projective classification of quadrics (over* **C** *and* **R***)*

Definition: A *quadric* is the set of all points satisfying a homogeneous quadratic equation in homogeneous coordinates: $\varphi(\xi_0, \cdots \xi_n) = 0$. By a suitable choice of coordinates this equation can be given a standard form. From theorem [14.3′] we now obtain

Theorem [20.4]: *Projective classification of quadrics. For any quadric in an n-dimensional projective space $P^n(\mathbf{F})$ there exist homogeneous coordinates $\xi_1, \cdots \xi_{n+1}$ such that the quadric has the following equation, when* **F** *is the field* **C** *of complex numbers*

$$\textstyle\sum_{i=1}^{r} \xi_i^2 = 0, \qquad 1 \leqslant r \leqslant n+1, \tag{20.4}$$

*and when* **F** *is the field* **R** *of real numbers it has the equation*

$$\textstyle\sum_{i=1}^{p} \xi_i^2 - \sum_{j=p+1}^{p+q} \xi_j^2 = 0, \quad 0 \leqslant q \leqslant p \leqslant n+1. \tag{20.5}$$

*Moreover to any quadric there corresponds exactly one of these representations.*

Thus the quadrics in a complex projective space can be divided into projective equivalence classes characterized by the number $r$. For the classes of quadrics in a real projective space the numbers $p$ and $q$ in (20.5) are characteristic. *They are projective invariants.* [1])

[1]) A function (or a value of such a function) associating numbers (or more generally elements of some set) to a set of figures or other objects in a projective space, such that projectively equivalent figures have the same function value, is called a *projective invariant.* The cross-ratio of four collinear points is an example.

The ellipse, hyperbola and parabola in a real affine plane cannot be distinguished in the corresponding real projective plane, as follows from the following table

ellipse: $\xi_1^2 + \xi_2^2 - 1 = 0,\ \xi_1^2 + \xi_2^2 - \xi_0^2 = 0;$

$$\xi_1 = \eta_1,\ \xi_2 = \eta_2,\ \xi_0 = \eta_0$$

hyperbola: $\xi_1^2 - \xi_2^2 - 1 = 0,\ \xi_1^2 - \xi_2^2 - \xi_0^2 = 0;$

$$\xi_1 = \eta_0,\ \xi_2 = \eta_1,\ \xi_0 = \eta_2$$

parabola: $\xi_1^2 - 2\xi_2 = 0,\ \xi_1^2 - 2\xi_0\xi_2 = 0;$

$$\xi_1 = \eta_1,\ 2\xi_0 = \eta_0 + \eta_2,\ \xi_2 = \eta_0 - \eta_2.$$

In terms of the new homogeneous projective coordinates $\eta_0, \eta_1, \eta_2$ the equations are identical: $\eta_1^2 + \eta_2^2 - \eta_0^2 = 0$.

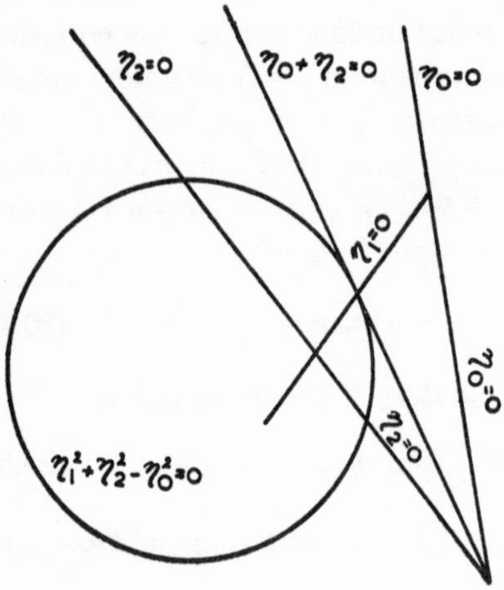

Fig. 20.7

The line at infinity has equation $\eta_0 = 0$, $\eta_2 = 0$ and $\eta_0 + \eta_2 = 0$ respectively, and it has 0, 2 or 1 points in common with the quadric. (cf. fig. 20.7). Hence: A real quadric of projective type (20.5) with $q = 1$, $p = 2$, $n = 2$ is an ellipse, a hyperbola or a parabola if it has 0, 2 or 1 infinite points respectively (cf. fig. 20.8).

There are two kinds of quadrics with $p + q = n + 1 = 4$ (see (20.5)) in the three-dimensional projective space if we disregard the empty set with equation $\xi_1^2 + \xi_2^2 + \xi_3^2 + \xi_4^2 = 0$.

The equation of type

$$\xi_1^2 + \xi_2^2 + \xi_3^2 - \xi_4^2 = 0$$

applies to the ellipsoid (sphere), the elliptic paraboloid as well as to the hyperboloid of two sheets in affine space. Thus these figures with their points at infinity added, are mutually projectively equivalent.

The equation of type

$$\xi_1^2 + \xi_2^2 - \xi_3^2 - \xi_4^2 = 0$$

applies to the hyperbolic paraboloid and the hyperboloid of one sheet in affine space.

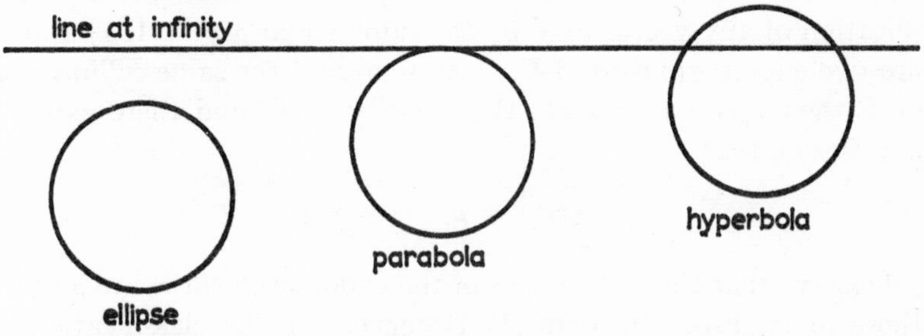


Fig. 20.8. An affine plane with ellipse, parabola and hyperbola, in a projection, such that the line at infinity is drawn as an ordinary line.

PROBLEMS. (20.2). Prove these last assertions making use of the affine classification of quadrics.

(20.3). On the last set of surfaces there exist two systems of lines, viz. with equations

I $\qquad (\xi_1 - \xi_3) = \lambda(\xi_2 - \xi_4), \; \lambda(\xi_1 + \xi_3) = -(\xi_2 + \xi_4)$

and

II $\qquad (\xi_1 - \xi_4) = \lambda(\xi_2 - \xi_3), \; \lambda(\xi_1 + \xi_4) = -(\xi_2 + \xi_3)$

where $\lambda$ is a parameter.

The quadrics in the real projective 3-dimensional space for which $p + q = n = 3$ in (20.5), excluding the case $\xi_1^2 + \xi_2^2 + \xi_3^2 = 0$, have, in suitable coordinates, the equation

$$\xi_1^2 + \xi_2^2 - \xi_3^2 = 0.$$

This equation applies in particular to the cone and to the elliptic, parabolic and hyperbolic cylinders in affine space with their points at infinity added. The quadric is called a *projective cone.*

*Classification of collineations (over* **C** *and* **R***)*

Definition: A projective mapping of a projective space $P$ onto itself is called a *collineation*. If V is an $(n+1)$-dimensional vector space over **F** and $P = (\mathrm{V} - \mathrm{O})/\mathbf{F}$ then the identical mapping of $P$ onto itself is represented by any endomorphism of V onto itself which leaves any 1-dimensional subspace invariant, i.e. a multiplication of any vector in V by the same scalar $\rho \neq 0$. If $\tau_1$ and $\tau_2$ are two endomorphisms of V which represent the same collineation of $P$ then $\tau_2\tau_1^{-1}$ represents the identity in $P$, and there exists a $\rho \neq 0$ such that

$$\tau_2\tau_1^{-1} = \rho, \quad \tau_2 = \rho\tau_1.$$

Observe that the eigenvalues of the endomorphism $\tau_2$ are $\rho$ times those of $\tau_1$. From theorem [17.1] concerning the classification of complex and real endomorphisms we now obtain:

Theorem [20.5]: *Projective classification of collineations in a complex projective space. An equivalence class of collineations of a complex projective space $P = (\mathrm{V} - \mathrm{O})/\mathbf{C}$ is characterized by the ratios of the eigenvalues, the multiplicities of the eigenvalues and the partitions of these multiplicities of any endomorphism $\tau$ of* V *which represents the given collineation. All eigenvalues of $\tau$ must be different from zero.*

In order to obtain the classification of the real collineations the complexification of the corresponding vector space is studied (cf. theorem [17.2]).

Problems. (20.4). A complete list of the classes of collineations in the projective 1-dimensional space over the complex and the real numbers is given by the normal forms (matrix of an endomorphism):

$$\text{complex:} \begin{pmatrix} 1 & 0 \\ 0 & \alpha \end{pmatrix} |\alpha| > 1; \begin{pmatrix} 1 & 0 \\ 0 & e^{i\varphi} \end{pmatrix} 0 \leqslant \varphi \leqslant \pi; \begin{pmatrix} 1 & 1 \\ 0 & 1 \end{pmatrix}$$

$$\text{real:} \quad \begin{pmatrix} 1 & 0 \\ 0 & \lambda \end{pmatrix} |\lambda| \geqslant 1; \begin{pmatrix} \cos\varphi & \sin\varphi \\ -\sin\varphi & \cos\varphi \end{pmatrix} 0 < \varphi \leqslant \frac{\pi}{2}; \begin{pmatrix} 1 & 1 \\ 0 & 1 \end{pmatrix}.$$

(20.5). A non-identical collineation in $P^n$ whose square is the identity is called an *involution* in $P^n$. Give a survey of all involutions in the complex and real projective spaces of dimension $\leqslant 3$.

(20.6). The collineations of a projective space form a group.

Theorem [20.6]: *If $S_i$, $i = 1, \cdots n+2$ are $n+2$ points in the projective $n$-dimensional space $P^n(\mathbf{F})$ no $n+1$ of which are contained in an $(n-1)$-dimensional projective space in $P^n(\mathbf{F})$, and if the same holds for the points $S_i'$, $i = 1, \cdots n+2$, then there exists exactly one collineation of $P^n(\mathbf{F})$ mapping $S_i$ onto $S_i'$ for $i = 1, \cdots n+2$.*

Example: There is exactly one projective mapping of the line $P^1(\mathbf{F})$ onto itself which maps three given distinct points $S_1$, $S_2$, $S_3$ to three given distinct points $S_1'$, $S_2'$, $S_3'$.

Proof of the theorem: (cf. fig. 20.9 for the case $n = 2$). Suppose that $P^n(\mathbf{F}) = P = (\mathrm{V} - \mathrm{O})/\mathbf{F}$. $S_i$ and $S_i'$ are 1-dimensional subspaces of V. Choose a vector a in the 1-dimensional subspace $S_{n+2}$ and choose as basis for the linear functions on V the functions $\xi_1, \cdots \xi_{n+1}$ such that $\xi_i$ has the value zero on $S_j$ for $j \neq i$, $j \neq n+2$ and $\xi_i(\mathrm{a}) = 1$. Choose a', $\xi_1', \cdots \xi'_{n+1}$ similarly for $S_1', \cdots S'_{n+2}$. The endomorphism $\sigma$ of V which maps $\xi_i'$ (dually) onto $\xi_i$ for $i = 1, \cdots n+1$, i.e. $\xi_i'\sigma = \xi_i$ gives the required collineation. The endomorphism $\sigma$ is determined apart from a scalar $\rho \neq 0$. But all endomorphisms obtained from $\sigma$ by multiplication by $\rho \neq 0$, give the same collineation in $P = (\mathrm{V} - \mathrm{O})/\mathbf{F}$. This implies that there cannot be more than one collineation with the required properties.

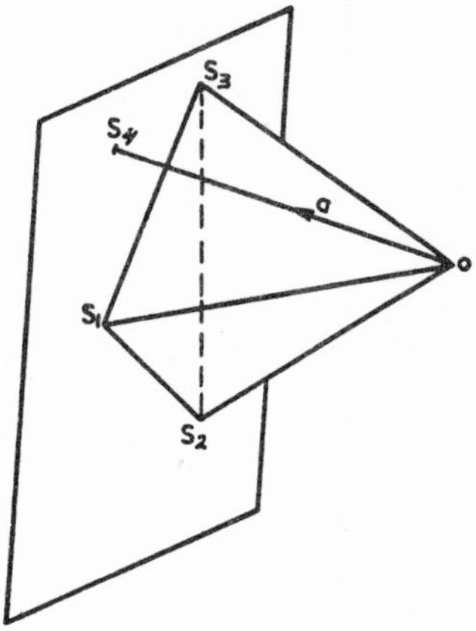

Fig. 20.9

*Cross-ratio*. The cross-ratio of four collinear points **F**a, **F**b, **F**c, **F**d in the projective space $(\mathrm{V} - \mathrm{O})/\mathbf{F}$ (a, b, c, d $\epsilon$ V) is defined as the cross-ratio of the one-dimensional subspaces **F**a, **F**b, **F**c, **F**d of the vector space V. (Cf. chapter 7). If the projective space is obtained from an affine space by adding the points at infinity then the cross-ratio of four collinear points in the affine space, as defined before, is equal to the cross-ratio of those points in the projective space under the definition just given.

Theorem [20.7]: *If $S_1$, $S_2$, $S_3$, $S_4$ are collinear points in a projective space P and if $\tau$ is a projective mapping of P onto the projective space P', for which $\tau S_i = S_i'$, $i = 1, \cdots 4$, then*

$$(S_1, S_2, S_3, S_4) = (S_1', S_2', S_3', S_4').$$

*The cross-ratio is invariant under projective mappings.*

(As an example of a projective mapping we mention the projection of a $P^1$ in a $P^2$ onto another $P^1$).

Proof: In suitable homogeneous coordinates $\xi_i$ for $P$ and $\xi_i'$ for $P'$, $\tau$ is represented by the equations

$$\xi_j' = \xi_j \qquad j = 1, \cdots n + 1.$$

In particular we have $\xi_j'(S_i') = \xi_j(S_i)$. Both cross-ratios are calculated in the same way from coordinate values, and so they are equal.

*N.B.* If $P$ and $P'$ are the same, i.e. we have a collineation of $P$, then the understanding of this proof requires extra effort, since in the same space we now use different coordinates for the points $S_i$ and $S_i'$.

*Functions on a projective space.* If $P = (\mathrm{V} - \mathrm{O})/\mathbf{F}$ and $\varphi$ and $\psi$ are homogeneous functions of degree $k$ on the vector space V, then for any $\mathrm{a} \in \mathrm{V}$, $\mathrm{a} \neq \mathrm{O}$ and $\lambda \in \mathbf{F}$

$$\varphi(\lambda \mathrm{a}) = \lambda^k \varphi(\mathrm{a}), \quad \psi(\lambda \mathrm{a}) = \lambda^k \psi(\mathrm{a}).$$

Hence $\dfrac{\varphi}{\psi}$ is a function on V which is constant on any one-dimensional subspace of V (from which the point O has been omitted) on which $\psi$ is not zero. Hence $\varphi/\psi$ is a function on the projective space $P$, which is not defined on the points for which $\psi = 0$. The analogue is true for $\psi/\varphi$. Instead of $\psi/\varphi = 0$ we write $\varphi/\psi = \infty$. *Then $\varphi/\psi$ associates to any point of the projective space for which not* *both $\varphi$ and $\psi$ are zero, an element of* $(\mathbf{F} \cup \infty)$. *$\varphi/\psi$ is called a rational k-th degree function on P.* On p. 46 we already considered such a function for $k = 1$. The set of level sets of the function $\varphi/\psi$ is called a *pencil of k-th degree varieties in P.* The points in $P$ for which $\varphi = \psi = 0$ are called the basic points of the pencil.

Theorem [20.8]: *The points of a projective n-dimensional space for which a given rational k-th degree function assumes the same value as another rational m-th degree function, are situated on an $(m + k)$-th degree variety.*

Proof: Let the given functions be $\varphi/\varphi'$ and $\psi/\psi'$ where $\varphi$ and $\varphi'$ are homogeneous of degree $k$, and $\psi$ and $\psi'$ homogeneous of degree $m$.

Any point for which $\varphi/\varphi' = \psi/\psi'$, satisfies $\varphi\psi' - \varphi'\psi = 0$, and the left-hand side of this equation is homogeneous of degree $k + m$. In particular equating two rational first-degree functions one obtains a quadratic curve. Before considering this in more detail, we note first:

Theorem [20.9]: *In a projective plane there is exactly one quadratic curve through any five points no four of which are collinear.*

Proof: Among the given five points there are certainly four no three of which are collinear. Choose coordinates $\xi_1$, $\xi_2$, $\xi_3$ such that these points become $(1, 0, 0)$, $(0, 1, 0)$, $(0, 0, 1)$ and $(1, 1, 1)$, and let the fifth point be $(\alpha_1, \alpha_2, \alpha_3)$. The equation of a quadratic curve is $\sum_{i \leq j} \gamma_{ij}\xi_i\xi_j = 0$, $i, j = 1, 2, 3$, $\gamma_{ij} \in \mathbf{F}$. Since the first three points are on the curve, $\gamma_{11} = \gamma_{22} = \gamma_{33} = 0$. Since the fourth point lies on it, the equation is of type

$$\lambda\xi_2\xi_3 + \mu\xi_3\xi_1 - (\lambda + \mu)\xi_1\xi_2 = 0,$$

and the coordinates of the fifth point then satisfy

$$\lambda\alpha_2(\alpha_3 - \alpha_1) + \mu\alpha_1(\alpha_3 - \alpha_2) = 0.$$

This determines the ratio of $\lambda$ and $\mu$, and thus the conic, unless

$$\alpha_2(\alpha_3 - \alpha_1) = \alpha_1(\alpha_3 - \alpha_2) = 0.$$

But the latter relation would mean that the fifth point coincides with one of the other four.

Another proof follows from the observation that substitution of the coordinate values of the five points gives five homogeneous equations in $\gamma_{ij}$ which determine the ratios of the $\gamma_{ij}$ completely provided that the equations are independent. The latter is the case if no four of the five points are collinear.

Let $S_i$, $i = 1, \cdots 5$ be five points of a projective ellipse and let no three of these points be collinear. Cf. fig. 20.10. Let $\varphi/\varphi'$ and $\psi/\psi'$ be the rational linear functions for which

$$\varphi(S_1) = \varphi(S_3) = \varphi'(S_1) = \varphi'(S_4) = 0$$

$$\psi(S_2) = \psi(S_3) = \psi'(S_2) = \psi'(S_4) = 0$$

and let $\varphi/\varphi' = \psi/\psi' = 1$ in the point $S_5$.

Then the points for which $\varphi/\varphi' = \psi/\psi'$ lie on the quadratic curve

$$\varphi\psi' - \varphi'\psi = 0$$

which, as follows from substitution, contains the points $S_1, \cdots S_5$, and this is the given ellipse.

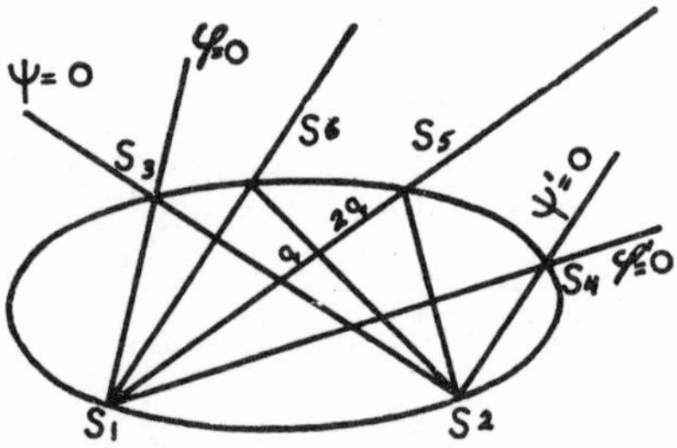

Fig. 20.10

If $S_6$ is a sixth point of the ellipse, then the cross-ratio of the four lines through $S_1$ and $S_3$, $S_1$ and $S_4$, $S_1$ and $S_5$, and $S_1$ and $S_6$ can be expressed in terms of the values of $\varphi/\varphi'$ at the points $S_5$ and $S_6$. If $S_5 = \mathbf{F}\mathbf{x}_5$ and $S_6 = \mathbf{F}\mathbf{x}_6$, and $\mathbf{x}_5$ and $\mathbf{x}_6$ are vectors in the three-dimensional vector space $\mathbf{V}^3$ with respect to which the projective plane is $P = (\mathbf{V}^3 - \mathrm{O})/\mathbf{F}$, then the cross-ratio in question is

$$\frac{\varphi(\mathbf{x}_5)}{\varphi'(\mathbf{x}_5)} : \frac{\varphi(\mathbf{x}_6)}{\varphi'(\mathbf{x}_6)}.$$

If the projective plane is considered as the extension of an affine plane with non-homogeneous linear functions $\varphi$, $\varphi'$, $\psi$, $\psi'$ and with an $\mathscr{A}$-map under which $S_5$ and $S_6$ are represented by the vectors $\mathbf{x}_5$ and $\mathbf{x}_6$ of a two-dimensional space, then the cross-ratio in question is

$$\frac{\varphi(\mathbf{x}_5)}{\varphi'(\mathbf{x}_5)} : \frac{\varphi(\mathbf{x}_6)}{\varphi'(\mathbf{x}_6)}$$

also.

Since the values of $\varphi/\varphi'$ and $\psi/\psi'$ are mutually the same for any point of the ellipse, we have:

Theorem [20.10]: *The joins of four points $S_3$, $S_4$, $S_5$, $S_6$ on a (projective) ellipse to a fifth point $S_1$ have the same cross-ratio as the joins to a point $S_2$, both $S_1$ and $S_2$ on the ellipse. This cross-ratio is called the cross-ratio of the points $S_3$, $S_4$, $S_5$, $S_6$ on the ellipse.*

*N.B.* In fig. 20.10 the cross-ratio $(S_3, S_4, S_5, S_6) = 4$.

Theorem [20.10] enables us to "construct" the second point of intersection of an ellipse and an arbitrary line through one of five given points of the ellipse.

As an application of theorem [20.10] we prove

Pascal's Theorem [20.11]: *Let $S_1, \cdots S_6$ be six points on an ellipse, and let $S_i + S_j$ be the join of $S_i$ and $S_j$, then the points $U = (S_1 + S_2) \cap (S_4 + S_5)$, $V = (S_2 + S_3) \cap (S_5 + S_6)$ and $W = (S_3 + S_4) \cap (S_6 + S_1)$ are collinear.*

Proof: In fig. 20.11 the cross-ratio $(S_4S_5TU)$ and $(S_4S_5S_3S_1)$ are both equal to the cross-ratio of the joins of these points to $S_2$: "projection from $S_2$ onto the ellipse". Hence $(S_4S_5TU) = (S_4S_5S_3S_1)$.

Similarly $(S_4RS_3W) = (S_4S_5S_3S_1)$ by projection from $S_6$ onto the ellipse. Hence $(S_4S_5TU) = (S_4RS_3W)$.

The lines joining $V$ to $S_4$, $S_5$, $T$ and $U$ thus have the same cross-ratio as the joins of $V$ to $S_4$, $R$, $S_3$ and $W$. However, the first three

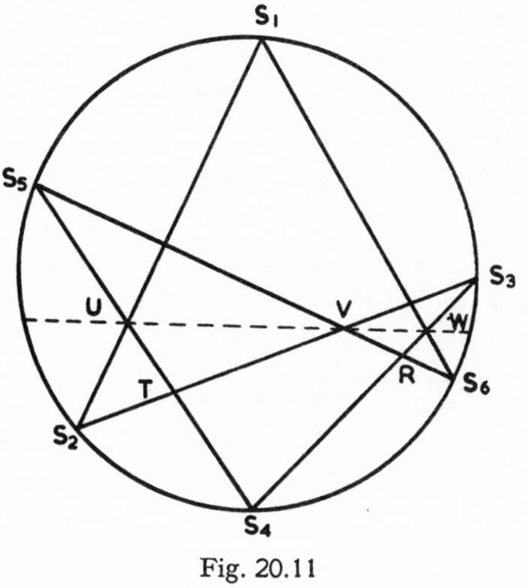

Fig. 20.11

lines in both cases are pair-wise the same, implying that the fourth pair is also identical, since there is only one line through $V$ which has a given cross-ratio with respect to three given lines through $V$. Thus the line through $V$ and $U$ is the same as that through $V$ and $W$.

*Polar theory. Spaces which are polar with respect to a quadric in a given projective space.* Let a quadric be given in the projective space $P = (\mathrm{V} - \mathrm{O})/\mathbf{F}$. The vectors in V representing points of the quadric form a cone with vertex O. Theorem [14.10] implies that if the quadric is not a real linear space, the quadratic equations $\varphi^{\cdot} = 0$ and $\psi^{\cdot} = 0$ represent the same cone if and only if there exists a $\lambda \neq 0$ such that

$$\psi^{\cdot} = \lambda\varphi^{\cdot}.$$

Two subspaces B and C of V are called polar (cf. chapter 14) with respect to the quadratic function $\varphi^{\cdot}$, if the bilinear symmetric function $\varphi$ satisfies $\varphi(\mathrm{x}, \mathrm{y}) = 0$ for all $\mathrm{x} \in \mathrm{B}$, $\mathrm{y} \in \mathrm{C}$. This is the case if and only if they are polar with respect to $\psi$. From this it will be clear that the following definition is independent of the special choice of $\varphi^{\cdot}$ (or $\psi^{\cdot}$) for a given quadric.

Definition: The projective subspaces $(\mathrm{B} - \mathrm{O})/\mathbf{F}$ and $(\mathrm{C}-\mathrm{O})/\mathbf{F}$ of $(\mathrm{V} - \mathrm{O})/\mathbf{F} = P$ are said to be *polar* with respect to the quadric $\varphi^{\cdot} = 0$, if B and C are polar with respect to the quadratic function $\varphi^{\cdot}$.

If $\varphi(\mathrm{x}, \mathrm{y}) = 0$ with $\mathrm{x}, \mathrm{y} \in \mathrm{V} = \mathrm{V}^{n+1}$, is the equation of the polar relation, then for given $\mathrm{x} \in \mathrm{V}$, the function $\mathrm{y} \to \varphi(\mathrm{x}, \mathrm{y})$ is a homogeneous linear function. This is not in general identically zero, and thus it has an $n$-dimensional subspace of $\mathrm{V}^{n+1}$ as kernel. This kernel determines a hyperplane in $P = P^n$, which will be called the *polar hyperplane of the point* $\mathbf{F}\mathrm{x} \in P^n$. (A polar hyperplane is called a pole in $P^1$, a polar in $P^2$, a polar plane in $P^3$).

PROBLEMS. (20.7). The locus of the points which are polar to themselves with respect to a given quadric is that quadric itself. They are the points which lie on their polar hyperplane.

(20.8). If any two of three different points in a projective plane are polar with respect to a given ellipse, then the triple is called a (self) *polar triangle* with respect to the ellipse. For a given ellipse with a given self polar triangle there exist homogeneous coordinates such that the equations of the ellipse and of the sides of the triangle are

$$\xi_1^2 + \xi_2^2 - \xi_3^2 = 0, \qquad \xi_1 = 0,\ \xi_2 = 0,\ \xi_3 = 0.$$

(20.9). If the polar of a point $S$ on a projective ellipse with respect to that ellipse intersects the ellipse in the point $S$ only, show that it is a tangent.

(20.10). If the points $S_1$ and $S_2 \neq S_1$ are polar with respect to the quadric $Q$ in a projective space, and if the join of $S_1$ and $S_2$ intersects $Q$ (only) in the points $S_3$ and $S_4$, then the points $S_1$ and $S_2$ separate the points $S_3$ and $S_4$ harmonically. The converse of this property is also true.

(20.11). Let in an affine space a quadric with centre $M$ be given. Any point at infinity is polar to $M$ with respect to the quadric; in other words the polar hyperplane of $M$ is the plane at infinity. A finite point which is polar to every point at infinity with respect to a quadric, is a centre of the quadric.

(20.12). If the projective ellipse in theorem [20.10] is an ordinary circle in the euclidean plane, then the assertion follows from elementary geometrical considerations.

(20.13). Theorem [20.10] also has a meaning if $S_3 = S_1$, the line $S_3S_4 = S_1S_4$, and $S_1S_3$ is the line which has only one point in common with the ellipse, i.e. is tangent at $S_1$.

(20.14). Construct the tangent at a point $S_1$ of a conic through five given points $S_1, \cdots S_5$ no three of which are collinear.

(20.15). A hyperbola in the ordinary plane is given by five points $S_1$, $S_2$, $S_4$, $S_5$, $S_6$ of which $S_1$ and $S_2$ are points at infinity (directions). Using theorem [20.11], construct more points and, in connection with problem (20.13), construct also the tangents at the points at infinity (the asymptotes).

Solution: In fig. 20.12 the lines $a, b, c, d, e, f, g, h$ are constructed in this order, and finally the asymptote $k$ with direction $S_1$. The lines $d, e, f$ and the line at infinity have the same cross-ratio as the lines $a, b, c, k$, equal to the cross-ratio of the points $S_4$, $S_5$, $S_6$, $S_1$.

*Duality*. If $P = (\mathrm{V} - \mathrm{O})/\mathbf{F}$ and $\mathrm{V}^*$ is the dual space of the $(n + 1)$-dimensional space V, then $(\mathrm{V}^* - \mathrm{O})/\mathbf{F} = P^*$ is called the *dual projective space* of $P$.

A point of $P^*$ is a set of linear functions $\lambda\varphi$ on V, $0 \neq \lambda \in \mathbf{F}$. All these functions have the same $n$-dimensional subspace of V as kernel. This kernel can be considered as a hyperplane of $P$. The points of $P^*$

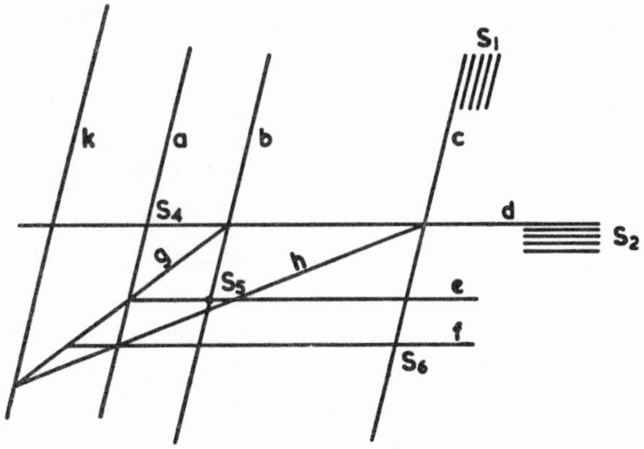


Fig. 20.12

are therefore in a one-to-one relationship with the hyperplanes of $P$. Another formulation is: the points of $P^*$ *are* the hyperplanes of $P$. Because of the symmetry of the relation "dual", similarly the points of $P$ "are" the hyperplanes of $P^*$. Also the $k$-dimensional subspaces $T^*$ of $P^*$ correspond to the $(n - k - 1)$-dimensional subspaces $T$ of $P$. The subspace $T^* \subset P^*$ corresponding to $T \subset P$ consists of the points of $P^*$ which "are" the hyperplanes of $P$ that contain $T$.

A theorem of the projective geometry of the space $P$ can also be formulated as a theorem of $P^*$. The theorem found in this manner is called the dual of the former. In order to obtain the dual of a plane projective theorem just replace the word

| | | |
|---|---|---|
| point | by | line |
| line | by | point |
| point of intersection | by | join |
| join | by | point of intersection. |

We apply this to theorem [7.3]:

Desargues's theorem (*in projective formulation*): *If for two given non-degenerate triangles with vertices a, b, c and a', b', c' there exists a line m which is concurrent with the sides bc and b'c', with the sides ca and c'a' and with the sides ab and a'b', then the lines aa', bb', cc' are concurrent.*

The dual theorem reads: *If for two given non-degenerate triangles with sides* $\alpha, \beta, \gamma$ *and* $\alpha', \beta', \gamma'$ *,there exists a point* $\mu$ *that is collinear with the points* $\beta \cap \gamma$ *and* $\beta' \cap \gamma'$*, with the points* $\gamma \cap \alpha$ *and* $\gamma' \cap \alpha'$ *and with the points* $\alpha \cap \beta$ *and* $\alpha' \cap \beta'$*, then the points* $\alpha \cap \alpha', \beta \cap \beta'$ *and* $\gamma \cap \gamma'$ *are collinear. In other words: If of two triangles with vertices a, b, c and a', b', c' and sides* $\alpha, \beta, \gamma$*, and* $\alpha', \beta', \gamma'$ *the lines aa', bb', cc' are concurrent then the points* $\alpha \cap \alpha', \beta \cap \beta'$ *and* $\gamma \cap \gamma'$ *are collinear*

Observe that the dual theorem happens to be the converse of the original theorem.

*Line coordinates.* Let $P = (\mathrm{V} - \mathrm{O})/\mathbf{F}$, $P^* = (\mathrm{V}^* - \mathrm{O})/\mathbf{F}$, dim $\mathrm{V} = 3$, $\mathrm{V}^*$ be the dual space of V. We choose a basis $(a_1, a_2, a_3)$ in V and the cobasis $(\xi_1, \xi_2, \xi_3)$ for $\mathrm{V}^*$

$$\xi_i(a_j) = \delta_{ij}.$$

$\xi_1, \xi_2, \xi_3$ are linear functions on V and homogeneous coordinates for the projective plane $P$. Dually $a_1, a_2, a_3$ can be considered as linear functions on $\mathrm{V}^*$. The values of these functions for $\xi \in \mathrm{V}^*$ are $\xi(a_1)$, $\xi(a_2)$ and $\xi(a_3)$. Then $a_1$, $a_2$ and $a_3$ can also be considered as homogeneous coordinates for $P^*$. They are called *line coordinates* for $P$ (more generally: hyperplane coordinates for the $n$-dimensional space). They assign a ratio of three scalars to any line.

Until now a point in $P$ has been characterized by a vector $x \in \mathrm{V}$ or by the three coordinate values $\xi_1(x), \xi_2(x), \xi_3(x)$.

Until now a line in $P$ has been characterized by an equation in the point coordinates $(\xi_1, \xi_2, \xi_3)$

$$\alpha_1\xi_1 + \alpha_2\xi_2 + \alpha_3\xi_3 = 0. \tag{20.6}$$

This line in $P$ is a point in $P^*$ and it can also be represented by a vector in $\mathrm{V}^*$, i.e. by a linear combination of the basis vectors $\xi_1, \xi_2, \xi_3$, viz.

$$\xi = \alpha_1\xi_1 + \alpha_2\xi_2 + \alpha_3\xi_3,$$

or by the line coordinates

$$\xi(a_1) = \alpha_1\xi_1(a_1) + \alpha_2\xi_2(a_1) + \alpha_3\xi_3(a_1) = \alpha_1$$
$$\xi(a_2) = \alpha_1\xi_1(a_2) + \alpha_2\xi_2(a_2) + \alpha_3\xi_3(a_2) = \alpha_2$$
$$\xi(a_3) = \alpha_1\xi_1(a_3) + \alpha_2\xi_2(a_3) + \alpha_3\xi_3(a_3) = \alpha_3$$

that is

$$(\alpha_1, \alpha_2, \alpha_3).$$

It is clear that equation (20.6) is completely determined by these line coordinates.

A point in $P$, that is a line in $P^*$, can also be characterized by a linear equation in the line coordinates $(\alpha_1, \alpha_2, \alpha_3)$:

$$\alpha_1\xi_1 + \alpha_2\xi_2 + \alpha_3\xi_3 = 0. \qquad (20.6)$$

For example the equation in $(\alpha_1, \alpha_2, \alpha_3)$ of the point x above is

$$\alpha_1\xi_1(x) + \alpha_2\xi_2(x) + \alpha_3\xi_3(x) = 0.$$

The point with ordinary coordinates $(\xi_1, \xi_2, \xi_3)$ lies on (or, more formally, "is *incident with*") the line with line coordinates $(\alpha_1, \alpha_2, \alpha_3)$ if the *incidence relation* (20.6) holds.

*Curves of the second class.* A second-degree curve in $P^*$ is called a *curve of the second class* of $P$. Such a projective ellipse in $P^*$ has, in suitable coordinates, the equation

$$\alpha_1^2 + \alpha_2^2 - \alpha_3^2 = 0. \qquad (20.7)$$

The polar of a point $(\beta_1, \beta_2, \beta_3)$ in $P^*$ with respect to this ellipse in $P^*$ has equation (think of the bilinear symmetric function in homogeneous coordinates)

$$\alpha_1\beta_1 + \alpha_2\beta_2 - \alpha_3\beta_3 = 0.$$

The point $(\beta_1, \beta_2, \beta_3)$ in $P^*$ is a line in $P$, viz. the line with line coordinates $(\beta_1, \beta_2, \beta_3)$ and with equation in point coordinates $(\xi_1, \xi_2, \xi_3)$

$$\beta_1\xi_1 + \beta_2\xi_2 + \beta_3\xi_3 = 0. \qquad (20.8)$$

The line in $P^*$ with equation (20.8) in the variables $\alpha_1, \alpha_2, \alpha_3$ is a point of $P$ with the same equation in line coordinates and with the

ordinary coordinate values $(\beta_1, \beta_2, -\beta_3)$. So we have found that the point $(\beta_1, \beta_2, -\beta_3)$ and the line (20.8) are pole and polar with respect to the curve of the second class (20.7). But the point and the line are also pole and polar with respect to the curve of second degree of $P$ with equation $\xi_1^2 + \xi_2^2 - \xi_3^2 = 0$.
Summarizing we have

Theorem [20.12]: *The relation "polar" with respect to a non-degenerate curve of the second class coincides with the relation "polar" with respect to a uniquely determined curve of second degree.*

A point of $P^*$ that lies on a non-degenerate quadratic curve of $P^*$ is incident with its polar in $P^*$. In $P$ it is the line incident with its pole with respect to a curve of the second class. Such a point in $P^*$ is then a tangent to the quadratic curve in $P$. Cf. problem (20.9).

The following theorem is obtained from Pascal's theorem [20.11] by duality.

Brianchon's Theorem [20.13]: *If* $S_1, \cdots S_6$ *are six tangents to a projective ellipse,* $S_i \cap S_j$ *is the intersection of* $S_i$ *and* $S_j$*, and* $(S_i \cap S_j) + (S_k \cap S_m)$ *the join of two such points, then the lines* $U = (S_1 \cap S_2) + (S_4 \cap S_5)$, $V = (S_2 \cap S_3) + (S_5 \cap S_6)$ *and* $W = (S_3 \cap S_4) + (S_6 \cap S_1)$ *are concurrent.*

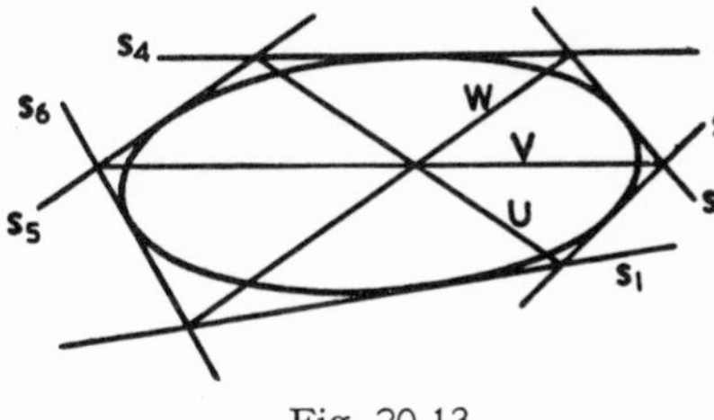


Fig. 20.13

PROBLEMS. (20.16). The quadratic curves $k_2$ in the projective plane $P$ form a projective space $P^5$ of dimension 5. The pencils of curves $k_2$ (cf. p. 227) are the lines in $P^5$. Those $k_2$ which contain a given point form a $P^4$ in $P^5$. The $k_2$ with respect to which two given points are polar also form a $P^4$. The $k_2$ with respect to which a given point and a given line are pole and polar, form a $P^3$ in $P^5$. The $k_2$ containing three given points form a $P^2$. The $k_2$ containing four given non-collinear points form a pencil. The circles in a euclidean plane form a $P^3$. The rectangular hyperbolas form a $P^4$. The $k_2$ touching a given line in a given point form a $P^2$. The $k_2$ touching two given lines in given points form a pencil.

(20.17). $\xi_1$ and $\xi_2$ are euclidean coordinates in a euclidean plane. $\xi_0$, $\xi_1$, $\xi_2$ are corresponding homogeneous coordinates. To prove: the isotropic directions ("isotropic points") have coordinate values $(0, 1, i)$ and $(0, 1, -i)$; a circle is a quadratic curve through the isotropic points.

(20.18)*. Study the 2-dimensional projective space over the finite field with 2, with 3, with 4, and with 5 elements. Cf. chapter 8.

# 21. NON-EUCLIDEAN PLANES

One of the axioms of plane euclidean geometry reads: Through any point $B$ not on a line $m$ there is exactly one line which does not meet $m$, or in other words, which is parallel to $m$.

If we consider the axioms of euclidean plane geometry as hypotheses concerning "planes" in the space in which we live, then this particular axiom is far less obvious, and appears as far less imperative than the other axioms. So much so that mathematicians searched for many centuries for a proof from the other more obvious axioms. Such a proof, however, can never be given, for the following reason. If, along with the other axioms, we choose as axiom

*a*) through any point outside $m$ there is more than one line not intersecting $m$, or, alternatively,

*b*) two different lines always intersect,

then a plane is obtained with a non-contradictory set of properties and much resemblance with the euclidean plane. These planes are called the non-euclidean planes, more precisely in case *a*) *the hyperbolic plane* (Gauss 1777–1855, Lobatchevski 1793–1856 and Bolyai 1802–1860 discovered this plane more or less independently) and in case *b*) *the elliptic plane* (studied by Gauss, Riemann 1826–866 and Klein 1849–1925).

In this chapter we shall demonstrate the hyperbolic and the elliptic plane by means of the *real* projective plane. In particular we shall show that the notion of distance to be defined gives rise to a large group of motions as is the case in the euclidean plane.

## *The hyperbolic plane*

In the real projective plane we consider the interior $H$ of a projective ellipse, which therefore is the boundary $\partial H$ of $H$. In suitable homogeneous coordinates $\partial H$ and $H$ are given by

$$\partial H: \xi_1^2 + \xi_2^2 - \xi_3^2 = 0; \qquad H: \xi_1^2 + \xi_2^2 - \xi_3^2 < 0.$$

In fig. 21.1 the line $\xi_3 = 0$ has been chosen as the line at infinity and $\xi_1$ and $\xi_2$ are orthogonal coordinates.

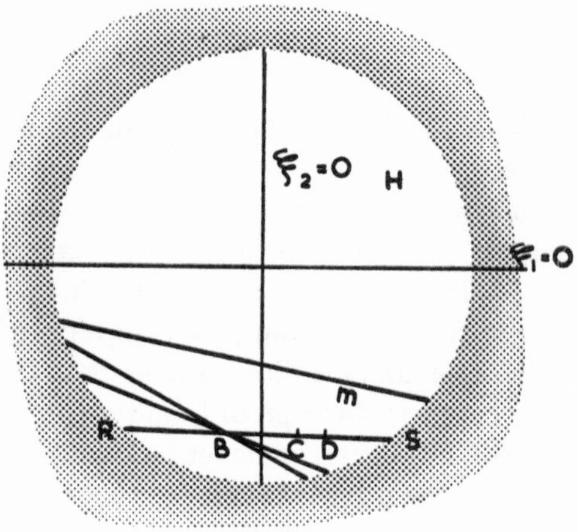


Fig. 21.1

As point set of the *hyperbolic plane* we take the set $H$. The non-empty intersection of a line in the projective plane $P$ with $H$ is called *a line in* $H$. It is then clear that through any point $B$ not lying on a line $m$ in $H$ there are many lines in $H$ which do not meet $m$.

We shall now define motions in $H$, and only later on shall we define the metric (distance), which then, of course, will have to be consistent with the motions. A *motion* of $H$ is a one-to-one mapping of $H$ onto itself which can be obtained from a projective *transformation* (= mapping) $\sigma$ of the projective plane $P$ by disregarding the points outside $H$. Of course $\sigma$ maps $H$ as well as $\partial H$ onto itself.

Theorem [21.1]: *If in the hyperbolic plane $H$, $B$ is a point on the line $m$ and $B'$ is a point on the line $m'$, then there are exactly four motions $\sigma$ with the action $\sigma B = B'$ and $\sigma m = m'$.*

This property is also true in the euclidean plane! As the choice of $B'$ and $m'$ is free, this implies that $H$ admits many motions.

Proof: As usual, let **R** be the field of real numbers and let $P = (V^3 - O)/\mathbf{R}$ where $V^3$ is a *real* three-dimensional vector space. Let $B_2$ be the pole of $m$ and $B_1$ be the pole of the line $BB_2$. Cf. fig. 21.2a or 21.2b.

Put $B = \mathbf{R}b$, $B_1 = \mathbf{R}b_1$, $B_2 = \mathbf{R}b_2$ with $b, b_1, b_2 \in V^3$. The polar relation with respect to the ellipse is given by a bilinear symmetric function $\varphi$ over $V^3$.

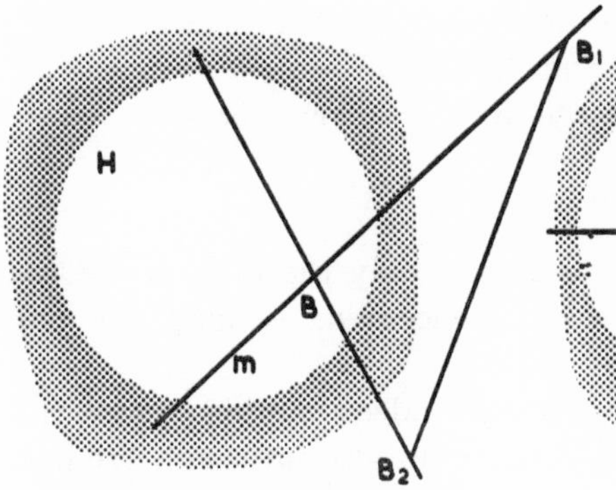

Fig. 21.2a

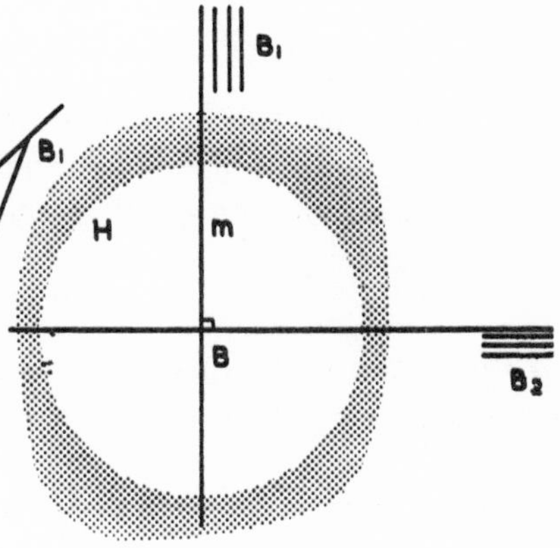

Fig. 21.2b

We remind the reader that apart from a scalar factor, $\varphi$ is determined by the ellipse. If we choose as homogeneous coordinates in $P$ the linearly independent functions that assume on $x \in V^3$ the values

$$\{\zeta_1(x), \zeta_2(x), \zeta_3(x)\} = \{\varphi(b_1, x), \varphi(b_2, x), \varphi(b, x)\}$$

then (cf. chapter 14)

$$\varepsilon\varphi^{\cdot}(x) = \lambda_1^2\zeta_1^2(x) + \lambda_2^2\zeta_2^2(x) - \lambda_3^2\zeta_3^2(x).$$

Here $\varepsilon = 1$ or $-1$. By another choice of $\varphi$ if necessary we can also obtain $\varepsilon = 1$. $\lambda_1, \lambda_2, \lambda_3$ are real numbers different from zero. By replacing $b_1, b_2, b$ by suitable multiples we are able to get new functions $\zeta_i$ such that

$$\varphi^{\cdot} = \zeta_1^2 + \zeta_2^2 - \zeta_3^2. \tag{21.1}$$

Similarly for $B'$ and $m'$ we find

$$\varphi^{\cdot} = \zeta_1'^2 + \zeta_2'^2 - \zeta_3'^2. \tag{21.2}$$

If now $\sigma$ is an endomorphism of V representing a motion of $H$ which maps $B$, $m$, $B_1$, $B_2$ onto $B'$, $m'$, $B_1'$, $B_2'$, then the kernel of the linear function $\zeta_i'\sigma$ on V is equal to the kernel of $\zeta_i$, and so there are real numbers $\nu_1$, $\nu_2$, $\nu_3$ such that

$$\zeta_i'\sigma = \nu_i\zeta_i.$$

Moreover, since the kernels of the quadratic functions
$$\zeta_1^2 + \zeta_2^2 - \zeta_3^2 \text{ and } \zeta_1'^2 + \zeta_2'^2 - \zeta_3'^2$$
are identical, viz. the given ellipse in $P$, it follows that

$$\nu_1^2 = \nu_2^2 = \nu_3^2.$$

We may put each equal to 1, and since only the ratio of the coordinates is relevant as far as $P$ is concerned, we may also put $\nu_3 = 1$.

The equations for $\sigma$ thus found are indeed motions, since the conditions above are not only necessary but also sufficient. We find the following four possibilities for $\sigma$:

$$\sigma = \sigma_1 \colon \zeta_1'\sigma = \zeta_1, \quad \zeta_2'\sigma = \zeta_2, \quad \zeta_3'\sigma = \zeta_3$$

i.e., if $x \in V^3$ is a point with coordinate values $\zeta_1(x) = \alpha_1$, $\zeta_2(x) = \alpha_2$, $\zeta_3(x) = \alpha_3$, then $\sigma x$ is a point with coordinates

$$\zeta_1'\sigma x = \alpha_1, \quad \zeta_2'\sigma x = \alpha_2, \quad \zeta_3'\sigma x = \alpha_3;$$

$$\sigma = \sigma_2 \colon \zeta_1'\sigma = \zeta_1, \quad \zeta_2'\sigma = -\zeta_2, \quad \zeta_3'\sigma = \zeta_3$$

$$\sigma = \sigma_3 \colon \zeta_1'\sigma = -\zeta_1, \quad \zeta_2'\sigma = \zeta_2, \quad \zeta_3'\sigma = \zeta_3$$

$$\sigma = \sigma_4 \colon \zeta_1'\sigma = -\zeta_1, \quad \zeta_2'\sigma = -\zeta_2, \quad \zeta_3'\sigma = \zeta_3.$$

$\sigma_j\sigma_i^{-1}$ is an involutory motion or reflection for $i \neq j$ (cf. problem 20.5))

$\sigma_2\sigma_1^{-1}$ is a reflection with respect to the line $m$

$\sigma_4\sigma_1^{-1}$ is a reflection with respect to the point $B$

$\sigma_3\sigma_1^{-1}$ is a reflection with respect to the line $BB_2$.

We shall now give a definition of *distance* (cf. chapter 15 and fig. 21.1). First we observe that if $\sigma$ is a motion of $H$, and $B$ and $C$ are points in $H$, and $R$ and $S$ are the intersections of $BC$ with $\partial H$, then because of the invariance of cross-ratios under projectivities:

$$(BCRS) = (\sigma B, \sigma C, \sigma R, \sigma S),$$

and because of the invariance of $\partial H$, $\sigma R$ and $\sigma S$ are the intersections of the line through $\sigma B$ and $\sigma C$ with $\partial H$. If we could call this cross-ratio, which is positive, the distance of $B$ and $C$, then we should have a notion of distance which indeed is invariant under motion. But the same would be true for $f\{(BCRS)\}$ for any fixed real function $f$.

If $D$ is a third point on the line $BC$ then

$$(BCRS)(CDRS) = (BDRS). \tag{21.3}$$

For, if by means of an $\mathscr{A}$-map we represent the points by vectors b, c, d, r, s then

$$(BCRS)(CDRS) = \left(\frac{\mathrm{b}-\mathrm{r}}{\mathrm{c}-\mathrm{r}} : \frac{\mathrm{b}-\mathrm{s}}{\mathrm{c}-\mathrm{s}}\right)\left(\frac{\mathrm{c}-\mathrm{r}}{\mathrm{d}-\mathrm{r}} : \frac{\mathrm{c}-\mathrm{s}}{\mathrm{d}-\mathrm{s}}\right) =$$

$$= \frac{\mathrm{b}-\mathrm{r}}{\mathrm{d}-\mathrm{r}} : \frac{\mathrm{b}-\mathrm{s}}{\mathrm{d}-\mathrm{s}} = (BDRS).$$

From (21.3) we derive

$$\ln (BCRS) + \ln (CDRS) = \ln (BDRS) \quad (\ln = \log_e). \tag{21.4}$$

As *distance* of the points $B$ and $C$ we now define [1]

$$d(B, C) = \gamma |\ln (BCRS)|, \quad \gamma \text{ constant} > 0. \tag{21.5}$$

Then (21.4) implies for any three consecutive points $B$, $C$, $D$ on a line

$$d(B, C) + d(C, D) = d(B, D). \tag{21.6}$$

---

[1]) The same formula can also be used if $H$ is an arbitrary strictly convex region with boundary $\partial H$ in a real affine plane. A metric so obtained is called a *Hilbert-metric*. Cf. Busemann-Kelly, Projective geometry and projective metrics.

For this distance $d$ we have

$$d(B, C) \begin{cases} = 0 \text{ for } B = C \\ > 0 \text{ for } B \neq C \end{cases}$$

$$d(B, C) = d(C, B)$$

and *invariance under motion.*

We must still prove the triangle inequality. In order to do this we first define perpendicularity of lines: the lines $m$ and $m'$ are said to be *perpendicular* if $m$ contains the pole of $m'$ with respect to $\partial H$. Perpendicularity is a symmetric relation.

Now we prove that in a non-degenerate right-angled triangle the side opposite the right angle is longer than the others.

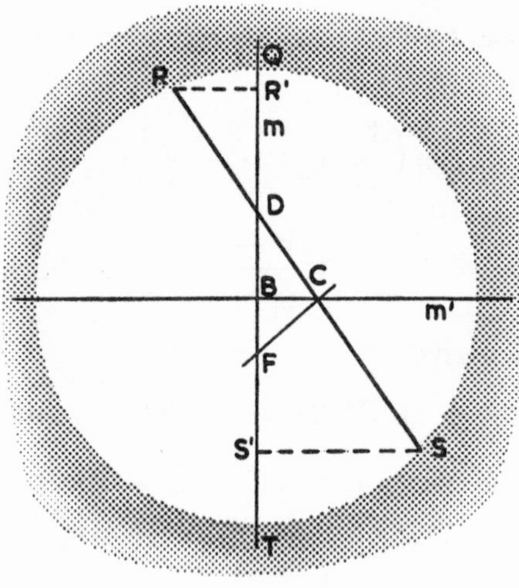


Fig. 21.3

In fig. 21.3 the triangle $BCD$ is *right-angled in* $B$. The drawing is such that the polar of $B$ with respect to $\partial H$ is the line at infinity. Furthermore the lines $RR'$ and $SS'$ are drawn through the pole of $BD$, that is, parallel to $m'$ in the figure. On an affine $\mathscr{A}$-map under which the image vectors are represented by lower case characters we have

$$d(CD) = \gamma\,|\ln(CDRS)|$$
$$= \gamma\,|\ln(BDR'S')| = \gamma\left|\ln\left(\frac{b-r'}{d-r'} : \frac{b-s'}{d-s'}\right)\right|$$
$$= \gamma\left\{\ln\frac{b-r'}{d-r'} + \ln\frac{d-s'}{b-s'}\right\}.$$

From the figure it is plain that $\frac{b-r'}{d-r'} > \frac{b-q}{d-q} > 1$ and $\frac{d-s'}{b-s'} > \frac{d-t}{b-t} > 1$, hence

$$d(CD) > \gamma\left\{\ln\frac{b-q}{d-q} + \ln\frac{d-t}{b-t}\right\} = \gamma\ln\left(\frac{b-q}{d-q} : \frac{b-t}{d-t}\right) =$$
$$= \gamma\,|\ln(BDQT)|$$
$$d(CD) > d(BD).$$

We apply this property to the triangle $DFC$ (cf. fig. 21.3) with altitude $CB$ from $C$. Then

$$d(DF) \leqslant d(DB) + d(BF) \leqslant d(DC) + d(CF)$$

(the first $\leqslant$-sign takes care of the possibility that $D$ and $F$ are on the same side of $B$)

$$d(DF) \leqslant d(DC) + d(CF).$$

Equality occurs only if $D$, $C$ and $F$ are collinear and lie on a line in this order.

Thus we see that the notions of distance and motion in $H$ display a certain similarity to the corresponding notions in the euclidean plane. However a discrepancy arises, for example if we consider the angles of the quadrangle $BCDE$ with three right angles (in $B$, $C$ and $E$) in fig. 21.4. It has a fourth angle which is *smaller* than a right angle: $\angle D_2 < \angle D_{2+1} = \angle E = \angle B = \angle C =$ right angle ($\angle$ denotes angle).

It is true, but we do not elaborate this, that the sum of the angles of a triangle in $H$ is always less than a straight angle.

Another interesting picture of the hyperbolic plane is encountered in the theory of complex functions of one variable. In order to obtain it, first consider the representation that was just given on a circular disc with boundary, which now however is the equator of a sphere with north pole $N$. If we project $H$ in the North-South direction onto the southern hemisphere, then lines in $H$ are projected onto vertical semi-circles. If the southern hemisphere is now projected stereographically (cf. problem (15.20)) from $N$ onto $H$, then the images of the semi-circles are the intersections with $H$ of circles perpendicular to $\partial H$. This gives a representation of the hyperbolic plane under which the "lines" are the circular arcs perpendicular to a fixed circle $\partial H$.

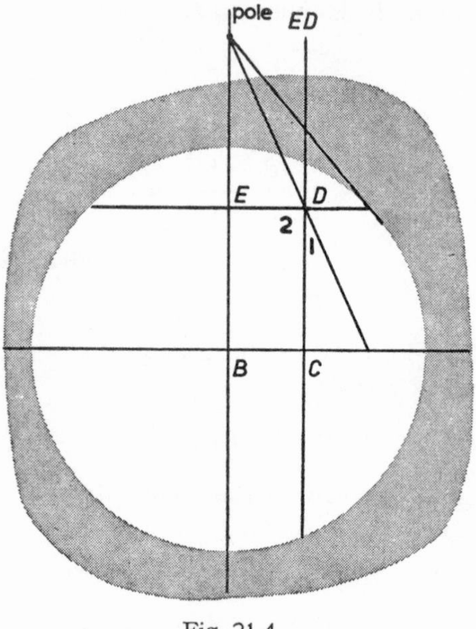


Fig. 21.4

*The elliptic plane*

As point set of the *elliptic plane* we choose the entire real projective plane. Then any two different lines intersect. Put $P = (\mathrm{V} - \mathrm{O})/\mathbf{R}$, as before. Again we consider a quadratic function on a real three-dimensional vectorspace $\mathrm{V}^3$, but now a positive definite one, which in suitable coordinates has the form

$$\varphi^{\cdot} = \zeta_1^2 + \zeta_2^2 + \zeta_3^2.$$

In the complexification of the real plane, that is the complex projective plane, the kernel of this function is a non-degenerate curve of the second degree containing no real point. The bilinear symmetric function $\varphi$ however determines a polarity whose restriction to the real plane does have a meaning. It has the equation

$$\varphi(x, y) = \zeta_1(x)\zeta_1(y) + \zeta_2(x)\zeta_2(y) + \zeta_3(x)\zeta_3(y) = 0 \qquad x, y \in V.$$

A *motion* $\sigma$ is a projective transformation which leaves this polarity invariant. Its complexification therefore leaves the complex second degree curve invariant. We may now restrict ourselves to the endomorphisms $\sigma$ of V that map $\varphi^{\cdot}$ (dually) onto itself:

$$\varphi(\sigma x, \sigma x) = \varphi(x, x).$$

V together with this invariant quadratic function is a euclidean vector space. Thus the elliptic plane can also be defined as $(E^3 - O)/\mathbf{R}$ where $E^3$ is a euclidean three-dimensional space. The motions are the euclidean endomorphisms of E considered as transformations on the set of one-dimensional subspaces of E.

Just as in the hyperbolic plane we have

Theorem [21.1′]: *If in the elliptic plane $B$ is a point on a line $m$ and $B'$ on $m'$, then there exist exactly four motions $\sigma$ for which $\sigma B = B'$ and $\sigma m = m'$.*

The proof is similar to that of theorem [21.1].

The *distance* of two real points $B$ and $C$ in the elliptic plane cannot simply be defined by formula (21.5), because the logarithmic function assumes no real value for a negative argument and it is multivalued in **C**. Instead, we take the formula

$$d(B, C) = \gamma \cdot \text{minimum } |\ln(xyuv)| \quad \gamma > 0 \qquad (21.7)$$

where the vectors x and y span the linear subspaces of $E^3$ that represent $B = \mathbf{R}x$ and $C = \mathbf{R}y$, and u and v are the (non-real) intersections of the line $x + \mathbf{C}(y - x)$ (consisting of the points $z = x + \lambda(y - x)$, $\lambda \in \mathbf{C}$) with $\varphi^{\cdot}(z) = 0$.

If x and y are unit vectors in $B$ and $C$ respectively, and $\alpha$ is the angle between x and y, $0 \leqslant \alpha \leqslant \frac{1}{2}\pi$ (when $\alpha > \frac{1}{2}\pi$ we take x and

$-$ y) then by chapter 15, p. 139

$$\alpha \equiv \frac{\varepsilon}{2i} \ln (\mathrm{xyuv}) \quad \text{modulo } \pi \qquad \varepsilon = 1 \text{ or } -1.$$

Substitution in (21.7) then gives

$$d(B, C) = 2\gamma\alpha.$$

Hence the distance of two points in the elliptic plane is proportional to the smallest angle between the one-dimensional subspaces in the euclidean three-dimensional vector space E that represent those points.

Thus an alternative description of the elliptic plane is as follows. Choose a 2-sphere $S^2$ with radius $2\gamma$ in the euclidean space $E^3$:

$$\varphi^{\cdot}(\mathrm{x}) = \mathrm{x}^2 = 4\gamma^2.$$

The spherical distance of two points x and y on the sphere is $2\gamma\alpha$ if $\alpha$ is the angle between the vectors x and y $(0 \leqslant \alpha \leqslant \pi)$.

Two vectors x and y $\epsilon\, S^2$ are linearly dependent if and only if y $=$ x or y $= -$ x, hence, if they are identical or antipodal. If $\mathfrak{A}$ stands for this restriction to $S^2$ of the linear dependence, then $\mathfrak{A}$ is an equivalence relation and the elliptic plane is the quotient

$$\text{2-sphere}/\mathfrak{A} = S^2/\mathfrak{A}.$$

The distance of two points (x, $-$ x) and (y, $-$ y) is the smaller of the spherical distances of x and y and of x and $-$ y.

The *motions* are the mappings of the equivalence classes each consisting of two diametrical points, obtained from euclidean endomorphisms of $E^3$.

The quantity $(4\gamma^2)^{-1}$ is called the *curvature* of the elliptic plane; $-(4\gamma^2)^{-1}$ ($\gamma$ from formula (21.5)) is the curvature of the hyperbolic plane. Curvature is an important notion in differential geometry.

The triangle inequality for the elliptic plane can be proved, for example, using the representation just given and the triangle inequality for sides of spherical triangles. Without proof we remark that in elliptic geometry (as well as for spherical triangles) the sum of the angles of a triangle exceeds a straight angle.

In this chapter we introduced non-euclidean geometries by specifying in the real projective plane a non-degenerate curve of degree two or, equivalently of class two, with or without real points. The euclidean geometry can be reconstructed from the real projective plane in a similar way. For that purpose we specify a non-real degenerate curve of class two in $P$, or a non-real pair of points in $P$. These play the role of two isotropic points (at infinity).

The group of all projective transformations which leave the isotropic points invariant is the group of equiformity transformations, which is generated by the euclidean motions *and* the geometrical multiplication with respect to a point, and is larger than the group of euclidean motions.

PROBLEMS. (21.1)* Any projective transformation of a real projective plane which leaves a real projective ellipse $\partial H$ invariant, has at least one invariant point, which may be inside, on or outside $\partial H$. Using this fact, give a classification of motions in the hyperbolic plane.

(21.2). For any motion $\sigma$ of the hyperbolic plane with

$$\sigma^4 = \text{identity} \neq \sigma^2,$$

there exists a point $Q$ with $\sigma Q = Q$ such that any line $m$ through $Q$ is perpendicular to its image $\sigma m$.

## 22*. SOME TOPOLOGICAL REMARKS

For our purpose in this chapter it will be sufficient to consider a restricted notion of topology, based on so-called continuous functions. A *topological space,* also called space with a topology, is a set $X$ of elements called points, and a set $X^c$ of pairs $(\varphi, U)$ with $U \subset X$ and $\varphi\colon U \to \mathbf{R}$ a real function on $U$ with the following properties. (Such a pair $(\varphi, U)$ is called a *continuous function* for $X$.)

*a.* Any point of $X$ is contained in at least one of the $U$.

*b.* *Combination.* If $(\varphi_1, U_1), \cdots (\varphi_r, U_r) \in X^c$ and $g(x_1, \cdots x_r)$ is a continuous real function of the real variables $x_1, \cdots x_r$ defined for $x_i \in \varphi_i(U_i) \subset \mathbf{R}$, then also

$$\{g(\varphi_1, \cdots \varphi_r),\ U_1 \cap \cdots \cap U_r\} \in X^c.$$

*c.* For any two different points $a, b \in X$ there exists a continuous function $\varphi$ such that $\varphi(a) \neq \varphi(b)$.

*d.* *Restriction.* If $(\varphi, U) \in X^c$ and if $W \subset U$ then also ($\varphi$ restricted to $W$, $W) \in X^c$.

A set of continuous functions is called a *set of generators* of $X^c$ if all other functions in $X^c$ can be obtained from them by combination and restriction.

If $Y \subset X$ and if any function $(\varphi, U)$ of $X^c$ is restricted to $U \cap Y$, then a set of functions is obtained which define a topology in $Y$. With this topology $Y$ is called a *topological subspace* of $X$.

Suppose now that $X$ and $Y$ are topological spaces and $X^c$ and $Y^c$ are their sets of continuous functions. Let furthermore $\tau\colon X \to Y$ be a mapping of $X$ into $Y$.

If $U \subset K$ and $g\colon \tau U \to \mathbf{R}$ is a real function on $\tau U \subset Y$ then $g \circ \tau\colon U \to \mathbf{R}$ is a real function on $U \subset X$. Thus we obtain from the set $Y^c$ of the continuous functions for $Y$ by means of $\tau$ a set $Y^c \circ \tau$ of real functions for $X$. The mapping $\tau$ is said to be *continuous* if $Y^c \circ \tau \subset X^c$. The mapping $\tau$ is called a "*topological mapping into*" if

$$Y^c \circ \tau = X^c.$$

Condition *c* above implies that a topological mapping is one-to-one.

Definition: A topological mapping into of $X$ onto $Y$ will be called a topological mapping or a *homeomorphism*.

If such a mapping exists then $X$ and $Y$ are called homeomorphic or topologically equivalent. Homeomorphism is an equivalence relation for topological spaces as is easily proved from the definitions. A classical problem in topology is to determine all equivalence classes of topological spaces.

In this chapter we mention the homeomorphy of a few topological spaces related to the spaces treated in this book. In proving that a mapping is a homeomorphism the following theorem is often useful:

Theorem [22.1]: *A one-to-one mapping of $X$ onto $Y$ which along with its inverse is continuous is a homeomorphism.*

The proof is an immediate consequence of the definitions.

If $X$ and $Y$ are topological spaces with $X^c$ and $Y^c$ as sets of continuous functions then a topology for the product set $X \times Y$ can be defined by taking as generating functions: 1°. any function associating to $(x, y) \in X \times Y$ the value $\varphi(x)$ if $x \in U \subset X$ and $(\varphi, U) \in X^c$; 2°. any function associating to $(x, y) \in X \times Y$ the value $\psi(y)$ if $y \in V \subset Y$ and $(\psi, V) \in Y^c$. From now on $X \times Y$ will mean the topological space so obtained, and it will be called the *topological product space*, or the product of $X$ and $Y$.

The real affine $n$-space becomes a topological space if we take as generating functions of the topology a system of $n$ coordinates $\xi_1, \cdots \xi_n$.

The product of $n$ copies of a real affine 1-dimensional space with coordinates $\eta_1, \cdots \eta_n$ respectively is homeomorphic to the real affine $n$-space. For, a topological mapping $\tau$ is obtained by mapping the point with coordinate values $(\xi_1, \cdots \xi_n) = (\alpha_1, \cdots \alpha_n)$, $\alpha_i \in \mathbf{R}$, to the point with coordinate values $(\eta_1, \cdots \eta_n) = (\alpha_1, \cdots \alpha_n)$. The dual mapping of functions satisfies $\eta_i\tau = \xi_i$, $i = 1, \cdots n$, and this maps a set of generators $\eta_1, \cdots \eta_n$ of the product space onto the set of generators $\xi_1, \cdots \xi_n$ of the affine $n$-space. We denote the topological class of this space by $\mathbf{R}^n$.

In each of the following examples we give a number of homeomorphic spaces with specific homeomorphisms. It is left to the reader to verify that the given mapping has the desired properties.

*Examples*

1. Some spaces homeomorphic to $\mathbf{R}^2$ with coordinates $\eta_1, \eta_2 \in \mathbf{R}$ are (cf. fig. 22.1):

(a) A solid parallelogram without boundary in a real affine plane $(-1 < \xi_1 < 1) \cap (-1 < \xi_2 < 1)$ with the topology generated by the functions $\xi_1$ and $\xi_2$. Homeomorphism: $\eta_i = \tan(\frac{1}{2}\pi\xi_i)$, $i = 1, 2$.

(b) The circular disc (or ellipse) without boundary: $\xi_1^2+\xi_2^2 < 1$. Homeomorphism: $\eta_i = \xi_i\rho^{-1} \tan \rho$ with $\rho = \frac{1}{2}\pi\sqrt{\xi_1^2 + \xi_2^2}$.

(c) The strip $-1 < \xi_2 < 1$ in the real affine plane with coordinates $\xi_1, \xi_2$. Homeomorphism: $(\eta_1, \eta_2) = (\xi_1, \tan(\frac{1}{2}\pi\xi_2))$.

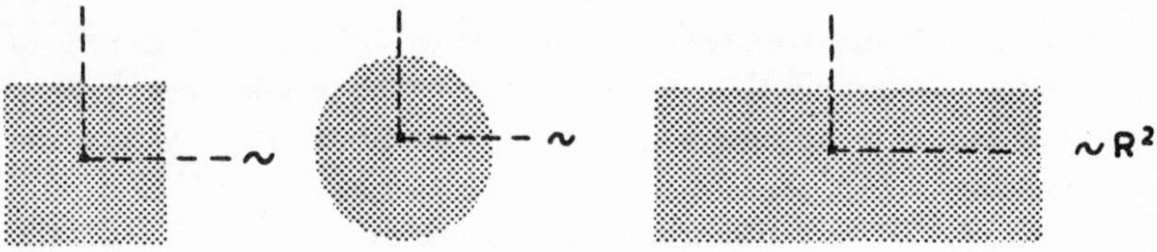


Fig. 22.1

Similarly the set of points with coordinates $\xi_1, \cdots \xi_n$ in the affine $n$-space $\mathbf{R}^n$ for which $\xi_1^2 + \cdots + \xi_r^2 < 1$, $r \leqslant n$, is homeomorphic to $\mathbf{R}^n$. Homeomorphism:

$$\eta_i = \xi_i\rho^{-1} \tan \rho \text{ for } i \leqslant r,\ \eta_j = \xi_j \text{ for } j > r,\ \rho = \tfrac{1}{2}\pi \sqrt{\xi_1^2+\cdots+\xi_r^2}.$$

2. *n-sphere and torus.*

Definition: A (*topological*) *n-sphere* $S^n$ is the subspace $\xi_1^2 + \cdots + \xi_{n+1}^2 = 1$ of an $(n + 1)$-dimensional affine space

$\mathbf{R}^{n+1}$ with $\xi_1, \cdots \xi_{n+1}$ as generating functions for the topology. $S^0$ is a pair of points, $S^1$ is a circle, $S^2$ is a sphere.

Definition: A (*topological*) *torus* in a 3-dimensional space with coordinates $\xi_1, \xi_2, \xi_3$ is a surface with parametric equations (parameters $u$ and $v$)

$$(\xi_1, \xi_2, \xi_3) = \{(a + \cos u) \cos v, (a + \cos u) \sin v, \sin u\} \quad a > 1.$$

If $(\eta_1, \eta_2)$ and $(\eta_3, \eta_4)$ are generating functions of two topological circles: $\eta_1{}^2 + \eta_2{}^2 = \eta_3{}^2 + \eta_4{}^2 = 1$, then the torus is homeomorphic to the product of those circles because of the homeomorphism

$$(\eta_1, \eta_2, \eta_3, \eta_4) = (\cos u, \sin u, \cos v, \sin v).$$

Generally the *n-dimensional torus* is the product space

$$S^1 \times S^1 \times \cdots \times S^1 \ (n \text{ factors}).$$

3. *Some real affine quadratic hypersurfaces* (*quadrics*). The real paraboloids and parabolic cylinders in the affine $n$-space are homeomorphic to $\mathbf{R}^{n-1}$. If the equation of the paraboloid or the parabolic cylinder is $\xi_n = \xi_1{}^2 + \cdots + \xi_p{}^2 - \xi^2{}_{p+1} - \cdots - \xi^2{}_{p+q}$ then a homeomorphism is

$$\eta_i = \xi_i \qquad i = 1, \cdots n-1.$$

Theorem [22.2]: *The real affine quadric with equation*

$$\xi_1{}^2 + \cdots + \xi_p{}^2 - \xi^2{}_{p+1} - \cdots - \xi^2{}_{p+q} = 1 \qquad p \geqslant 1$$

*is homeomorphic to* $S^{p-1} \times \mathbf{R}^{n-p}$.

Proof: Consider the homeomorphism

$$\eta_i = \rho\xi_i \quad i = 1, \cdots n, \rho = (\xi_1{}^2 + \cdots + \xi_p{}^2)^{-\frac{1}{2}} = (1 - \eta^2{}_{p+1} - \cdots - \eta^2{}_{p+q})^{\frac{1}{2}}$$

of the given quadric onto the image in $\mathbf{R}^n$:

$$\eta_1{}^2 + \cdots + \eta_p{}^2 = 1, \ \eta^2{}_{p+1} + \cdots + \eta^2{}_{p+q} < 1, \ \eta_{p+q+1}, \cdots \eta_n \in \mathbf{R},$$

which is homeomorphic to (cf. the first example) $S^{p-1} \times \mathbf{R}^q \times \times \mathbf{R}^{n-p-q}$, hence to $S^{p-1} \times \mathbf{R}^{n-p}$.

This is shown in fig. 22.2 for the hyperbola homeomorphic to $S^0 \times \mathbf{R}^1$. Rotation of the figure around the axis $\xi_1 = 0$ yields a hyperboloid of one sheet homeomorphic to the surface of a (vertical) cylinder $S^1 \times \mathbf{R}^1$.

PROBLEM (22.1). Investigate the quadrics in the real affine 2- and 3-space in more detail.

4. *The complex affine spaces and quadratic curves.* In the complex affine $n$-space $\mathbf{C}^n$ with complex coordinates $\zeta_1, \cdots \zeta_n$ the real functions re$(\zeta_j)$ and re$(i\zeta_j)$ $j = 1, \cdots n$, are a set of generators of the topology customary for this case [1]. It follows that $\mathbf{C}^n$ is homeomorphic to $\mathbf{R}^{2n}$. $\mathbf{C}^1$ is called the complex plane.

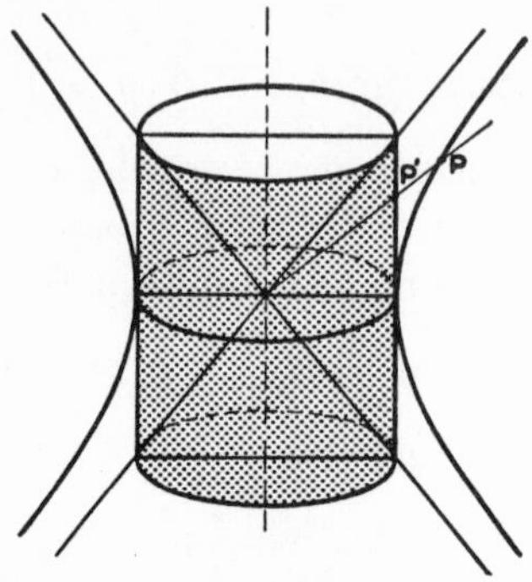

Fig. 22.2 $\xi_1 = 0$

In suitable coordinates any complex affine non-degenerate quadratic curve has the equation $\zeta_1\zeta_2 = 1$. It is homeomorphic to the complex plane from which one point has been removed ($\zeta_1 \neq 0$), i.e. to $S^1 \times \mathbf{R}^1$. Generators of the real continuous functions are

$$\eta_1, \eta_2, \eta_3; \qquad \eta_1^2 + \eta_2^2 = 1$$

given by the homeomorphism

$$(\eta_1, \eta_2, \eta_3) = \{re \frac{\zeta_1}{|\zeta_1|}, re \frac{i\zeta_1}{|\zeta_1|}, \ln |\zeta_1|\}.$$

5. *Real projective spaces and their quadrics.* If $\xi_1, \cdots \xi_{n+1}$ are homogeneous coordinates of a real projective space $P^n(\mathbf{R})$ then the functions $\xi_i/\xi_j$ form a set of generators of the topology. The $\frac{1}{2}n(n+1)$ functions $\eta_{ij} = \xi_i\xi_j(\Sigma_{k=1}^{n+1} \xi_k^2)^{-1}$ $1 \leqslant i \leqslant j \leqslant n+1$ give a topological mapping of $P^n(\mathbf{R})$ into $\mathbf{R}^N$, $N = (n+1)^2$.

The 1-dimensional real projective space $P^1(\mathbf{R})$ is homeomorphic to $S^1$ by the homeomorphism

$$(\eta_1, \eta_2) = \left(\frac{2\xi_1\xi_2}{\xi_1^2 + \xi_2^2}, \frac{\xi_1^2 - \xi_2^2}{\xi_1^2 + \xi_2^2}\right) \qquad (\eta_1^2 + \eta_2^2 = 1).$$

In suitable non-homogeneous coordinates any non-degenerate

[1]) *re* means: "the real part of". Thus $re(-3 + 5i) = -3$.

real projective quadratic curve has equation $\xi_1^2 + \xi_2^2 = 1$, and thus is also homeomorphic to $S^1$.

The real quadratic surfaces with standard equation

$$\xi_1^2 + \xi_2^2 + \xi_3^2 - \xi_4^2 = 0$$

are homeomorphic to $S^2$, as is seen by taking $\xi_i/\xi_4$, $i = 1, 2, 3$, as non-homogeneous coordinates. The ellipsoids belong to this class as do the hyperboloids of two sheets including their points at infinity.

The real quadratic surfaces with standard equation

$$\xi_1^2 + \xi_2^2 - \xi_3^2 - \xi_4^2 = 0 = (\xi_1 + \xi_3)(\xi_1 - \xi_3) + (\xi_2+\xi_4)(\xi_2-\xi_4)$$

or, in other coordinates

$$Q\colon\ \xi_1\xi_2 - \xi_3\xi_4 = 0 \qquad (22.1)$$

are homeomorphic to $P^1(\mathbf{R}) \times P^1(\mathbf{R})$, i.e. to $S^1 \times S^1$, that is the 2-dimensional torus. This holds for the hyperbolic paraboloid and the hyperboloid of one sheet, both including their points at infinity.

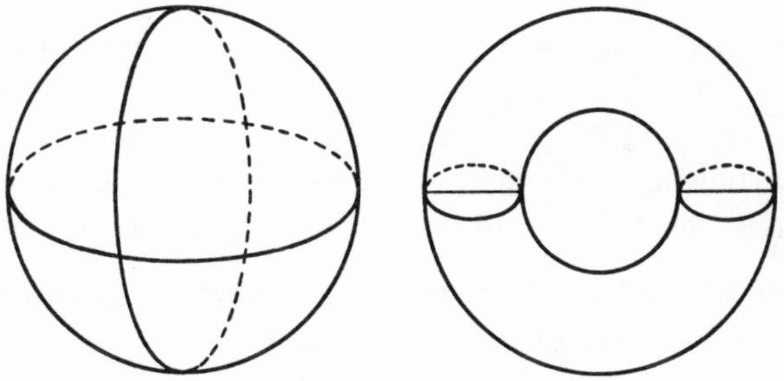

Fig. 22.3 Topological classification of the real quadratic surfaces in $P^3(\mathbf{R})$

If $\eta_1$, $\eta_2$ are homogeneous coordinates for $P^1$ and $\eta_3$, $\eta_4$ similar coordinates for a copy of $P^1$, then we obtain a homeomorphism of $Q$ onto $P^1 \times P^1$ as follows. For $\eta_1/\eta_2$ we take the function equal to $\xi_1/\xi_3$, or in points where the latter is not defined, equal to $\xi_4/\xi_2$; similarly for $\eta_2/\eta_1 : \xi_3/\xi_1$ or $\xi_2/\xi_4$. Similarly for $\eta_3/\eta_4 : \xi_1/\xi_4$ or $\xi_3/\xi_2$ and for $\eta_4/\eta_3$: $\xi_4/\xi_1$ or $\xi_2/\xi_3$.

A homeomorphism directly between $Q$ and the torus $S^1 \times S^1$ is given by

$$(\eta_1, \eta_2, \eta_3, \eta_4) =$$
$$\left(\frac{2\xi_1\xi_3}{\xi_1^2+\xi_3^2} = \frac{2\xi_4\xi_2}{\xi_2^2+\xi_4^2}, \frac{\xi_1^2-\xi_3^2}{\xi_1^2+\xi_3^2} = \frac{\xi_4^2-\xi_2^2}{\xi_4^2+\xi_2^2}, \right.$$
$$\left. \frac{2\xi_1\xi_4}{\xi_1^2+\xi_4^2} = \frac{2\xi_3\xi_2}{\xi_3^2+\xi_2^2}, \frac{\xi_1^2-\xi_4^2}{\xi_1^2+\xi_4^2} = \frac{\xi_3^2-\xi_2^2}{\xi_3^2+\xi_2^2}\right)$$
$$\eta_1^2+\eta_2^2 = \eta_3^2+\eta_4^2 = 1.$$

6. *Some complex projective varieties.* In the complex projective space $P^n(\mathbf{C})$ with complex homogeneous coordinates $\zeta_1, \cdots \zeta_{n+1}$, the real functions $\mathrm{re}(\zeta_j/\zeta_k)$ and $\mathrm{re}(i\zeta_j/\zeta_k)$ form a set of generators for the topology.

Theorem [22.3]: *$P^1(\mathbf{C})$ is homeomorphic to $S^2$.*

Proof: The mapping

$$(\eta_1, \eta_2, \eta_3) = \left(\frac{\zeta_1\bar{\zeta}_2+\bar{\zeta}_1\zeta_2}{\zeta_1\bar{\zeta}_1+\zeta_2\bar{\zeta}_2}, \frac{i(\zeta_1\bar{\zeta}_2-\bar{\zeta}_1\zeta_2)}{\zeta_1\bar{\zeta}_1+\zeta_2\bar{\zeta}_2}, \frac{\zeta_1\bar{\zeta}_1-\zeta_2\bar{\zeta}_2}{\zeta_1\bar{\zeta}_1+\zeta_2\bar{\zeta}_2}\right)$$

with $\eta_1^2+\eta_2^2+\eta_3^2 = 1$ provides the homeomorphism ($\bar{\zeta}_i$ is the complex conjugate of $\zeta_i$).

A non-degenerate complex projective second-degree curve is homeomorphic to $P^1(\mathbf{C})$, hence to $S^2$. A homeomorphism is given by, for example, the rational linear functions $\varphi/\varphi'$ belonging to fig. 20.10.

Theorem [22.4]: *The non-singular complex quadratic surface with equation in homogeneous coordinates*

$$\zeta_1^2+\zeta_2^2+\zeta_3^2+\zeta_4^2 = 0$$

*is homeomorphic to $S^2 \times S^2$.*

Proof: In the new coordinates $\zeta_1 + i\zeta_2$, $\zeta_1 - i\zeta_2$, $\zeta_3 + i\zeta_4$ and $-\zeta_3 + i\zeta_4$ the equation takes the form as in (22.1)

$$Q(\mathbf{C}){:}\ \zeta_1'\zeta_2' - \zeta'_3\zeta'_4 = 0.$$

The argument for the real quadratic surface (22.1) applied to our case then results in the homeomorphism of $Q(\mathbf{C})$ and $P^1(\mathbf{C}) \times P^1(\mathbf{C})$. But since $P^1(\mathbf{C})$ is homeomorphic to $S^2$, the assertion follows.

# HINTS AND ANSWERS TO THE PROBLEMS IN CHAPTERS 3—21

(3.2): Prove $A_3, \cdots A_9$ under the natural definition of $A_1$ and $A_2$.

(3.3): Prove $A_3, \cdots A_9$ for multiples $\lambda a_1$ of $a_1$.

(3.4): $\lambda a + \mu b = \lambda a + (-\mu)(-b) = \lambda a + \mu'(-b)$

$$\alpha a + \beta b = \frac{\alpha}{\lambda}(\lambda a) + \beta b = \alpha'(\lambda a) + \beta b$$

$$\lambda a + \mu b = \lambda(a + b) + (\mu - \lambda)b = \lambda(a + b) + \mu' b.$$

(3.5): $\sum_1^m \lambda_i a_i = (\lambda_1 - \lambda_2)a_1 + \lambda_2(a_1 + a_2) + \sum_3^m \lambda_i a_i$.

(3.6): Prove $A_3, \cdots A_9$ for the set B.

(3.7): $a + W$ is obtained from $W$ by a parallel displacement.

(3.9): Any vector of $\frac{1}{2}(U + U)$ belongs to $U$ and conversely.

(4.1): From $(b' - a') = \alpha(b - a)$, $(d' - c') = \beta(d - c)$ and $(d - c) = \lambda(b - a)$ it follows that $(d' - c') = \dfrac{\beta\lambda}{\alpha}(b' - a')$; $\alpha, \beta$ and $\lambda \neq 0$.

(4.3): From $d - c = \lambda(b - a)$, $f - e = \mu(b' - a')$, and $b' - a' = \nu(b - a)$, it follows that $(f - e) = \dfrac{\mu\nu}{\lambda}(d - c)$; $\lambda, \mu, \nu \neq 0$.

(4.4): If c is on the line through a and b, then $c = a + \lambda(b - a)$, $c + (\lambda - 1)a - \lambda b = O$ and $(\alpha, \beta, \gamma) = (\lambda - 1, -\lambda, 1)$. If conversely $\alpha a + \beta b + \gamma c = O$, $\alpha + \beta + \gamma = 0$ and for example $\gamma \neq 0$, then we put $\lambda = -\beta/\gamma$.

(4.5): $d - c = a - b$. (4.6): $\frac{1}{2}(d + b) = \frac{1}{2}(c + a)$.

(4.7): $\frac{1}{2}(a + b) - \frac{1}{2}(a + d) = \frac{1}{2}(c + b) - \frac{1}{2}(c + d)$.

(4.8): From $p = 2b - a$, $q = 2c - b$ and $r = \lambda p + (1 - \lambda)q = \mu a + (1 - \mu)c$ or $\lambda p + (1 - \lambda)q - \mu a - (1 - \mu)c = O$ we obtain by substitution $-(\lambda + \mu)a + (3\lambda - 1)b +$

$+ (1 - 2\lambda + \mu)\mathrm{c} = \mathrm{O}$ or $\lambda + \mu = 0,\ 3\lambda - 1 = 0,$
$1 - 2\lambda + \mu = 0,\ \lambda = -\mu = \frac{1}{3}$ and $\dfrac{\mathrm{r}-\mathrm{c}}{\mathrm{c}-\mathrm{a}} = \frac{1}{3}$.

(4.9): Put a, b, c, d = $\mathrm{a}_1, \mathrm{a}_2, \mathrm{a}_3, \mathrm{a}_4$; $\frac{1}{4}(\mathrm{a}_1 + \mathrm{a}_2 + \mathrm{a}_3 + \mathrm{a}_4) = \lambda \mathrm{a}_1 + (1-\lambda).\ \frac{1}{3}(\mathrm{a}_2 + \mathrm{a}_3 + \mathrm{a}_4)$ etc. (cyclically) with $\lambda = \frac{1}{4}$.

(4.10): $$\frac{1}{m}(\mathrm{a}_1 + \cdots + \mathrm{a}_m) = \frac{p}{m}\left\{\frac{1}{p}(\mathrm{a}_1 + \cdots + \mathrm{a}_p)\right\} + \frac{m-p}{m}\left\{\frac{1}{m-p}(\mathrm{a}_{p+1} + \cdots + \mathrm{a}_m)\right\}.$$
Medians and joins of midpoints of opposite edges in a tetrahedron pass through one point.

(4.11): It is the centroid of the hexagon.

(4.12): $\mathrm{c} - \mathrm{d} = \mathrm{b} - \mathrm{a}$ and $\mathrm{e} - \mathrm{a} = \mathrm{f} - \mathrm{b} = \mathrm{g} - \mathrm{c} = \mathrm{h} - \mathrm{d}$
$\mathrm{w} = \frac{1}{8}(\mathrm{a} + \mathrm{b} + \mathrm{c} + \mathrm{d} + \mathrm{e} + \mathrm{f} + \mathrm{g} + \mathrm{h})$;
$\mathrm{u} - \mathrm{a} = \frac{1}{3}(\mathrm{g} - \mathrm{a})$; $\mathrm{v} - \mathrm{a} = \frac{2}{3}(\mathrm{g} - \mathrm{a})$; $\mathrm{w} - \mathrm{a} = \frac{1}{2}(\mathrm{g} - \mathrm{a})$.

(4.13): If a and b belong to $G \cap H$, then $\lambda \mathrm{a} + (1-\lambda)\mathrm{b}$ with $0 < \lambda < 1$ also belongs to $G$ and $H$, and hence to $G \cap H$.

(4.14): If $\mathrm{x} = \sum_1^m \alpha_i \mathrm{a}_i$ and $\mathrm{y} = \sum_1^m \beta_i \mathrm{a}_i$ with $\sum \alpha_i = \sum \beta_i = 1$ are points of $G$, then $\lambda \mathrm{x} + (1-\lambda)\mathrm{y} = \sum\{\lambda\alpha_i + (1-\lambda)\beta_i\}\mathrm{a}_i = \sum \delta_i \mathrm{a}_i$ $0 < \lambda < 1$ with $\sum \delta_i = \lambda + 1 - \lambda = 1$ also is in $G$. If moreover $\alpha_i \geqslant 0$, $\beta_i \geqslant 0$ then also $\delta_i \geqslant 0$.
Any convex point set containing $\mathrm{a}_1, \cdots \mathrm{a}_m$ also contains $\dfrac{\gamma_1 \mathrm{a}_1 + \cdots + \gamma_r \mathrm{a}_r}{\gamma_1 + \cdots + \gamma_r}$ for $\gamma_i \geqslant 0$ and $\sum \gamma_i \neq 0$, in case $r = 2$.
The same is true for $r = 3$, for $$\frac{\gamma_1 + \gamma_2}{\gamma_1 + \gamma_2 + \gamma_3} \cdot \frac{\gamma_1 \mathrm{a}_1 + \gamma_2 \mathrm{a}_2}{\gamma_1 + \gamma_2} + \frac{\gamma_3 \mathrm{a}_3}{\gamma_1 + \gamma_2 + \gamma_3} = \frac{\gamma_1 \mathrm{a}_1 + \gamma_2 \mathrm{a}_2 + \gamma_3 \mathrm{a}_3}{\gamma_1 + \gamma_2 + \gamma_3}$$ etc, until $r = m$.
The set consisting of all these points is convex and hence is the smallest convex set containing $\mathrm{a}_1, \cdots \mathrm{a}_m$.

(4.15): $$\mathrm{x} = \mathrm{a} + \frac{\mu}{\lambda + \mu}(\mathrm{b} - \mathrm{a}).$$

(4.16): Use (4.15). $\mathrm{x} = \dfrac{\alpha \mathrm{a} + \beta \mathrm{b} + \gamma \mathrm{c}}{\alpha + \beta + \gamma}$ is collinear with a and

$$a' = \frac{\beta b + \gamma c}{\beta + \gamma} \quad \text{(similarly cyclically)}; \quad \frac{c - a'}{b - a'} = -\frac{\beta}{\gamma}$$

(cyclically). Hence $\left(-\frac{\beta}{\gamma}\right) \cdot \left(-\frac{\gamma}{\alpha}\right) \cdot \left(-\frac{\alpha}{\beta}\right) = -1.$

If conversely $-1 = \left(-\frac{\beta}{\gamma}\right) \cdot \left(-\frac{\gamma}{\alpha}\right) \cdot \left(\frac{b - c'}{a - c'}\right)$, so that

$\frac{b - c'}{a - c'} = -\frac{\alpha}{\beta}$, then $x = \frac{\alpha a + \beta b + \gamma c}{\alpha + \beta + \gamma}$ is common to the lines aa′, bb′, cc′.

(4.17): The join of $\lambda a$ and $\nu c$ meets the join of O and the centroid of the parallelogram in

$$\frac{\nu}{\lambda+\nu}\lambda a + \frac{\lambda}{\lambda+\nu}\nu c = \frac{\nu\lambda}{\lambda+\nu}(a+c) = \frac{\nu\lambda}{\lambda+\nu}(b+d) = \frac{\mu\omega}{\mu+\omega}(b+d).$$

(4.18): Let $\alpha : \beta$ be the ratio of the segments $PS : SQ$ on the secant $PQ$. For fixed $S$, the ratio varies from $\alpha : \beta$ to $\beta : \alpha$, hence passes the value 1, in which case $S$ is the midpoint of $PQ$.

$\frac{1}{2}(\partial G + \partial G) \subset G \cup \partial G$ since any midpoint belongs to $G \cup \partial G$. $G \cup \partial G \subset \frac{1}{2}(\partial G + \partial G)$ since any point of $G$ is midpoint of a secant and any point of $\partial G$ is midpoint of itself.

(4.19): If the point $z \in G$ is outside $(1 - 2\omega)G$, then the diameter through z is divided into pieces $\beta : 1 - \beta$ with $\beta < \omega$. Rotation around z then yields at least once the ratio $1 : 1$, and consequently also at least once the ratio $\omega : 1 - \omega$. If, conversely, a secant (x, y) of $G$ is divided by a point z in the ratio $\omega : (1 - \omega)$, so that $(x - z) = \omega(x - y)$, then $x' = (1 - 2\omega)x$, $y' = (1 - 2\omega)\cdot(-y)$ and z are collinear, and $z = x' - \frac{\omega}{1-2\omega}(y' - x')$. x′ and y′ are on $(1 - 2\omega)\partial G$ and z lies on the extension of this secant. This proves the assertion.

(4.20): From $x_1 + y_1,\ x_2 + y_2 \in U + W$ with $x_1, x_2 \in U$ and $y_1, y_2 \in W$ follows: $\lambda(x_1 + y_1) + (1 - \lambda)(x_2 + y_2) = (\lambda x_1 + (1 - \lambda)x_2) + (\lambda y_1 + (1 - \lambda)y_2) \in U + W$
$0 < \lambda < 1$.

(5.1): If $a_1$ is linearly dependent on $a_2, \cdots a_m$, hence $a_1 = - \lambda_2 a_2 - \cdots - \lambda_m a_m$, then equation (5.2) is satisfied with $\lambda_1 = 1$. If (5.2) holds for $\lambda_p \neq 0$, then $a_p$ can be solved from (5.2).

(5.2): $a = \frac{1}{2}(2a + b) - \frac{1}{2}b$; $1 \cdot 2a + 2 \cdot (-a) = O$.
$1 \cdot O + 0 \cdot a + 0 \cdot b = O$; $2a = 2(a + b) + (-2)b$.

(5.4): $3; -8; -9; 2; -3$.

(5.7): The space of the homogeneous $r$-th degree functions has as basis the products, in which repetitions may occur, of $r$ out of $n$ basis functions $\varphi_1, \cdots \varphi_n$. Number of possibilities: $\binom{n+r-1}{r}$. The non-homogeneous $r$-th degree functions are the sums of $s$-th degree homogeneous functions, $0 \leqslant s \leqslant r$.

(5.8): $0, 0, -1$ and $1$; $2, -2, 2$ and $-1$.

(6.1): *Parallellism*: If in general $x' = x + d$ and $(g - f) = \lambda(b - a)$, then it follows that $(g' - f') = \lambda(b' - a')$ and conversely.
*Between*: If $x = \lambda a + (1 - \lambda)b$, $0 < \lambda < 1$, then $x' = \lambda a' + (1 - \lambda)b'$.

(6.2): If $\kappa$ is an $\mathscr{A}$-map mapping this linear variety onto a subspace P of V, then there exists a vector d such that its image under $\kappa'$ is equal to $P + d$. According to the assumption $O \in P + d$, hence $-d \in P$ and $P + d = P$.

(6.3): Choose an $\mathscr{A}$-map such that one of the $r + 1$ points is mapped to O. A basis of the first image-subspace (cf. problem (6.2)) then lies in the second image-subspace, from which the assertion follows.

(6.4): Choose an $\mathscr{A}$-map such that one point of $\xi^{-1}(0)$ is mapped to O, and apply theorem [5.10]. Observe that $\xi$ and $\eta$ have the same collection of level sets.

(6.5): Proof by substitution. Interpretation: three concurrent lines or planes.

(6.6): For $a \neq b \in \xi^{-1}(0)$ we have $\eta(a) = \lambda$ and $\eta(b) = \mu$ $(\lambda, \mu \neq 0)$. From $\lambda \neq \mu$ it follows that $\eta\{\alpha a + (1 - \alpha)b\} = \alpha\lambda + (1 - \alpha)\mu$ is zero for $\alpha = - \dfrac{\mu}{\lambda - \mu}$. But $\alpha a +$

$+ (1 - \alpha)b \in \xi^{-1}(0)$ *and* $\in \eta^{-1}(0)$ · contradictory to our assumption; hence $\lambda = \mu$.
From $\eta(a) = \eta(b) = \lambda$ for all a, $b \in \xi^{-1}(0)$ it follows that $\xi^{-1}(0) = \eta^{-1}(\lambda)$, $\eta - \lambda = \mu\xi$ or $\alpha\xi + \beta\eta = 1$, $\alpha = -\mu\lambda^{-1}$, $\beta = \lambda^{-1}$.

(6.7): *A*: Put $\alpha\xi + \beta\eta + \gamma\zeta = 0$ and for example $\gamma \neq 0$ (if not, change the notation). If $\xi^{-1}(0)$ and $\eta^{-1}(0)$ meet in a, then $\zeta(a) = 0$, hence $\zeta^{-1}(0)$ also passes through a.
If $\xi^{-1}(0)$ and $\eta^{-1}(0)$ are parallel then $\eta = \mu\xi + \nu$, $\mu$ and $\nu$ constants, and a similar expression for $\zeta$ is obtained by substitution. The three lines are parallel.
*B*: If the kernels $\xi^{-1}(0)$, $\eta^{-1}(0)$ and $\zeta^{-1}(0)$ intersect in a point *S*, and we use an $\mathscr{A}$-map $\kappa: A \to V$ which maps *S* to the vector O, then the linear functions $\xi\kappa^{-1}$, $\eta\kappa^{-1}$ and $\zeta\kappa^{-1}$ on V are homogeneous. The space of such functions is two-dimensional, hence the three functions are linearly dependent: $\alpha\xi + \beta\eta + \gamma\zeta = 0$. If the kernels are parallel and different then from $\eta = \mu\xi + \nu$ and $\zeta = \mu'\xi + \nu'$ it follows that $\nu'\eta - \nu\zeta - (\nu'\mu - \nu\mu')\xi = 0$.

(6.8): Under a suitable $\mathscr{A}$-map the sets *a*), *b*) and *h*) are represented by subspaces. In that case, together with a and b also $\lambda a + (1 - \lambda)b$ belongs to the subspace. Without loss of generality we may replace $A^n$, via an $\mathscr{A}$-map, by a vector space V with homogeneous linear functions $\varphi$ and $\psi$.
If now $\alpha < \varphi(a) < \beta$, $\alpha < \varphi(b) < \beta$ then *c*) follows from
$\alpha = \lambda\alpha + (1 - \lambda)\alpha < \lambda\varphi(a) + (1 - \lambda)\varphi(b) =$
$= \varphi\{\lambda a + (1 - \lambda)b\} < \beta$, $0 < \lambda < 1$.
Case *f*) For all $\lambda$ and $\mu$ we have
$\varphi^2[\lambda a + (1-\mu)b] + \psi^2[\lambda a + (1-\mu)b] = \lambda^2(\varphi^2(a) + \psi^2(a)) +$
$+ (1-\mu)^2(\varphi^2(b) + \psi^2(b)) + 2\lambda(1-\mu)[\varphi(a)\cdot\varphi(b) + \psi(a)\cdot\psi(b)]$
$\geqslant 0$. If $\varphi^2(a) + \psi^2(a) \leqslant 1$ and $\varphi^2(b) + \psi^2(b) \leqslant 1$, then $\lambda$ real (no or one root) and $\mu = 0$ implies that the discriminant of the quadratic expression is $\leqslant 0$, or
$[\varphi(a)\cdot\varphi(b) + \psi(a)\cdot\psi(b)]^2 \leqslant [\varphi^2(a) + \psi^2(a)][\varphi^2(b) + \psi^2(b)] \leqslant 1$.
If we put, on the other hand, $0 < \lambda = \mu < 1$ then
$\varphi^2[\lambda a + (1 - \lambda)b] + \psi^2[\lambda a + (1 - \lambda)b] \leqslant 1$.

(7.2): A side of the parallelogram is bisected by one of the lines, and is parallel to the other one. Cf. fig. 7.7.

(7.3): The projections onto $\varphi = 1$ of lines through p are parallel. The same holds for the lines through r. The assertion follows from the invariance of the cross-ratio and from the fact that the image of q is midpoint of the join of the images of s and t.

(7.4): Choose $\varphi$ such that $\varphi(b_i) = 0$ for $i = 1, \cdots m$. Then

$$\Pi_1^m \frac{a_i - b_i}{a_{i+1} - b_i} = \Pi_1^m \frac{\varphi(a_i)}{\varphi(a_{i+1})} = 1.$$

Conversely: If $\varphi$ is such that for $m - 1$ points $\varphi(b_i) = 0$, and $\varphi(a_j) \neq 0$, then

$$1 = \Pi_{i=1}^{m-1} \left[ \frac{\varphi(a_i)}{\varphi(a_i+1)} \right] \cdot \frac{a_m - b_m}{a_1 - b_m} = \frac{\varphi(a_1)(a_m - b_m)}{\varphi(a_m)(a_1 - b_m)},$$

hence $[\varphi(a_1) - \varphi(a_m)]\varphi(b_m) = 0$.

If $\varphi(a_1)$ were equal to $\varphi(a_m)$ then $1 = \dfrac{a_m - b_m}{a_1 - b_m}$ and $a_m = a_1$, contrary to the assumption. Hence $\varphi(b_m) = 0$.

(7.5): Cf. problems (7.4) and (4.7).

(7.6): If $a_2a_4a_6$ are non-collinear, then at least one of the sides of the triangle $a_2a_4a_6$ is not parallel to $a_1a_3$. Suppose this side is $a_2a_4$, intersecting $a_1a_3$ in O. Put $a_1 = a$; $a_3 = \lambda a$; $a_5 = \mu\lambda a$; $a_2 = b$; $a_4 = \nu b$.

Now $\nu = \mu\lambda$ since $a_4a_5$ and $a_2a_1$ are parallel. The line through $a_1$ parallel to $a_3a_4$ intersects $a_2a_4$ in the point $\mu b$. The line through $a_5$ parallel to $a_2a_3$ intersects $a_2a_4$ in the point. $\mu b$ Hence $a_6 = \mu b$.

(8.1): 4, 2, 2, 3, 4, 2, 2, 2, 4, 4, 3, 2, 1, 2.

(8.2): 0,0. (8.3): $\eta + 3\xi = 0$. (8.4): $(\xi, \eta) = (2, 1)$.

(8.5): *a)* $\eta + 3\xi = 0$; *b)* $\frac{1}{2}\{(3, 1) + (2, 4)\} = (0, 0)$; *c)* through a: $\eta + 4\xi = 3$; through b: $\eta + 2\xi = 3$; through c: $\xi = 0$; centroid $(0, 3)$; *d)* 3; f) For the $\eta$-coordinates we have $\dfrac{2-0}{4-0} : \dfrac{2-1}{4-1} = 4 = -1$; *g)* Choose for example $a = (0, 0)$, $b = (1, 2)$, $c = (3, 2)$, then $d = (2, 0)$; a and c are on $\eta + \xi = 0$ and b and d on $\eta + 2\xi \doteq 4$. Intersection $(4, 1) = \frac{1}{2}(a + c) = \frac{1}{2}(b + d)$.

(8.6):

| | | | |
|---|---|---|---|
| 2 | 02 | 12 | 22 |
| 1 | 01 | 11 | 21 |
| $\eta=0$ | 00 | 10 | 20 |
| | $\xi=0$ | 1 | 2 |

| $\xi$ | $\eta$ | $\xi+\eta$ | $\xi+2\eta$ |
|---|---|---|---|
| 012 | 222 | 201 | 120 |
| 012 | 111 | 120 | 201 |
| 012 | 000 | 012 | 012 |

*a*) The midpoint of two points on a line is always the third point on that line. *b*) The three medians of a triangle are parallel (concurrent). *c*) For cross-ratio and Menelaus's theorem the number of points is too small. *d*) Through any point there are four lines.

(8.7):

| | | |
|---|---|---|
| 1 | 01 | 11 |
| $\eta=0$ | 00 | 10 |
| | $\xi=0$ | 1 |

| $\xi$ | $\eta$ | $\xi+\eta$ |
|---|---|---|
| 01 | 11 | 10 |
| 01 | 00 | 01 |

The midpoint of two points does not exist ($\frac{1}{2}$ is not defined).

(8.8):

| | | | | |
|---|---|---|---|---|
| $\omega^2$ | $0\omega^2$ | $1\omega^2$ | $\omega\omega^2$ | $\omega^2\omega^2$ |
| $\omega$ | $0\omega$ | $1\omega$ | $\omega\omega$ | $\omega^2\omega$ |
| 1 | 01 | 11 | $\omega 1$ | $\omega^2 1$ |
| $\eta=0$ | 00 | 10 | $\omega 0$ | $\omega^2 0$ |
| | $\xi=0$ | 1 | $\omega$ | $\omega^2$ |

| $\xi$ | $\eta$ | $\xi+\eta$ | $\xi+\omega\eta$ | $\xi+\omega^2\eta$ |
|---|---|---|---|---|
| $0\ 1\ \omega\ \omega^2$ | $\omega^2\ \omega^2\ \omega^2\ \omega^2$ | $\omega^2\ \omega\ 1\ 0$ | $1\ 0\ \omega^2\ \omega$ | $\omega\ \omega^2\ 0\ 1$ |
| $0\ 1\ \omega\ \omega^2$ | $\omega\ \omega\ \omega\ \omega$ | $\omega\ \omega^2\ 0\ 1$ | $\omega^2\ \omega\ 1\ 0$ | $1\ 0\ \omega^2\ \omega$ |
| $0\ 1\ \omega\ \omega^2$ | $1\ 1\ 1\ 1$ | $1\ 0\ \omega^2\ \omega$ | $\omega\ \omega^2\ 0\ 1$ | $\omega^2\ \omega\ 1\ 0$ |
| $0\ 1\ \omega\ \omega^2$ | $0\ 0\ 0\ 0$ | $0\ 1\ \omega\ \omega^2$ | $0\ 1\ \omega\ \omega^2$ | $0\ 1\ \omega\ \omega^2$ |

Take for example the points $a = (\omega, \omega^2)$, $b = (1, 0)$, $c = (0, \omega)$, then $d = (\omega^2, 1)$ and $b - d = a - c = (\omega, 1)$.
Other proof:
$c = d + b - a \rightarrow c - a = d + b - 2a = d + b = d - b$.

(8.9): There are $5^3$ points; $5^3$ linear functions $\alpha x + \beta y + \gamma z$. Functions with different level planes are $x + \delta y + \varepsilon z$ (25 possibilities), $y + \eta z$ (5), and $z$ (1), hence 31 possibilities in total. Then there are $31 \times 5 = 155$ level planes $\alpha x + \beta y + \gamma z = \delta$ ($\delta = 0, 1, \cdots 4$). Two planes intersect in a line of 5 points or are parallel.
The intersection of three non-coinciding planes is a point, a line or empty. The number of directions (= number of lines through (0, 0, 0)) is 31.

(8.10): The hyperplane $\alpha x + \beta y + \gamma z + \delta w = \varepsilon$ has $2^3 = 8$ points, viz. $2^3$ choices for x, y and z give one solution for w each. Any of the $(2^4 - 1) = 15$ possibilities for the set $(\alpha, \beta, \gamma, \delta) \neq (0, 0, 0, 0)$ gives a function $\alpha x+\beta y+\gamma z+\delta w$ with exactly two level hyperplanes, and thus a division of the 16 points into two classes of 8. Any hyperplane of one function has four points in common with a hyperplane of any other function, since the equations $\alpha x+\beta y+\gamma z+\delta w=\varepsilon$ and $\alpha' x+\beta' y+\gamma' z+\delta' w = \varepsilon'$ have one solution for any of the four choices of (x, y).

(9.1): $2b_1 + 2b_2$; $\sigma(A) = \sigma\{(\lambda_1 a_1 + \lambda_2 a_2 + \lambda_3 a_3)\} = \{(\lambda_1+\lambda_3)b_1+ + (\lambda_2 + \lambda_3)b_2\} = B$; $\sigma^{-1}(O)$ has as basis $(a_1 + a_2 - a_3)$; rank $\sigma$ + dim $\sigma^{-1}(O) = 2 + 1 = 3 =$ dim A.
$\rho^{-1}(O)$ has as basis $a_1 - a_3$ and $a_2 - a_3$; rank $\rho$ is 1.

(9.2): $\sigma + \varepsilon$: rotation through $\pi/4$ and multiplication by $\sqrt{2}$; $(\rho + \varepsilon)(a_1, a_2) = (3a_1, 2a_2)$; $\rho - \varepsilon$: orthogonal projection on the space with basis $a_1$; $(3a_2, - 3a_1)$; $2\varepsilon$: multiplication by factor 2; $(a_2 - 2a_1, - a_1 - a_2)$; $(- 2a_1, - a_2)$; $(3a_2, - 3a_1 + 2a_2)$.

(9.4): Rotation through $\pi/2$; $(2a_1, a_2)$; rotation through $\pi$; identity; $\sigma$; $(2a_2 - a_1)$; $(a_2, - 2a_1)$, projection onto $a_1$ and then reflection with respect to the line $\lambda(a_1 + a_2)$; mapping to (0, 0); $\sigma(\rho - \varepsilon)$; rotation through $3\pi/2$; $(a_1, 2a_2)$.

(9.5): The zero vector acts as identity $= \varepsilon$. The opposite vector is the inverse.

(9.6): Subgroup of the automorphism group with $\sigma^4$ = identity = 1.

Table:

| | 1 | $\sigma$ | $\sigma^2$ | $\sigma^3$ |
|---|---|---|---|---|
| 1 | 1 | $\sigma$ | $\sigma^2$ | $\sigma^3$ |
| $\sigma$ | $\sigma$ | $\sigma^2$ | $\sigma^3$ | 1 |
| $\sigma^2$ | $\sigma^2$ | $\sigma^3$ | 1 | $\sigma$ |
| $\sigma^3$ | $\sigma^3$ | 1 | $\sigma$ | $\sigma^2$ |

(9.7): Put $A \xrightarrow{\tau} B \xrightarrow{\sigma} \sigma(B)$. Since dim image $\leqslant$ dim source we have $\dim \sigma(\tau(A)) \leqslant \dim \tau(A)$, hence rank $\sigma\tau \leqslant$ rank $\tau$. Since $\tau(A) \in B$, $\dim \sigma(\tau A) \leqslant \dim \sigma B$, hence rank $\sigma\tau \leqslant$ rank $\sigma$.

(9.8): $\sigma(a) = a + b$ $\quad\quad \sigma(b) = -a$
$\sigma^2(a) = b$ $\quad\quad \sigma^2(b) = -a - b$
etc.
$\sigma^6(a) = a$ $\quad\quad \sigma^6(b) = b.$
If a and b are vectors of equal length making an angle of $2\pi/3$ in the ordinary plane, then $\sigma$ is a rotation through an angle of $\pi/3$.
${}^t(2a+3b)(3a-b)=(2{}^ta+3{}^tb)(3a-b)=6{}^ta\cdot a-2{}^tab+ +9{}^tba-3{}^tbb=6.1-2.0+9.0-3.1=3.$

(10.1): $\begin{bmatrix} 8 \\ 12 \end{bmatrix}, \begin{bmatrix} 4 \\ 3 \end{bmatrix}, \begin{bmatrix} 1 \\ 0 \end{bmatrix}, \begin{bmatrix} 8 \\ 0 \end{bmatrix}, \begin{bmatrix} 1 \\ 0 \end{bmatrix}, \begin{bmatrix} 1 \\ 0 \end{bmatrix}, \begin{bmatrix} 1 \\ 3 \end{bmatrix}$

$\sigma: \begin{bmatrix} 1 & 1 & 1 \\ 3 & 0 & 0 \end{bmatrix}.$ (10.2): $\begin{bmatrix} 6 \\ 5 \\ 2 \end{bmatrix}, \begin{bmatrix} 3 \\ 4 \\ 1 \end{bmatrix}.$

(10.3): $\sigma: \begin{bmatrix} 1 & 3 & 0 \\ 4 & 12 & 0 \\ 2 & 6 & 0 \end{bmatrix}$ rank $\sigma = 1$.

(10.4): ${}^t\sigma = \begin{bmatrix} 1 & 2 & -1 \\ 2 & 4 & -2 \\ -5 & -10 & 5 \\ -1 & -2 & 1 \end{bmatrix}$ rank ${}^t\sigma$ = rank $\sigma = 1$.

(10.5): $\sigma^6 = \varepsilon = \begin{bmatrix} 1 & 0 \\ 0 & 1 \end{bmatrix}$. Relation: $\begin{bmatrix} 1 \\ 0 \end{bmatrix}$ and $\begin{bmatrix} 0 \\ 1 \end{bmatrix}$ act as a and b respectively.

(10.6): $a = 0, c = 1; a = 8, b = 46; a = 0, b = 0.$

(10.7): $\sigma^{-1} = \begin{bmatrix} 1 & -1 & 0 \\ 1 & 0 & -2 \\ 1 & 1 & 1 \end{bmatrix}$.

(10.8): $\sigma^k = \begin{bmatrix} 1 & k \\ 0 & 1 \end{bmatrix}$; $({}^t\sigma)^k = \begin{bmatrix} 1 & 0 \\ k & 1 \end{bmatrix}$.

(10.9): $\sigma$: $(e_1, e_2, e_3, e_4) \to (e_4, e_1, e_2, e_3)$,
$\sigma$ is a cyclical rearrangement of the basis vectors.
$\sigma^2 = (e_3, e_4, e_1, e_2)$, $\sigma^3 = \sigma^{-1}$, $\sigma^4 =$ identity.

$$\sigma + \sigma^2 + \sigma^3 + \sigma^4 = \begin{bmatrix} 1 & 1 & 1 & 1 \\ 1 & 1 & 1 & 1 \\ 1 & 1 & 1 & 1 \\ 1 & 1 & 1 & 1 \end{bmatrix}; \text{ rank } 1.$$

(10.10): ${}^t\sigma\sigma = (\alpha^2 + \beta^2)\,\underline{1}$. (10.11): ${}^t\sigma\sigma = \underline{1}$.

(10.13): $k \pmod 8$ 1, 2, 3, 4, $\cdots$ 8

$$\sigma^k = \begin{bmatrix} 1 & 2 \\ 3 & 4 \end{bmatrix}, \begin{bmatrix} 2 & 0 \\ 0 & 2 \end{bmatrix}, \begin{bmatrix} 2 & 4 \\ 1 & 3 \end{bmatrix}, \begin{bmatrix} 4 & 0 \\ 0 & 4 \end{bmatrix}, \cdots \begin{bmatrix} 1 & 0 \\ 0 & 1 \end{bmatrix}$$

(10.14): Apply the definition of a ring.

(10.15): $\sigma^{-1} = \begin{bmatrix} 2 & -7 \\ -1 & 4 \end{bmatrix}$.

(10.16): ${}^t\sigma = \dfrac{1}{\sqrt{6}} \begin{bmatrix} 1 & \sqrt{2} & -\sqrt{3} \\ -2 & \sqrt{2} & 0 \\ 1 & \sqrt{2} & \sqrt{3} \end{bmatrix}$.

${}^t\sigma\sigma =$ identity; $\sigma^{-1} = {}^t\sigma$. Consider ${}^t$a and b etc. as homomorphisms. Then ${}^t(\sigma a)(\sigma b) = ({}^ta\,{}^t\sigma)(\sigma b) = {}^ta({}^t\sigma\sigma)b = {}^tab$.

(10.17): If $\sigma$ and $\tau$ belong to the given set of matrices then $\sigma + \tau$ and $\sigma\tau$ also belong to it. The set then is a ring.
The unit matrix belongs to the subset of the elements with $\alpha_{ii} \neq 0$ for $i = 1, \cdots n$. The inverse of any element of this subset also belongs to it, as does the product of any two elements of the subset. The associative law holds since it holds in the ring of all matrices. According to the definition on p. 67 the subset then is a group.

(10.18): From $\sigma\mu = \mu\sigma$ and $\tau\mu = \mu\tau$ for all $\mu \in M$, it follows that $(\sigma+\tau)\mu = \mu(\sigma+\tau)$, $(\sigma\tau)\mu = \sigma(\mu\tau) = (\sigma\mu)\tau = (\mu\sigma)\tau = \mu(\sigma\tau)$.

Moreover $0\mu = \mu 0$, $1\mu = \mu 1$ for all $\mu \in M$. The associative and distributive laws hold since they hold for the set of all $n \times n$-matrices. This proves the first part of the assertion. In case $M$ contains all real $n \times n$-matrices, the ring consists of the matrices with elements $a_{ij} = \lambda\delta_{ij}$.

(10.19): $\sigma = \begin{bmatrix} 0 & 1 & 0 \\ 0 & 0 & 1 \\ 1 & 0 & 0 \end{bmatrix}$.

(10.20): Apply the given interchanges to the columns of the unit matrix.

(11.1): *a)* $(\xi_1, \xi_2, \xi_3) = (3, -1, 2)$
*b)* $(\frac{5}{4} - 5\lambda; \frac{3}{4} + \lambda, 4\lambda)$, $\lambda$ real.

(11.2): $(2 + i, 0)$. (11.3): $(\xi_1, \xi_2, \xi_3) = (3, 2, 1)$.

(12.2): $2; -1; -4; 1; 1; 2; 0.$

(12.3): $-30; -1; 2; \frac{1}{2}; 0.$

(12.4): 1234, 1342, 1423, 2143, 2314, 2431, 3124, 3241, 3412, 4132, 4213, 4321.

(12.5): 6. (12.6): 14.

(12.7): $\det \sigma = \varepsilon(j_1, \cdots j_n) = (-1)^{N(j_1, \ldots j_n)} = 1$ for $N$ even and $= -1$ for $N$ odd.

(12.8): $1 = \det(\tau\tau^{-1}) = \det \tau \det \tau^{-1}$; $\det(\tau\sigma\tau^{-1}) = \det \tau \cdot \det \sigma \cdot \det \tau^{-1} = \det \tau \cdot \det \sigma \cdot (\det \tau)^{-1} = \det \sigma$. By induction $\det \sigma^k = (\det \sigma)^k$.

(12.9): $30; \beta-\alpha; (\alpha-\beta)(\beta-\gamma)(\gamma-\alpha); \alpha\delta-\beta\gamma$; cf. problem (12.1).

(12.10): $6; \alpha^2; 0.$

(12.11): $\det \sigma = -\det(-\sigma) = -\det {}^t\sigma = -\det \sigma$. Hence $\det \sigma = -\det \sigma = 0$.

(12.12): $\det \sigma^{-1} = \det {}^t\sigma = \det \sigma; \sigma \cdot \sigma^{-1} = 1$, hence $1 = \det \sigma \cdot \det \sigma^{-1} = (\det \sigma)^2$; $\det \sigma = 1$ or $-1$.

(12.13): ${}^t\sigma = \sigma^{-1}$ and ${}^t\tau = \tau^{-1}$.
$\det(\sigma - \tau)(\sigma + \tau) = \det(\sigma - \tau)({}^t\sigma + {}^t\tau) =$
$= \det(\sigma{}^t\sigma - \tau{}^t\sigma + \sigma{}^t\tau - \tau{}^t\tau) = \det(\sigma{}^t\tau - \tau{}^t\sigma)$.
This is an antisymmetric matrix with an odd number of rows and columns, and hence, by problem (12.11) its determinant is zero.

(12.14): Since $\overline{\det \sigma} = \det \bar{\sigma} = \det {}^t\sigma^{-1} = \det \sigma^{-1} = (\det \sigma)^{-1}$,

$|\det\sigma|^2 = |\det\sigma|\cdot\overline{|\det\sigma|} = |\det\sigma\cdot(\det\sigma)^{-1}| = 1$, hence $|\det\sigma| = 1$.
(The vertical dashes mean "absolute value of").

(12.15): $\det(\bar\sigma - \bar\tau)\det(\sigma+\tau) = \det({}^t\sigma^{-1} - {}^t\tau^{-1})\det(\sigma+\tau) =$
$= \det(\sigma^{-1} - \tau^{-1})(\sigma+\tau) = \det(\sigma^{-1}\tau - \tau^{-1}\sigma)$.
The complex conjugate of this is $\det(\sigma-\tau)\det(\bar\sigma+\bar\tau) =$
$= \det(-\sigma^{-1}\tau + \tau^{-1}\sigma) = (-1)^n\cdot\det(\sigma^{-1}\tau - \tau^{-1}\sigma)$.
For $n$ even (odd) $\det(\sigma^{-1}\tau - \tau^{-1}\sigma)$ is opposite (equal) to its complex conjugate, from which the assertion follows.

(12.16): ${}^t(\overline{\tau^{-1}\sigma\tau}) = {}^t(\bar\tau^{-1}\bar\sigma\bar\tau) = {}^t\bar\tau\,{}^t\bar\sigma({}^t\bar\tau^{-1}) = \tau^{-1}\sigma\tau$.

(12.17): For a permutation with $j_0 = 0$ the assertion follows from problem (12.7).
For a permutation which is an interchange of $a_0$ and $a_1$ the assertion follows from the following property of each multilinear antisymmetric function $\varphi$:
$\varphi(a_1 - a_0, a_2 - a_0, \cdots, a_n - a_0) =$
$= \varphi(a_1 - a_0, (a_2 - a_0) - (a_1 - a_0), \cdots, (a_n - a_0) - (a_1 - a_0)) =$
$= -\varphi(a_0 - a_1, a_2 - a_1, \cdots, a_n - a_1)$.
Since any permutation can be considered as product of a number of permutations of the types used above, the assertion follows.

(12.18): According to equation (12.11) the term $\sum_{j=1}^n \sigma_{ij}\omega_{kj}$ of $\sigma{}^t\omega$ can be considered as an expression for the determinant of the matrix obtained from $\sigma$ by replacing the $k$-th row by the $i$-th row, leaving all other rows unchanged. Its value then is $\delta_{ik}\det\sigma$.

(13.1): A necessary and sufficient condition (*n.s.c.*) is that the vectors in $\mathbf{F}^{n+1}$:
$\{\xi_1(a_i) - \xi_1(a_r), \cdots, \xi_n(a_i) - \xi_1(a_r), 0\}$
are linearly dependent for $i = 1, \cdots r-1$.
Another n.s.c. is that these vectors together with $\{\xi_1(a_r), \cdots, \xi_n(a_r), 1\}$ (which is independent of them) form a linearly dependent set. Adding this last vector to each of the first $r-1$ vectors, we find another n.s.c.: $\{\xi_1(a_i), \cdots, \xi_n(a_i), 1\}$ are linearly dependent for $i=1, \cdots n$. According to the theory of matrices this is equivalent to the assertion.

(13.2): In the first case the determinants of the given endomorphisms $a_i \to b_i$ are positive, in the second case negative.

(13.3): As (13.2).

(13.4): Choose coordinates such that $d = (0, 0)$, $b = (1, 0)$, $c = (0, 1)$ then $a = (\alpha_1, \alpha_2)$ with $\alpha_1 < 0$, $\alpha_2 < 0$. Now the assertion follows as in problems (13.2) and (13.3) by calculating the determinants. The results can be obtained geometrically as on page 85. The second part, concerning fig. 13.6 follows from problem (12.16).

(13.6): For parallel lines the assertion is trivial both ways. Choose an $\mathscr{A}$-map such that $a + b + c = 0$ and put $a, b, c = a_1, a_2, a_3$.
$\chi_i = \varphi_i - \varphi_i(O)$ is a homogeneous function and $\varphi_i = \chi_i - \chi_i(a_i)$, $\psi_i = \chi_i - \chi_i(-\frac{1}{2}a_i) = \chi_i + \frac{1}{2}\chi_i(a_i)$. (Make a drawing). If now $\varphi_i(p) = 0$ then $\psi_i(-\frac{1}{2}p) = 0$ and conversely. The lines $\varphi_i$ have the point p in common if and only if the lines $\psi_i$ have the point $q = -\frac{1}{2}p$ in common.

(14.1): See main theorem [14.3′].

(14.2): From $v_1 = \lambda u_1 + (1-\lambda)u_2$, $v_2 = \mu u_1 + (1-\mu)u_2$, $\varphi(u_1, u_2) = \varphi(v_1, v_1) = \varphi(v_2, v_2) = 0$ and $\xi(x) = \varphi(x, v_1)$; $\eta(x) = \varphi(x, v_2)$ it follows that

$$(u_1u_2v_1v_2) = \frac{\xi(u_1 - v_1)}{\xi(u_2 - v_1)} : \frac{\eta(u_1 - v_2)}{\eta(u_2 - v_2)} = \frac{\xi(u_1)}{\xi(u_2)} : \frac{\eta(u_1)}{\eta(u_2)} =$$

$$= \frac{\varphi(u_1, v_1)}{\varphi(u_2, v_1)} : \frac{\varphi(u_1, v_2)}{\varphi(u_2, v_2)} = \frac{\lambda}{1-\lambda} : \frac{\mu}{1-\mu}.$$

Moreover from $0 = \varphi(v_1, v_1) = \lambda^2\varphi(u_1, u_1) + (1-\lambda)^2\varphi(u_2, u_2)$ and $0 = \varphi(v_2, v_2) = \mu^2\varphi(u_1, u_1) + (1-\mu)^2\varphi(u_2, u_2)$ it follows that $\frac{\lambda}{1-\lambda} = \frac{\pm\mu}{1-\mu}$. The plus sign makes no sense since $v_1 \neq v_2$, hence $(u_1u_2v_1v_2) = -1$.

If conversely the cross-ratio is $-1$, so that $\frac{\lambda}{1-\lambda} = \frac{-\mu}{1-\mu}$ and $\varphi(v_1, v_1) = 0$ and $\varphi(v_2, v_2) = 0$, then $\varphi(u_1, u_2) = 0$ follows.

(14.3): Put $\psi = \sum_{k=1}^{p} \eta_k^2 - \sum_{k=p+1}^{r} \eta_k^2$. Then the assertion follows from theorem [14.7].

(14.4): ${}^t\mathrm{x}\alpha\mathrm{y} = \sum_{ij} \alpha_{ij}\mathrm{x}_i\mathrm{y}_j$ hence symmetric if $\alpha_{ij} = \alpha_{ji}$, i.e. if ${}^t\alpha = \alpha$.

(14.5): If ${}^t\mathrm{x} = (\xi, \eta, \zeta)$, then ${}^t\mathrm{x}\alpha\mathrm{x} = 2\xi^2 + 20\xi\eta - 4\xi\zeta + 11\eta^2 - 28\eta\zeta - \zeta^2 = 2(\xi + 5\eta - \zeta)^2 - 39\eta^2 - 8\eta\zeta - 3\zeta^2 = (\xi')^2 - 3(\zeta + \eta\tfrac{4}{3})^2 - (\eta')^2 = (\xi')^2 - (\eta')^2 - (\zeta')^2$.

(14.6):
a) $\psi_1^2 + \psi_2^2 - 4$    $\varphi = 0$ : ellipse in $A^2$
b) $\psi_1^2 + 1$    : empty
c) $\psi_1^2 - \psi_2^2 + \psi_3^2 - 1$    : hyperboloid of one sheet
d) $\psi_1^2 - \psi_2^2 - \psi_3^2 - 1$    : hyperboloid of two sheets
e) $\psi_1^2 - \psi_2^2 + \psi_3^2 - \frac{577}{4}$: hyperboloid of one sheet.

(14.7): The intersection of a plane and a quadratic variety is always a conic. If $\xi_1^2 + \xi_2^2 - \xi_3^2 = 0$ is the cone, then $\xi_3 = \text{constant} \neq 0$ yields an ellipse, $\xi_1$ or $\xi_2 = \text{constant} \neq 0$ a hyperbola, $\xi_1 = 0$ a pair of lines, $\xi_2 - \xi_3 = \text{constant} \neq 0$ a parabola, $\xi_2 - \xi_3 = 0$ a line.

(14.8): Let the hyperboloid have equation $\varphi = \xi_1^2 + \xi_2^2 + \xi_3^2 - 1 = 0$. Then the systems of lines with parameter $\lambda$ (or $\mu$ resp.) have equations $\xi_1 - \xi_3 = \lambda(1 - \xi_2)$, $\lambda(\xi_1 + \xi_3) = 1 + \xi_2$ and the line $1 - \xi_2 = \xi_1 + \xi_3 = 0$; and $\xi_1 - \xi_3 = \mu(1 + \xi_2)$, $\mu(\xi_1 + \xi_3) = 1 - \xi_2$ and the line $1 + \xi_2 = \xi_1 + \xi_3 = 0$.

(14.9): The hyperbolic paraboloid $\varphi = \xi_1^2 - \xi_2^2 - \xi_3 = 0$ has the systems of lines $\xi_1 - \xi_2 = \lambda$, $\lambda(\xi_1 + \xi_2) = \xi_3$, and $\xi_1 + \xi_2 = \mu$, $\mu(\xi_1 - \xi_2) = \xi_3$.

(15.1): Immediate consequence of the definition.

(15.2): Choose suitable euclidean coordinates, $W$: $\xi_1 = 0$; $U$: $(p, 0)$.
locus: $d^2(\mathrm{x}, W) = \xi_1^2 = \lambda^2 d^2(\mathrm{x}, U) = \lambda^2\{(\xi_1 - p)^2 + \xi_2^2\}$, $\lambda > 0$. The assertion follows from inspection of the corresponding quadratic form $(\lambda^2 - 1)\xi_1^2 + \lambda^2\xi_2^2 - 2p\lambda^2\xi_1 + p^2\lambda^2 = 0$.

(15.3): $U$: $(p, 0)$; $W$: $(-p, 0)$.
locus: $(\xi_1 + p)^2 + \xi_2^2 = \lambda^2\{(\xi_1 - p)^2 + \xi_2^2\}$; $\lambda = 1$ yields $\xi_1 = 0$; for $\lambda \neq 1$: circle $(\xi_1 - \alpha)^2 + \xi_2^2 = \rho^2$ with $-\alpha(1 - \lambda^2) = (1 + \lambda^2)p$ and $\rho^2 = \alpha^2 - p^2 > 0$, centre $(\alpha, 0)$, radius $\rho$. Similarly

the second case gives spheres and the plane containing the perpendicular bisectors.

(15.4): Let $\xi$ and $\eta$ be linear functions each of which can be considered as one of a euclidean coordinate system, and which have the given lines as zero-level sets. Hence $|\xi|$ is the distance to the first line etc. The locus in question has equation $\xi^2 = \lambda^2\eta^2$ and consists of the lines $\xi = \lambda\eta$ and $\xi = -\lambda\eta$.

(15.5): Suppose that $\mathscr{A}$-map $\kappa$ maps $U$ onto a subspace $\kappa U$ of V of dimension, say $p$, and maps $W$ onto a variety which is parallel to the subspace $\kappa W^*$ of dimension $q$, $\mathrm{a} + \kappa W^* = \kappa W$. Since $\kappa U$ and $\kappa W^*$ have no direction in common, they span a subspace of dimension $p + q$. $\kappa U$, $\kappa W^*$ and a span a space of dimension $p + q + 1$. For, if $\mathrm{a} = \mathrm{b} + \mathrm{c}$ with $\mathrm{b} \in \kappa U$, $\mathrm{c} \in \kappa W^*$, then $\kappa W = \mathrm{b} + \mathrm{c} + \kappa W^* = \mathrm{b} + \kappa W$, with $\mathrm{b} \in \kappa U$ *and* $\mathrm{b} \in \kappa W$, which is clearly impossible since $\kappa U$ and $\kappa W$ are disjoint. This space generated by $\kappa U$, $\kappa W^*$ and a contains $\kappa W$. Now in the space generated by $\kappa U$ and $\kappa W^*$ choose a basis with $\mathrm{a}_1, \cdots \mathrm{a}_p \in \kappa U$; $\mathrm{a}_{p+1}, \cdots \mathrm{a}_{p+q} \in \kappa W^*$. If $\mathrm{u} = \sum_{i=1}^{p} \alpha_i \mathrm{a}_i \in \kappa U$ and $\mathrm{w} = \mathrm{a} + \sum_{j=p+1}^{p+q} \beta_j \mathrm{a}_j \in \kappa W$ and if the line through u and w is perpendicular to $\kappa U$ and $\kappa W^*$, then $\mathrm{w} - \mathrm{u}$ is perpendicular to $\mathrm{a}_i$ for $i = 1, \cdots p + q$. This determines the coefficients $\alpha_i$ and $\beta_j$.

(15.6): Suppose that $\mathscr{A}$-map $\kappa$ maps $U$ onto a subspace $\kappa U$, and that $\kappa W$ is parallel to the subspace $\kappa W^*$ with $\kappa W = \mathrm{a} + \kappa W^*$. The dimension of the space Z generated by $\kappa U$, $\kappa W^*$ and a is $p + q + 1$ (cf. problem (15.5)). This space contains $\kappa W$. Choose an *orthonormal* [1] basis with $\mathrm{a}_1, \cdots \mathrm{a}_p \in \kappa U$, $\mathrm{a}_{p+1}, \cdots \mathrm{a}_{p+q} \in \kappa W^*$, $\mathrm{a}_{p+q+1}$ in the space Z (cobasis $\xi_1, \cdots \xi_n$). Let $\kappa W$ be the level $\alpha > 0$ for the function $\xi_{p+q+1}$ on Z. In E we have:

$d^2(P, U) = \xi^2_{p+1}(\mathrm{x}) + \cdots + \xi_n^2(\mathrm{x}) = \sum_{i=p+1}^{n} \xi_i^2(\mathrm{x})$;

$d^2(P, W) = \xi_1^2(\mathrm{x}) + \cdots + \xi_p^2(\mathrm{x}) + (\xi_{p+q+1} - \alpha)^2 + \xi^2_{p+q+2} + \cdots + \xi_n^2$;

---

[1] *Orthonormal* vectors are *orthogonal unit* vectors.

locus: $0 = -d^2(P, U) + d^2(P, W) = \Sigma_1^p \xi_i^2 - \Sigma_{p+1}^{p+q} \xi_i^2 - 2\alpha\xi_{p+q+1} + \alpha^2 = \varphi(\mathrm{x}) = \varphi(\kappa(P))$.
A change of $\mathscr{A}$-map with $\kappa'\kappa^{-1}\mathrm{x} = \mathrm{x} - \frac{1}{2}\mathrm{d}$, $\mathrm{d} = \alpha \mathrm{a}_{p+q+1}$ yields $\varphi'\kappa'P = \varphi'(\mathrm{x} - \frac{1}{2}\mathrm{d}) = \Sigma_1^p \xi_i^2 - \Sigma_{p+1}^{p+q} \xi_i^2 - 2\alpha\xi_{p+q+1}$.

(15.7): If in coordinates $B_1 = (\gamma, 0)$, $B_2 = (-\gamma, 0)$, then for a point $(\xi_1, \xi_2)$, $d_1^2 = d^2(\mathrm{x}, B_1) = (\xi_1 - \gamma)^2 + \xi_2^2$; $d_2^2 = d^2(\mathrm{x}, B_2) = (\xi_1 + \gamma)^2 + \xi_2^2$ and from $d(\mathrm{x}, B_1) + d(\mathrm{x}, B_2) = 2\alpha > d(B_1, B_2) = 2\gamma$ or equivalently $d_1^2 + d_2^2 + 2d_1d_2 = 4\alpha^2$ or $(2d_1d_2)^2 = (4\alpha^2 - d_1^2 - d_2^2)^2$ it follows by substitution: $(\alpha^2 - \gamma^2)\xi_1^2 + \alpha^2\xi_2^2 = \alpha^2(\alpha^2 - \gamma^2)$, which is an ellipse, since $2\alpha > 2\gamma$. Similarly $d(\mathrm{x}_1, B) - d(x_2, B) = 2\alpha > 0$ with $2\gamma > 2\alpha$ yields a hyperbola.

(15.8): $\xi_1, \cdots \xi_n$ form an orthonormal basis for the homogeneous linear functions on V. The $(n-1)$-variety $W$ then has as equation $\mathrm{ax} + \alpha = 0$. The vector a is perpendicular to $W$. The foot $\mathrm{x} + \lambda\mathrm{a}$ of the perpendicular from x to $W$ satisfies $\mathrm{a}(\mathrm{x} + \lambda\mathrm{a}) + \alpha = 0$. Hence $\lambda = -(\mathrm{ax} + \alpha)/\mathrm{a}^2$ and the distance from x to $W$ is $\sqrt{(\lambda\mathrm{a})^2} = \sqrt{\frac{(\mathrm{ax} + \alpha)^2}{\mathrm{a}^2}}$, from which the assertion follows.

(15.9): Choose the origin in the centre of the ellipse. Let $\varphi$ be the homogeneous quadratic function which has the value 1 on the ellipse. Let $\psi$ be the quadratic function $\mathrm{x} \to \mathrm{x}^2$ (inner product). Apply problem (14.3).

(15.10): Like (15.9) with $\psi = \eta^2$, $\eta$ is the distance from $m$. Special case: one conjugate diameter along $m$.

(15.11): Choose the origin in the centre. Let $\xi$ and $\eta$ be two orthonormal coordinates; let $\mathrm{a}_1$ and $\mathrm{a}_2$ be endpoints of two conjugate diameters; then the sum of the squares of the distances from the origin of two tangents to the ellipse with directions $\xi^{-1}(0)$ and $\eta^{-1}(0)$ is equal to $\xi^2(\mathrm{a}_1) + \xi^2(\mathrm{a}_2) + \eta^2(\mathrm{a}_1) + \eta^2(\mathrm{a}_2) = \mathrm{a}_1^2 + \mathrm{a}_2^2$ according to problem (15.10). Hence it is independent of the choice of the orthonormal coordinates. It is also the square of the distance of the variable vertex of the rectangle from O.

(15.13): Cf. Problem (15.2). The line $(p + \alpha, 0) + \mu(1, i)$ with parameter $\mu$ intersects the conic $\xi_1^2 = \lambda^2(\xi_1 - p)^2 + \xi_2^2$ in points whose $\mu$-values are the roots of $(p + \alpha + \mu)^2 = \lambda^2\{(\alpha + \mu)^2 + (i\mu)^2\}$.

The equation has two equal roots $\mu$ if $\alpha = 0$ or $\alpha = 2p/(\lambda^2 - 1)$. $\alpha = 0$ gives the focus $(p, 0)$. The other point (for $\lambda^2 \neq 1$) is the symmetric image of the former, as appears from calculation, and is therefore also a focus of the conic.

(15.14): Cf. formula (15.8).

(15.15): The line $x = y + \lambda b$, $b^2 = 1$, intersects the circle $(x - m)^2 = r^2$ in those points x for which $\lambda$ satisfies $(y + \lambda b - m)^2 = r^2$ or $\lambda^2 + 2\lambda b(y - m) + (y - m)^2 - r^2 = 0$. The roots $\lambda_1$, $\lambda_2$ satisfy $|\lambda_1\lambda_2| = |(y - m)^2 - r^2|$, which is independent of b. Similarly for the higher dimensional cases.

(15.16): Equating the powers with respect to the circles: $(y - m)^2 - r^2 = (y - n)^2 - s^2$ yields $2y(n - m) = r^2 - s^2$, a line through each point lying on both circles. If the powers $M_1$, $M_2$, $M_3$ of a point with respect to three circles satisfy: $M_1 = M_2$ *and* $M_2 = M_3$, then also $M_1 = M_3$; if there is no point for which $M_1 = M_2$ *and* $M_2 = M_3$, there is no point either for which $M_1 = M_2$ *and* $M_1 = M_3$ (parallel).

(15.17): Conjugate directions with respect to a circle are perpendicular, hence a tangent is perpendicular to the radius. $(x_0 - m)(x - x_0) = 0$ is a line through $x_0$ perpendicular to $x_0 - m$. Cf. fig. 14.4.

(15.18): The tangents are perpendicular if and only if the radii are, that is when the triangle ($m$, $n$, point of intersection) is right-angled in the point of intersection. Pythagoras's theorem then proves the assertion.

(15.19): *c.* $u = \dfrac{\alpha x}{x^2}$ substituted in $z = \dfrac{\alpha u}{u^2}$ yields $z = x$.

*d.* If an image point u satisfies $f(u) = 0$ then its original x satisfies $f\left(\dfrac{\alpha x}{x^2}\right) = 0$. The other assertions now follow from a special choice of $f$, using *c*.

(16.1): $\mathrm{x_A}$ is obtained from x by replacing each number by its row-mean.

(16.2): $\mathrm{x} - \mathrm{x_A} \perp \mathrm{A}$, hence $\perp \bar{\mathrm{x}}$ and $\perp \mathrm{x_A} - \bar{\mathrm{x}}$, both $\in \mathrm{A}$; hence $\mathrm{x_A} - \bar{\mathrm{x}} = (\mathrm{x} - \bar{\mathrm{x}}) - (\mathrm{x} - \mathrm{x_A}) \perp \bar{\mathrm{x}}$. ($\perp$ indicates perpendicularity). The last assertion now follows from $\mathrm{x} = \bar{\mathrm{x}} + (\mathrm{x_A} - \bar{\mathrm{x}}) + (\mathrm{x} - \mathrm{x_A})$.

(16.3): For $p \geqslant n$ we have more than $n$ vectors in an $n$-dimensional space, and these are dependent. If for $p < n$ the vectors were dependent, then there would exist numbers $\alpha_i$, not all zero, such that $\sum_{i=0}^{p} \alpha_i x^i = 0$ has $n$ distinct roots $x = x_1, \cdots x_n$, which is a contradiction.

(16.4): $\mathrm{z_A} = 22\mathrm{a}_0 + 2\mathrm{a}_1 + \mathrm{a}_2 + 3\mathrm{a}_3 = (2, 36, 28, 8, 6, 52)$.

(16.5): Suppose classification $A$ has $h$ classes and classification $B$ has $k$ classes. Let for $i = 1, \cdots h - 1$, $\mathrm{a}_i$ be the vector with elements $-(n_i)^{-1}$ in the $i$-th class of classification $A$ and elements $(n_h)^{-1}$ in the last class of classification $A$, and zeros elsewhere. $(\mathrm{a}_1, \cdots \mathrm{a}_{h-1})$ is a basis of $\mathrm{A}^0$.
Let for $j = 1, \cdots k$, $\mathrm{b}_j$ be the vector with elements 1 in the $j$-th class of classification $B$ and zeros elsewhere.
Let the number of elements that are in the intersection of the $i$-th class of $A$ and the $j$-th class of $B$ be $r_{ij}$. $(\mathrm{b}_1, \cdots \mathrm{b}_k)$ is a basis of B. $\mathrm{A}^0$ is orthogonal to $\mathrm{B}^0$ if and only if $\mathrm{A}^0$ is orthogonal to B. This is the case if and only if for $i = 1, \cdots h - 1$ and $j = 1, \cdots k$:

$$\mathrm{a}_i \mathrm{b}_j = r_{hj}(n_h)^{-1} + r_{ij}(-n_i)^{-1} = 0;$$

$$\frac{r_{hj}}{n_h} = \frac{r_{ij}}{n_i}.$$

Hence for an arbitrary class $j$ of $B$ it follows that

$$\frac{r_{1j}}{n_1} = \cdots = \frac{r_{ij}}{n_i} = \cdots = \frac{r_{hj}}{n_h} = \frac{\sum_{i=1}^{h} r_{ij}}{\sum_{i=1}^{h} n_i} = \frac{m_j}{n}$$

and for arbitrary $i$ and $j$ we have $\dfrac{r_{ij}}{n_i} = \dfrac{m_j}{n}$ or $r_{ij} = \dfrac{m_j \cdot n_i}{n}$.

(16.6): Let the image space of the homomorphism $A\colon \mathbf{F}^m \to \mathbf{F}^n$ be called "image $A$", and similarly for other homomorphisms. Since $D$ is an automorphism of $\mathbf{F}^m$, image $A$ and image $AD$ are identical; the same holds for image ${}^tAA$

and image ${}^tAAD$, whilst, since ${}^tD$ is an automorphism, ${}^tAAD$ has the same dimension as ${}^tD{}^tAAD$. This proves our first assertion. Take for $D$ a suitable matrix with elements $d_{ii} \neq 0$, $d_{ij} = 0$ for $i < j$, such that the columns of $AD$ are orthogonal. On carrying out the necessarycalc ulations, this turns out to be possible! Now $r =$ rank $AD =$ = (number of columns different from zero). ${}^t(AD)AD$ is a matrix with $r$ elements $\neq 0$ in the diagonal and zeros elsewhere. The last assertion is now obvious.

(16.7): Substitution of $\overline{\mathrm{x}^2}=\overline{\mathrm{y}^2}=1^2+\cdots+n^2=\frac{1}{6}n(n+1)(2n+1)$; $\bar{\mathrm{x}}\mathrm{y}=\bar{\mathrm{x}}\bar{\mathrm{y}}=\bar{\mathrm{x}}^2 = \text{etc.} = n\left(\frac{n+1}{2}\right)^2$; $(\mathrm{x}-\mathrm{y})^2=\mathrm{x}^2+\mathrm{y}^2-2\mathrm{xy}$ in the two formulas for $r$ yields equality, after some computation.

(16.8): Substitution yields the formula.

(16.9): *a*) and *b*) follow by repeated application of the triangle inequality to the sum of the unit vectors $\mathrm{X}_i$, $i=1, \cdots k$, for $k = 2, 3, \cdots m$. *c*) and *d*) follow by working out at length the formula for $M$. For *e*) use formula *d*) and observe that the mean of the $(n!)^m$ contributions $r(\mathrm{x}_1, \mathrm{x}_2)$ is zero, and likewise for $r(\mathrm{x}_1, \mathrm{x}_3)$ etc. Only the mean of the $(n!)^m$ contributions $m$ remains. *f*): According to *d*) $(M - m)^2 =$ $= 4\{\sum_{i<j} r(\mathrm{x}_i, \mathrm{x}_j)\}^2 = 4\sum_{i<j}\sum_{k<l} r(\mathrm{x}_i, \mathrm{x}_j)r(\mathrm{x}_k, \mathrm{x}_l)$.
The mean over the $(n!)^m$ numbers of a term $r(\mathrm{x}_i, \mathrm{x}_j)r(\mathrm{x}_k, \mathrm{x}_l)$ is $\frac{1}{n-1}$ for $i = k$ and $j = l$, and 0 for all other cases.
Hence

$$(M - m)^2 = 4\sum_{i<j} \frac{1}{n-1} = \frac{2m(m-1)}{n-1}.$$

(16.10): $r(\mathrm{y}, \mathrm{z}) = -\frac{1}{2}$ ;the angle between $\mathrm{y} - \bar{\mathrm{y}}$ and $\mathrm{z} - \bar{\mathrm{z}}$ is $\frac{2}{3}\pi$.
Note that $\sqrt{(\mathrm{y} - \bar{\mathrm{y}})^2} = \sqrt{(\mathrm{z} - \bar{\mathrm{z}})^2} = 5\sqrt{2}$.
The projection $\bar{\mathrm{x}}$ of x on the vector (1, 1, 1, 1) has length $10 \cos \pi/4 = 5\sqrt{2}$, and also $\mathrm{x} - \bar{\mathrm{x}}$ has length $5\sqrt{2}$. On the other hand $\bar{\mathrm{x}} = \lambda(1, 1, 1, 1)$, hence $\lambda\sqrt{4} = 5\sqrt{2}$ so that $\bar{\mathrm{x}} = \frac{5}{2}\sqrt{2}(1, 1, 1, 1)$.

Since the coefficient of multiple correlation is 1, we have $x - \bar{x} = \alpha(y - \bar{y}) + \beta(z - \bar{z})$.
Since $r(x, y) = \frac{1}{2}$, the angle between $x - \bar{x}$ and $y - \bar{y}$ is $\pi/3$; from a drawing it appears that $x - \bar{x} = \lambda[-(z - \bar{z})]$ or $\mu[(y - \bar{y}) + (z - \bar{z})]$.
Substitution in $\dfrac{(x - \bar{x})(y - \bar{y})}{\sqrt{(x - \bar{x})^2 \cdot (y - \bar{y})^2}} = \frac{1}{2}$ yields

$$\frac{\lambda \cdot 25}{5\sqrt{2} \cdot 5\sqrt{2}} = \frac{1}{2} \text{ and } \frac{\mu \cdot 25}{5\sqrt{2} \cdot 5\sqrt{2}} = \frac{1}{2};\ \mu = \lambda = 1.$$

$x_1 - \bar{x} = (-4, -3, 3, 4)$ and $x_2 - \bar{x} = (-2, 6, -1, -3)$.
For calculating the Spearman correlation coefficient we must construct the Spearman vectors $x_1' = (1, 2, 3, 4)$; $x_2' = (2, 4, 3, 1)$ and $y' = (1, 4, 3, 2)$. It follows that the Spearman corr. coeff. of $x_2'$ and $y'$ is greater than the one of $x_1'$ and $y'$. The required vector is $x = \frac{5}{2}\sqrt{2}\ (1, 1, 1, 1) + + (-2, 6, -1, -3) = (1{,}535;\ 9{,}535;\ 2{,}535;\ 0{,}535)$.

(17.1): Check the definition of equivalence in chapter 2.

(17.2): The required matrix is obtained by placing the following matrices along the diagonal of a $16 \times 16$-matrix with zeros elsewhere:

$$\begin{bmatrix} \lambda_1 & 1 & & \\ & \lambda_1 & 1 & \\ & & \lambda_1 & \\ & & & \lambda_1 \end{bmatrix} \begin{bmatrix} \lambda_1 & & & \\ & \lambda_1 & & \\ & & \lambda_1 & \\ & & & \lambda_1 \end{bmatrix} \begin{bmatrix} \lambda_2 & & & \\ & \lambda_2 & & \\ & & \lambda_2 & \\ & & & \lambda_2 \end{bmatrix} \begin{bmatrix} \lambda_3 & 1 & & \\ & \lambda_3 & 1 & \\ & & \lambda_3 & 1 \\ & & & \lambda_3 \end{bmatrix}.$$

(17.3): $\begin{bmatrix} \lambda & 0 \\ 0 & \lambda \end{bmatrix}, \begin{bmatrix} \lambda & 1 \\ 0 & \lambda \end{bmatrix}, \begin{bmatrix} \lambda_1 & 0 \\ 0 & \lambda_2 \end{bmatrix}.$

(17.4): $\begin{bmatrix} \lambda & & \\ & \lambda & \\ & & \lambda \end{bmatrix}, \begin{bmatrix} \lambda & 1 & \\ & \lambda & \\ & & \lambda \end{bmatrix}, \begin{bmatrix} \lambda & 1 & \\ & \lambda & 1 \\ & & \lambda \end{bmatrix}, \begin{bmatrix} \lambda_1 & & \\ & \lambda_1 & \\ & & \lambda_2 \end{bmatrix},$

$\begin{bmatrix} \lambda_1 & 1 & \\ & \lambda_1 & \\ & & \lambda_2 \end{bmatrix}, \begin{bmatrix} \lambda_1 & & \\ & \lambda_2 & \\ & & \lambda_3 \end{bmatrix}.$

(17.5): Similar to (17.4).

(17.6): The complexification of $\sigma$ has the normal form: $\begin{bmatrix} \lambda & 1 & & \\ & \lambda & & \\ & & \bar{\lambda} & 1 \\ & & & \bar{\lambda} \end{bmatrix}$;

$\begin{bmatrix} \rho\cos\varphi & \rho\sin\varphi & 1 & 0 \\ -\rho\sin\varphi & \rho\cos\varphi & 0 & 1 \\ 0 & 0 & \rho\cos\varphi & \rho\sin\varphi \\ 0 & 0 & -\rho\sin\varphi & \rho\cos\varphi \end{bmatrix}$ is the real normal form of $\sigma$.

(17.7): Since the characteristic equation is real and of odd degree, it has a real root, to which there corresponds a real eigenvector which is basis of an invariant real 1-dimensional subspace.

(17.8): $\begin{bmatrix} \lambda & 0 \\ 0 & \lambda' \end{bmatrix}$, $\begin{bmatrix} \lambda & 1 \\ 0 & \lambda \end{bmatrix}$, $\begin{bmatrix} \rho\cos\varphi & \rho\sin\varphi \\ -\rho\sin\varphi & \rho\cos\varphi \end{bmatrix}$, $\lambda, \lambda', \rho$, real.

(17.9) and (17.10): Like (17.4) and (17.5) if all eigenvalues are real. Moreover

$$\begin{bmatrix} \rho\cos\varphi & \rho\sin\varphi & 0 \\ -\rho\sin\varphi & \rho\cos\varphi & 0 \\ 0 & 0 & \lambda \end{bmatrix}; \quad \begin{bmatrix} P & 0 \\ 0 & Q \end{bmatrix}$$

with $P$ and $Q$ equal to the matrices mentioned in the answers to problems (17.8) and (17.6).

(17.11): $\sum_{i=1}^{n} \lambda_i \xi_i^2$ with $\lambda_i \leqslant \lambda_{i+1}$ for $i = 1, \cdots n - 1$.

(17.12): $\begin{bmatrix} 1 & 0 \\ 0 & -1 \end{bmatrix}$, $\begin{bmatrix} \cos\varphi & \sin\varphi \\ -\sin\varphi & \cos\varphi \end{bmatrix}$; $\begin{bmatrix} \cos\varphi & \sin\varphi & 0 \\ -\sin\varphi & \cos\varphi & 0 \\ 0 & 0 & \varepsilon \end{bmatrix}$

with $\varepsilon^2 = 1$;

$$\begin{bmatrix} \cos\varphi & \sin\varphi & 0 & 0 \\ -\sin\varphi & \cos\varphi & 0 & 0 \\ 0 & 0 & \cos\psi & \sin\psi \\ 0 & 0 & -\sin\psi & \cos\psi \end{bmatrix}, \begin{bmatrix} \cos\varphi & \sin\varphi & 0 & 0 \\ -\sin\varphi & \cos\varphi & 0 & 0 \\ 0 & 0 & 1 & 0 \\ 0 & 0 & 0 & -1 \end{bmatrix}.$$

(18.1): *a*) $5\left[\dfrac{x + 2y - 3}{\sqrt{5}}\right]^2 - 1$

*b*) $20\left[\dfrac{x - 3y + 3}{\sqrt{10}}\right]^2 + 10\left[\dfrac{3x + y - 1}{\sqrt{10}}\right]^2 - 4$

*c*) $(x + 2)^2 + (y - 3)^2 - 27$

*d*) $4(x+1)^2 + 10\left[\dfrac{2y+z+5}{\sqrt{5}}\right]^2 + 5\left[\dfrac{y-2z}{\sqrt{5}}\right]^2 - 20$

*e*) $2\left[\dfrac{x+y}{\sqrt{2}}\right]^2 - 2\left[\dfrac{x-y}{\sqrt{2}}\right]^2 + z^2 - 1$

*f*) $2\left[\dfrac{x+y}{\sqrt{2}}\right]^2 - 2\left[\dfrac{x-y}{\sqrt{2}}\right]^2 - z^2 - 1$

*g*) $18[\frac{1}{3}(x+2y+2z)-\frac{2}{27}]^2+\frac{1}{9}(-64x+169y-137z)+3\frac{73}{81}$

*h*) $10\left[\dfrac{2x-2y+z-u}{\sqrt{10}}\right]^2 - 10\left[\dfrac{-x+y+2z-2u}{\sqrt{10}}\right]^2 +$

$+ 2\left[\dfrac{x+y-2}{\sqrt{2}}\right]^2 - 2\left[\dfrac{z+u}{\sqrt{2}}\right]^2$

*i*) $(x-2)^2 + (y+3)^2 + z^2 + (u-1)^2 - 32.$

(18.2): The planes in question are the planes through the centre of each of the level sets of $f$, perpendicular to the $n$ one-dimensional eigenspaces of the endomorphism determined by $f$.

(19.1): Together with $\sigma$ and $\tau$ also $\sigma^{-1}\sigma = \varepsilon$, $\sigma^{-1}\varepsilon = \sigma^{-1}$, $(\sigma^{-1})^{-1}\tau = \sigma\tau$ belong to $G$.

(19.2): The only axes of symmetry of $\lambda_1\xi_1^2+\lambda_2\xi_2^2+\alpha=0$, $\lambda_1\neq\lambda_2$, are $\xi_1 = 0$ and $\xi_2 = 0$.

(19.3): $\lambda\xi_1^2 + \lambda\xi_2^2 + \lambda_3\xi_3^2 + \alpha\xi_3 + \beta = 0$ is a rotational surface with respect to the axis $\xi_1 = \xi_2 = 0$.

(19.4): *a*. The motions with an invariant point can be classified according to the orthogonal endomorphisms with respect to that point. Cf. problem (17.12).

*b*. The motions that have no invariant point:

translation $\xi_1\sigma = \xi_1 + \beta$, $\xi_i\sigma = \xi_i$ for $i > 1$,

screwing, $\varphi \not\equiv 0 \bmod 2\pi$, $\varepsilon = 1$ or $-1$:

$$\begin{cases} \xi_1\sigma = \cos\varphi\cdot\xi_1 + \sin\varphi\cdot\xi_2 \\ \xi_2\sigma = -\sin\varphi\cdot\xi_1 + \cos\varphi\cdot\xi_2 \\ \xi_3\sigma = \xi_3 + \beta \\ \xi_4\sigma = \varepsilon\xi_4 \end{cases}$$

(19.5): Define a set of euclidean coordinates $\xi_1, \cdots \xi_n$ satisfying $\xi_i(P_j) = 0$, $j < i$, for $i = n, n-1, \cdots 1$ and $\xi_i(P_i) > 0$;

and similarly $\eta_1, \cdots \eta_n$ with respect to $Q_0, \cdots Q_n$. Now $\sigma$ is uniquely determined by the action $\eta_i \sigma = \xi_i$. Subsequently it should be verified by elementary means that $\xi_i(P_j) = \eta_i(Q_j)$ for $n = 2$ or 3.

(19.6): Choose two $\mathscr{A}$-maps $\kappa$ and $\kappa'$: $A \to$ V for the plane, such that the affinity $\sigma$ is represented by the identity $\kappa' \sigma \kappa^{-1} = \underline{1}$ in the vector space V. Then the assertion is evident.

(19.7): For the first three points $P_0$, $P_1$, $P_2$ we consider coordinates $(\xi_1, \xi_2)$ such that $P_0 = (0, 0)$, $P_1 = (1, 0)$, $P_2 = (0, 1)$, and similarly coordinates $(\eta_1, \eta_2)$ with respect to the other three points $Q_0, Q_1, Q_2$. The affinity $\sigma$ with the action $\eta_i \sigma = \xi_i$, $i = 1, 2$, is the uniquely determined affinity which was required.

(19.8): For the proof of the last assertion we take an affinity $\tau$ which transforms the positive definite quadratic function $\psi = \sum_{i=0}^{n-1} \chi \sigma^i$ into a quadratic function $\psi\tau$ with concentric circles as level curves.

(19.9): Apply an affinity under which the ellipse has a circle as image.

(19.10): Apply an affinity under which the triangle has as image an equilateral triangle.

(19.11): Construct the axes of the ellipse and subsequently the tangents which make angles of $\pi/4$ with the axes.

(20.1): 31.

(20.3): Cf. problems (14.8) and (14.9).

(20.4): Cf. problems (17.3) and (17.8).

(20.5): Matrices with diagonalelements $+1$ and $-1$ and zeros elsewhere.

(20.6): Theorem [9.5].

(20.7): **F**x, **F**y $\epsilon$ V are polar with respect to the quadric $\varphi(\mathrm{x}, \mathrm{x}) = 0$ if $\varphi(\mathrm{x}, \mathrm{y}) = 0$.

(20.8): Choose coordinates $\eta_i$ such that the given polar triangle has sides $\xi_i = 0$. The equation of the ellipse then is $\sum_{i=1}^{3} \lambda_i \eta_i^2 = 0$. After possible renumbering and by putting $\eta_i = \nu_i \xi_i$, where $\nu_i$ are conveniently chosen scalars, we find the desired equation.

(20.10): Cf. problem (14.2).

(20.12): The two figures consisting of the four lines through $S_1$ and $S_2$ respectively, are congruent.

(20.14): Apply problem (20.13).

(20.17): The directions which are perpendicular to themselves satisfy $\xi_0 = 0$, $\xi_1^2 + \xi_2^2 = 0$. Hence they are $(0, 1, i)$ and $(0, 1, -i)$. A circle $(\xi_1 - \alpha_1)^2 + (\xi_2 - \alpha_2)^2 = \rho^2$ or $(\xi_1 - \alpha_1\xi_0)^2 + (\xi_2 - \alpha_2\xi_0)^2 = \rho^2$ passes through those points. A quadratic curve passing through these points, should have an equation of type $\xi_0(\beta_0\xi_0 + \beta_1\xi_1 + \beta_2\xi_2) + \gamma(\xi_1^2 + \xi_2^2) = 0$, and this is a circle if $\gamma \neq 0$ and a pair of lines if $\gamma = 0$. In the latter case one of these lines is the line at infinity and the other line of the pair can be considered as a special circle.

(20.18): $P^2(GFp^r)$, the projective plane over the field with $p^r$ elements has $p^{2r} + p^r + 1$ points and as many lines. Any line has $p^r + 1$ points and through any point there pass $p^r + 1$ lines. If $p^r = 2$ then a representation is obtained by calling the sides and altitudes and the inscribed circle of an equilateral triangle "lines" and the vertices, pedal points and centroid: "points".

(21.1): Let $Q$ be the invariant point and $q$ its polar. We have the following possibilities: $Q$ inside $\partial H$: rotation around $Q$; $q$ partly inside $\partial H$ :translation in the direction of $q$; no point or line inside $\partial H$ invariant: $Q$ on $\partial H$.

(21.2): Only in the first case of problem (21.1) can $\sigma$ generate a finite group, as may be seen by inspection of the projectivity which is induced in the pencil of lines through $Q$. In suitable coordinates $\partial H$ is $\xi_1^2 + \xi_2^2 - \xi_3^2 = 0$; $Q = (0, 0, 1)$; $\sigma$: $\xi_1' = \xi_2$, $\xi_2' = -\xi_1$; $\alpha_1\xi_1 + \alpha_2\xi_2 = 0$ perpendicular to $\alpha_2\xi_1 - \alpha_1\xi_2 = 0$; from which the assertion follows by substitution.

# INDEX

$A^n$ = n-dimensional affine space, 13, 32
Abelian-group, 67
addition of homomorphisms, 63
— — matrices, 73
— — vectors, 2, 8
adjoint matrix, 97
adjustment of x on A, 143
affine property, 203
— regular n-gon, 204
— space, 13, 32
affinely equivalent, 202
affinity, 202
$\mathscr{A}$-map, 32
antilinear function, 119
antisymmetric function, 86, 107
— matrix, 96
Apollonius's circles, 136
area, 99
associative law, 3, 9
augmented matrix, 82
automorphism, 66

basis of a vector space, 9
between, 15
bilinear function, 106
— symmetric function, 108
Brianchon's theorem, 235

**C** = complex number field, 8
canonical form, 164
centre, 19
centre of quadratic function, 122
centre of variety, 124
centroid, 14, 17
Ceva's theorem, 19, 40
characteristic function, 194
— polynomial, 159
— root, 158
circle, 106, 135, 137, 182, 189
circumscribed, 140
classification, 55
— , orthogonal, 55
— , one way, 145
cobasis, 27
coefficient of concordance, 155
— — multiple correlation, 153
— — partial correlation, 153
co-factor, 94
collinear, 16
collineation, 224
commutative law, 3, 9
complex conjugate matrix, 96
— — vectors, 167
complexification of real vector space, 138, 167
composition of homomorphisms, 65
— — relations, 7
concurrent, 16
cone, 113
conformal mapping, 141
congruent figures, 182, 194
conic sections, 112
conjugate vectors, 115
constant function, 7, 29
constructions, 205, 207
continuous function, 248
— mapping, 248
contrast, 145

contrast vector, 149
— — , normalized, 150
convex sets, 18
coordinate system, 38
coordinates, 28, 38
correlation coefficient, 150
cosine of the angle between vectors, 130
cosine rule, 131
Cramer's rule, 105
cross-ratio, 44
curvature, 246
curve of degree k in projective plane, 218
curves of the second class, 234
cylinder, 135

dependent, 20
Desargues's configuration, 44
— theorem, 41, 232
determinant of endomorphism, 91
— — matrix, 92
development of determinant, 93
diagonal of a function, 85
diameter, 124
difference vector, 11
dimension of vector space, 10, 22, 25
direction, 138, 209
— , isotropic, 138
directrix, 136
distance, 131, 134
— in hyperbolic plane, 241
— in elliptic plane, 245
distributive law, 3, 9
dual homomorphism, 68
— image of f under $\sigma$: $\sigma^*$ f or f$\sigma$, 192
— numbers, 79
— projective space, 231
— vector space V*, 27

eigenspace, 160
eigenvalue, 158
eigenvector, 158
ellipse, 112, 182, 189, 222
ellipsoid, 113, 189
elliptic cylinder, 112
— paraboloid, 124, 187
— plane, 244
endomorphism, 58
— , hermitian, 176
— , orthogonal, 173
— , singular, 66
— , symmytric, 170
— , unitary, 177
epimorphism, 58
equivalence, 5
equivalent endomorphisms, 156
— functions, 193
euclidean $\mathscr{A}$-map, 132
— coordinates, 128, 132
— invariant, 182
— property, 203
— space $E$, 131
— vector space E, 128
exact sequence of homomorphisms, 63

**F**, field, 8
$\mathbf{F}^n$, n-dimensional space, 28
field, 68
— , skew, 50
— with characteristic 0, 16
finite affine plane, 53
— field, 53
— set of generators, 10
focus, 136, 137
foot, 133
frame, 103
function, 6
— , antilinear, 119
— , antisymmetric, 86, 107
— , hermitian, 119
— , quadratic, 30, 35
— , r-linear, 86
— , sesquilinear, 119
— , symmetric, 107, 198
— of degree r, 30
— — — zero, 29

function, zero, 7
— — n variables, 85

$GF(n)$ = Galois field, 53
generators of a vector space, 9
— — $X^c$, 248
group, 67

harmonic separation, 48
hermitian endomorphism, 176
— function, 119
— — , positive, 121
— matrix, 97
Hesse's function, 135, 139
Hilbert-metric, 241
Hom (A, B), 63
homeomorphism, 249
homogenous coordinates, 216
— function, 30
— linear function, 21
homomorphism, 58
— onto, 58
— , transposed, 70, 72
hyperbola, 112, 182, 184, 222
— , rectangular, 182
hyperbolic cylinder, 112
— paraboloid, 124
— plane, 238
hyperboloid of one sheet, 113, 189
— — two sheets, 113, 189
hypercone, 189
hyperplane, 36
hypersphere, 135, 189

identity, 4
image, 6
— of homomorphism, 60
incidence relation, 234
indefinite real quadratic function, 111
index of inertia, 110, 121
inner product of vectors with respect to a basis, 70, 72, 128
intersection of sets, 4
invariant of endomorphisms, 157
invariant, euclidean, 182
— subspace, 159
inverse mapping, 7
— matrix, 75
inversion, 88, 141
involution in $P^n$, 225
isomorphic, 28
isomorphism, 66
isotropic cone, 138
— direction, 138

join of two spaces, 215
Jordan's normalform, 165

kernel of a homomorphism, 60
— — - mapping, 7

Laguerre's formula for angle, 139
latent root, 158
Latin square, 56
Latin squares, orthogonal, 56
least squares, method of, 144
length of a vector, 128
level curve, 54
— set, 7
**line**, 209
line, 14, 35
line at infinity, 209
line coordinates, 233
linear combination, 20
— equations, 81
— function on $A$, 35
— — on V, 21, 35
— group $Gl(m, \mathbf{F})$, 75
— mapping, 58
— regression, 145
— space, 8
— transformation, 58
— variety, 35
linearly dependent, 20
— independent, 20

mapping into, 6
— onto, 7

matrix, 72
— , adjoint, 97
— , antisymmetric, 96
— , augmented, 82
— , hermitian, 97
— , orthogonal, 96, 174
— , similar, 157
— , singular, 75
— , square, 74
— , transposed, 76
— , unit, 75
— , unitary, 96
mean, 144
measure on a point set, 99
Menelaus's theorem, 39, 51
method of least squares, 144
metric, 131
middle, 14
Monge's circle, 140
motion, 190
multiplication, geometrical, 3
— of homomorphisms, 65
— — — by a scalar, 63
— — matrices, 74
— — vectors by a scalar, 2, 8
multiplicity, 159

negative definite real quadratic function, 111
non-degenerate quadratic curve, 140
non-singular quadratic forms, 111
norm of a vector, 128
normal equations, 145
normal forms of quadratic functions, 111, 122

O, zero vector, 10
one-to-one mapping, 7
orientation, 103
orthogonal classifications, 55, 149
— endomorphism, 173
orthogonal group, 96, 176
— matrix, 96, 174
— polynomials, 149
orthonormal vectors, 269

Pappus's theorem, 49, 51
parabola, 124, 189, 222
parabolic cylinder, 124, 189
— variety, 124
paraboloid of revolution, 189
parallel, 16
par. = parallelopiped, 99
parametric representation, 14
partition, 160
Pascal's theorem, 229
pedal point, 133
permutation, 87
— , even and odd, 88
perpendicular, 133
— circles, 140
— vectors, 129
plane, 36
**point**, 209
point, 13
— at infinity, 209
polar, 230
— hyperplane, 230
— plane, 230
— projective spaces, 230
— triangle, 230
— vectors, 115
pole, 230
positive definite real quadratic function, 111
power, 140
product mapping, 7
— set, 4
— of homomorphisms, 65
— of matrices, 74
— of vector and scalar, 2, 8
projective cone, 223
— invariants, 221
— mapping, 220

projective n-dimensional space over **F**, 215
— plane, 209
— property, 220
projectively equivalent, 220
proper first-degree function, 30
— linear function, 29
— subset, 4
— value, 158
Pythagoras's theorem, 130

quadratic curve, nondegenerate, 140
— function on vector space, 30, 35
— — — affine space, 35
— variety, 124
quadric, 221
quaternions, 79
quotient of a set and an equivalence, 5

**R** = real number field, 8
rank correlation coefficient, 154
rank of a homomorphism, 60
— — - matrix, 74
— — $\varphi$· (quadratic function), 109
ratio of line segments, 16
ratio of line segments, 16
— — vectors, 15, 212
reflection, 174, 195, 196, 197
— , with respect to a linear r-space, 198
reflexive relation, 5
regression with respect to a one-way classification, 145
regular n-gon, 204
relation, 4
— , composite, 7
— , reflexive, 5
— , symmetric, 4
— , transitive, 4
— **F**, vectors in the, 215
representative, 5

ring, 67
rotation, 174, 196, 197
rotational k-th degree function on *P*, 227
— symmetric function, 199

scalars, 8
screwmotion, 197
semi-definite (positive, negative) real quadratic function, 111
sesquilinear function, 119
similar matrices, 157
simplex, 101
singular endomorphism, 66
— matrices, 75
— quadratic function, 109
— real quadratic function, 111
skew fields, 50
source of a homomorphism, 60
spanning a vectorspace, 9
Spearman vector, 154
spectrum, 158
spur, 159
square matrix, 74
standard basis vectors, 71
Steiner's ellipse, 208
stereographic projection, 142
subset, 4
subspace, vector, 11, 24
sum of vectors, 2, 8
symmetric endomorphism, 170
— function, 107, 198
— relation, 4

topological mapping, 249
— product space, 249
— space, 248
— sphere, 250
— torus, 251
trace, 159
transflection, 197
transitive relation, 4
translation, 32, 195, 196, 197
transposed homomorphism, 70, 72

transposed matrix, 76
triangle inequality, 131
two-class vector, 154
two-simplex, 18

union, 4
unit element of group, 67
— matrix, 75
— vector, 129
unitary endomorphism, 177
— group, 96, 178
— matrix, 96
— vector space, 142

V = vectorspace, 8
$V^n$ = n-dimensional vector space, 10
Van-der-Waerden vector, 154
variety, 219
vector, 1, 8
vector space, 2-dimensional, 1
— — , n- — , 8
volume, 99
— of parallelopiped, 100
— — simplex, 102

weighted mean, 18

zero vector O, 1, 10

# LIST OF SYMBOLS

**A**, B, V vector spaces
a, b, . . . x, y, vectors
$\alpha$, $\beta$, $\gamma$, . . . $\lambda$, $\mu$, scalars
$A$, affine space
O, zero vector
$\xi$, $\eta$, linear functions
**F**, field
**R**, real number field
**C**, complex number field
$a \in A$, 4
$A \subset B, B \supset A$, 4
$A \cap B, A \cup B$, 4
$A \times B$, 4
$a \sim b$, 5
$A/R$, 5
$f : A \to B$, 6
$fa$, $fV$, 6
$f^{-1}(b)$, $f^{-1}(0)$, 7
$gf(a)$, 7
**F**, 8
**R**, 8
**C**, 8
$V^n$, 10
O, 11
**F**a, 11
$U + W$, 11
$\lambda U$, 11
$A^n$, 13, 32
$\varphi$, $\xi$, $\eta$, 21, 39
$V^*$, 26
$\delta_{ij}$, 26
$\binom{n}{k}$, 30
$\mathscr{A}$-map $\kappa$, 32, 34
$//$, 41
$Cf(10_3, 10_3)$; 44
$GF(5) = Z/(5)$, 53
Hom(A, B), 63
$\sigma^*$, 68
${}^t$, 69, 76
Gl(m, **F**), 75
$\sigma^k$, 78
$f^\cdot$, 85
$\varepsilon(\sigma) = \varepsilon(j_1, \ldots j_n)$, 89
$\varphi_\sigma$, 91, 116
$\det \sigma = |\sigma|$, 91
$\Lambda_{ij}$, 94
$\bar{\sigma}$, 96
par., 99
$\dfrac{\partial f}{\partial \xi_j}$, 123
E, 128
xy, 128
$\|x\|$, 128
$E$, 131
$d(P, Q)$, 131
$\tilde{x}$, 144
$\bar{x} = (\tilde{x}, \ldots \tilde{x})$, 144
$(\mathbf{R}^n)^\circ$, 145
X, 149
$r(x,y)$, 150
$V^m_\lambda$, 160
V, 167
$\sigma^* f$, $f\sigma$, 192
$(V^{n+1} - O) / \mathbf{F} = P^n(\mathbf{F})$, 215
$(V^* - O) / \mathbf{F} = P^*$, 231
$X^c$, 248